THERMODYNAMICS
FOR
GEOLOGISTS

RAYMOND KERN

University of Aix-Marseilles

ALAIN WEISBROD

University of Nancy

THERMODYNAMICS
FOR
GEOLOGISTS

Translated by
Duncan McKie
Cambridge University

 Freeman, Cooper and Company
1736 Stockton Street
San Francisco 94133

From *Thermodynamique de Base pour Minéralogistes, Pétrographes et Géologues*, by R. Kern and A. Weisbrod, published by Masson & Cie, 1964, Paris

Preface to the English Edition

Three years ago I discovered a book, *Thermodynamique de Base pour Minéralogistes, Pétrographes, et Géologues* by Professors Kern and Weisbrod. It took no more than two minutes of leafing through the pages to know that it was a book long overdue, and needed to be translated into English as soon as possible to make it widely available to geologists like me whose French is willing but not able.

The timing of this translation is almost perfect. Thermodynamics is perhaps the single great tool of Science that never ages; it flowers in each science in succession, and then returns to flower again. First the applications of thermodynamics were to physics, then to chemistry, then to engineering; today its widest use is in biology and geology. In each instance, it simply awaits the availability of data good enough to fit its elegant structure, and then permits rapid progress in solving problems of the particular discipline. In geology, after a slow start, data amenable to thermodynamic treatment have accumulated rapidly, and an increasing number of publications have appeared over the past decade that employ the methods of thermodynamics in one way or another. Brilliant applications to particular problems have been accomplished, but they have been scattered through a wide variety of journals in many different languages. As Kern and Weisbrod state, concerning available books in thermodynamics, ". . . their examples of the application of thermodynamics to real problems and their exercises are far removed from any geological field of interest."

In their book, Kern and Weisbrod have put into one volume the basic thermodynamics of particular interest to geologists, and have demonstrated application in detail over a tremendous range of representative geologic material. For the first time it should not be

5

necessary to search through a half-dozen texts on chemical thermo-dynamics to find how to treat in detail problems involving such topics as phase changes at elevated temperature and pressure, the relation of chemical equilibrium to the earth's gravitational field, or the effects of differences of pressure within a given system.

One of the striking aspects of the book is the step-by-step detailing of all the calculations required in solving the various types of prob-lems. Although this approach gives an initial impression of austerity, it does in fact make the book easier to use. The accompanying exposi-tion, even in translation, retains the stamp of the personalities of the authors, and is generally terse but lucid.

It also seems likely that this book will speed up a tendency that history says is inevitable—the actual teaching of basic thermody-namics, as well as its application, within departments of earth science. For the first time a book is available for this purpose, and we are deeply indebted to Professors Kern and Weisbrod for making this first text a comprehensive and distinguished one.

ROBERT M. GARRELS

Preface to the Original Edition

". . . *Maintenant je te prie de me parler des pierres: d'autant que tu m'as dit qu'en parlant d'icelles je connaîtrais de beaux secrets. Je voudrais bien savoir (ce) que tu en veux dire: car les uns disent qu'elles ont été formées dès la création du monde, et les autres disent qu'elles croissent tous les jours.*"

Bernard Palissy,
Discours admirables, 1580*

The interpretation of natural mineral assemblages requires some knowledge of the stability fields of the minerals involved; and such knowledge may be gained by the study either of lattice energies or of thermodynamic properties.

Lattice energy is a function of atomic positions. Therefore, if the coordinates of every atom in a crystalline solid have been determined precisely by X-ray diffraction and if an equally precise theory of structural energy can be applied to them, it should be possible to calculate the lattice energy of the structure and in time to perform such calculations for every mineral structure.

The goal to be attained is the explanation of the natural crystallization of minerals as a function of the physical laws that govern the interaction of atoms, that is, ultimately, the determination of the stability of minerals and of mineral assemblages.

There is a clever, if qualitative, solution of this difficult problem

---

* Bernard Palissy (1510–1589) was known not only as a philosopher, but as an artist in ceramics so that this observation of his from those less sophisticated days of science is particularly apt: "Now I beg you to tell me about rocks, since you have told me that from our discussions of them I would come to comprehend their engrossing secrets. I would like to know about them whatever you can tell me, for some people say that rocks took their present form at the time of this earth's creation, while others say that they still grow and change from day to day."

to be found in Jacques de Lapparent's "Logique des minéraux du granite" (1941). By using the simple device of structural models in place of merely theoretical speculation he was able, thanks to his intimate knowledge of granitic rocks on every scale, to substitute for classical descriptive petrography an attractive interpretation of the order of crystallization of the granitic minerals and then of their alteration.

In the present book Raymond Kern and Alain Weisbrod have expounded in an admirable manner the other explanatory technique: that of thermodynamic calculations based on experimental data. Suppose that for a rock-forming reaction the specific heat, specific volume, coefficient of thermal expansion, and coefficient of compressibility of each of the minerals involved were known; that the heat of reaction had been measured; and that the temperature-dependence and pressure-dependence of such properties as volume and entropy could be calculated. It would then be possible to predict the physical conditions of reaction. And it then becomes possible to compare calculated with experimentally determined equilibrium curves: from that comparison the petrologist can learn much about mineral stability.

Major programs of precise thermal study have been concerned over the past few decades with the fusion of silicates in the presence of a gas phase at high pressure and temperature; with the synthesis of silicates under dry conditions or in the presence of water vapor; with the study of the inversion characteristics of quartz as a function of temperature of formation and composition of the medium; and with the effect of pressure on the temperatures of polymorphic transformations in various minerals.

Thus a highly developed field of research has now emerged and a considerable quantity of data is available; but it requires very costly and highly specialized equipment. Although it may be possible in many laboratories to experiment on a large scale in open crucibles at atmospheric pressure, technical problems of quite another order of magnitude arise when the experiments have to be performed in bombs maintained at known, constant, and high temperatures and pressures for long periods of time. Certain laboratories have made this their own special field. In other centers of mineralogical and petrological research experimental study has now become a tradition too, but with equipment on a more modest scale: for instance, thermogravimetric analysis and differential thermal analysis.

Whatever the experimental facilities available, the purpose remains essentially the same: first to decipher the thermal record obtained directly or culled from the literature, and then to apply it to the rocks.

This book is intended to further that aim. Anyone wishing to approach mineralogy and petrology from this untraditional angle and not wanting to base his understanding of the subject primarily on descriptive observations—I do not decry the merits of the latter approach—will find here a well-chosen collection of pilot problems.

RAYMOND HOCART

Translator's Preface

When I was invited in the summer of 1964 to translate *Thermodynamique de Base pour Minéralogistes, Pétrographes et Géologues,* I accepted the task with alacrity. I was already giving a course of lectures that embraced the field covered by Kern and Weisbrod, and those lectures and their accompanying demonstrations have, I believe, benefited from the close study that translation required me to make of Kern and Weisbrod and especially from use of the impressive array of worked numerical examples culled from their pages. The immediate relevance to geology of every problem they discuss is obviously one of the chief merits of the book. Another is their clear exposition of the principles of chemical thermodynamics.

This does not claim to be a rigorous text of thermodynamics. It is rather a quasi-rigorous text of the sort generally acceptable to chemists, but here given a geological slant that is so far unique and therefore geologically valuable. The opportunity to make this stimulating work available to a wider audience has given me much personal pleasure.

That some geologists tend to fight shy of purely theoretical physico-chemical or even algebraic arguments unless they can see an immediate application to the solution of a geological problem is understandable. Kern and Weisbrod have made it their practice, therefore, always to provide worked examples relevant to geology. These have proved an effective vehicle for making the abstractions of chemical thermodynamics acceptable to my pupils.

The French text was published in 1964 and no attempt has been made systematically to bring it up to date; it is a textbook and not a research monograph, and for the former pedagogical quality is a more relevant criterion than comprehensiveness. But in one field in which there have been significant and instructive advances I have, with the agreement of the authors, written two entirely new sections (*2.4* and *2.5* in Chapter XI) on distribution ratios, for which I accept full responsibility. In addition several recently published works have been added to the bibliography.

A full discussion of the text with Professor Kern was an invaluable help in the production of this translation as was his careful checking of the whole typescript of the translation.

DUNCAN McKIE

Table of Contents

THERMODYNAMICS
FOR
GEOLOGISTS

I

Introduction

1. Thermodynamics and geology

The brilliant memoirs of Goldschmidt (1911, 1912), Van't Hoff (1912), and Grubenmann and Niggli (1924) have been followed over the succeeding years by a splendid display of mineralogical, petrological, and geological papers soundly based in thermodynamics. Many geologists have not been trained in classical thermodynamics and it has consequently become increasingly difficult for them to read such papers, although these would certainly be of interest to them.

The situation becomes acute when the geologist, whether a beginner or a man of experience, foregoes the reading of papers that may capture his interest in such journals as the *American Journal of Science*, the *Journal of Geology*, the *American Mineralogist*, the *Journal of Geophysical Research*, the *Journal of Petrology*, and others—solely because he lacks adequate familiarity with thermodynamics.

There are in the world a number of geologists, petrologists, and mineralogists who relate their observations of natural phenomena to calculations of a thermodynamic character. Such thermodynamic considerations have as their object the marshaling of observations, descriptions, and analytical data in order to put them on a plane more accessible to discussion and at the same time to guarantee a minimum of logical error. Often such scientists have recourse to experiment in order to make their field observations more pertinent, just as they reinforce their theoretical calculations with study in the field.

Classical thermodynamics is an exact science and moreover made to measure for the geologist in that it is one of the few disciplines that have achieved an extreme degree of elaboration with a quite restricted mathematical apparatus. The algebra taught in elementary classes,

19

supplemented by the concept of partial derivatives, constitutes an adequate mathematical background. The mode of thermodynamic argument has, moreover, nothing disconcerting in it: it is typically cartesian in the sense that a complex transformation is split into the sum of such simple parts as may be necessary for convenient description (partial derivatives). The difficulties commonly experienced by petrologists and geologists when they find that they need to make use of the methods and thinking of modern crystallography, are, for instance, of a quite different order.

Good textbooks of thermodynamics are not lacking,* but experience does seem to have shown that in general they are not easy reading for the geologist. It is not that they are commonly too abstract or advanced, but rather that their examples of the application of thermodynamics to real problems and their exercises are far removed from any geological field of interest.

A number of recent books on petrology and on mineralogy have been embellished with thermodynamical introductions; but all too often a reading of the remainder of the text leaves the reader with the impression that the introduction is not wholly relevant. There are however a limited number of works devoted wholly or in large measure to the thermodynamics of rocks and minerals; notable among recent publications are Ramberg (1952), Korzhinskii (1959), Lafitte (1957), and Thompson (1955). A gap remains to be bridged and it is the purpose of the present volume to attempt to bridge it by providing for the student a treatise on the elements of thermodynamics couched in such a form as to equip him—indeed to stimulate him— to read the multitude of papers that have appeared in recent years, and are appearing with ever increasing frequency, on the application of thermodynamics to the earth sciences. We begin, very classically, with the most down to earth of the many statements of the two Laws and proceed from there toward more abstract expressions, from which we deduce rigorously the various theorems, rules, and laws of thermodynamics. As each result is obtained, its mineralogical or petrological application is discussed with numerical calculations performed in detail; it is often the details of thermodynamic calculations that

---

* Some textbooks of chemical thermodynamics that have been used extensively in the preparation of this book are listed in the bibliography.

are responsible for the student's greatest difficulties with the subject.

The reader may be surprised not to find a number of pages devoted to Carnot's cycle in the treatment of the Second Law. It is our belief that Carnot's cycle is of use only to the pure thermodynamicist; in chemistry and in our field it has no immediate application. We have therefore followed Planck in adopting a treatment that, while less faithful historically, is certainly more appropriate here.

We have taken care to avoid mixing the interpretative approach of statistical thermodynamics with our exposition of classical thermodynamics although it is true that statistical thermodynamics can make some of the classical abstract ideas appear more realistic. In our view an exposition of thermodynamics, whether classical or statistical, should be self-contained; and moreover the practical applications that concern us are essentially classical in nature.

All the applications to the earth sciences that are discussed in the text are taken from the primary literature of the past twenty years.* Both the scope of the calculations and the conclusions of the original authors have often been extended; and sometimes their errors have been corrected or the enthusiasm of their interpretation curbed.

The material treated in this volume has been taught in part to the students of the Faculté des Sciences of the Université de Nancy and to those of the École Nationale Supérieure de Géologie Appliquée et de Prospection Minière of the same university. The authors will feel that their object has been achieved if even a few more young geologists are enabled to enjoy reading the very many excellent papers currently being published in this field.

We wish to express our gratitude to Raymond Hocart, Professor of Mineralogy and Crystallography at the Sorbonne, for the interest that he has shown in this work. One of us (R.K.) is particularly indebted to him for his introduction to the problems of the application of thermodynamics to chemistry and to the earth sciences.

Raymond Kern and Alain Weisbrod

---

* Their great number makes it inconvenient to give every reference relating to a particular problem. The bibliography at the end of the book includes mainly secondary sources.

2.   The purpose of thermodynamics

Thermodynamics can conveniently be divided into two parts, *classical* (or macroscopic) and *statistical* (or microscopic).

The former is formally *phenomenological*, that is, it attempts to find equations to describe the possible evolution of a system, of a chemical reaction, etc. It could alternatively be called phenomenological thermodynamics. Such equations, of universal application, having been established for a number of experimentally realizable reactions, can be extrapolated to predict reactions that are more difficult, or even impossible, of practical achievement. Therein lies their interest: they permit calculation and prediction in advance of prolonged discussion and experimentation.

Obviously, thermodynamic equations do not do away with the need for experimental studies, if only because experimentally determined macroscopic coefficients, such as specific heat, heat of reaction, thermal expansion and compressibility may appear as parameters in the equations; it is however only fair to add that these coefficients are always readily measurable.

The equations of classical thermodynamics follow from the two Laws. The First Law expresses our belief in energy, the Second Law that reactions have a natural direction of evolution. The thermodynamic equations giving the direction of evolution of a reaction are logically derived from the two Laws: equations as concrete in their application as the Law of Mass Action, the Phase Rule, and Clapeyron's Equation are likewise deduced without further assumptions from the two Laws.

Running on a course parallel to classical thermodynamics is statistical thermodynamics. The latter seeks, ideally, to be independent of experimental determinations of the coefficients of classical thermodynamics. This aim can evidently only be achieved by introducing hypotheses about the nature of the matter under consideration. Statistical thermodynamics makes use of imaginary models, often on an atomic (microscopic) scale, to determine macroscopic thermodynamic functions by statistical argument, and, if the models are well chosen, agreement with experiment may be found. In such a case, the model is said to provide an interpretation of the mechanism of reaction;

statistical thermodynamics then becomes *causal* in contrast to the simply phenomenological nature of classical thermodynamics. In this text we shall not have recourse to statistical arguments even though in certain cases they might be able to provide successful interpretations of classical descriptions.

Thermodynamics in general makes possible the likelihood of predicting a reaction; it does not tell us whether the reaction will take place effectively, for instance by setting a value to its rate; it simply indicates that under favorable conditions the reaction could take place.*

Following Cassel we can say that *thermodynamics represents the legislative power:* no phenomenon can run counter to the thermodynamic equations without invalidating their foundations, the two Laws of Thermodynamics. For *kinetics*, a discipline of quite another kind, it is necessary to inquire in what manner a reaction proceeds; *kinetics represents the executive power*. It is divided into two quite distinct parts, phenomenological kinetics which analyzes mathematically the laws of reaction rate† and mechanistic kinetics which relates such analysis to reaction models. In the following, reference will not be made to kinetic studies.

---

* The "thermodynamics of irreversible phenomena" of the Belgian school led by De Donder has established a formal phenomenological treatment of rates of reaction, diffusion, and transport in general.

† The "thermodynamics of irreversible phenomena" forms a transition between kinetics and phenomenological thermodynamics.

II

Symbols, Units, and Constants

Note on nomenclature.

Thermodynamics knowing no geographic limits, it has been decided to retain the European usage in this edition both to help avoid errors and to prepare readers for further reading of the literature written outside of the United States, especially on the European continent.

The symbols used are therefore those of the French original and they correspond in the main to those recommended by both the International Union of Physics (1948) and the International Union of Chemistry (1947) in that the four thermodynamic potentials are denoted by U, H, F, and G. Following the French text, F is described as free energy rather than as Helmholtz free energy or the Helmholtz function. The significant departure from common English and American usage comes in the description of G as free enthalpy instead of as Gibbs free energy or the Gibbs function. Herein we have followed the practice of Kern and Weisbrod because it is logical although unfamiliar to English-speaking readers; G is after all related to H as F is to U. That one should be named free enthalpy and the other free energy would seem sensible and convenient for the student. This is expanded upon further on page 37 of the French edition and page 64 of this edition.

1.   Symbols

Symbols relating to any physical quantity

J. . . . .   a quantity
dJ. . . . .   its differential

x, y, z......   parameters of state (variables)

$X = \left(\dfrac{\partial J}{\partial x}\right)_{y,z}$ the partial derivative of the quantity J

ΔJ........   a change in magnitude of the quantity J

(ΔJ).......   the same, but due to a reaction

If P and T are total pressure and absolute temperature:

$\left.\begin{array}{l} \Delta J_T^P ...... \\ (\Delta J)_T^P ..... \end{array}\right\}$ are changes in the quantity J at given P and T

$\left.\begin{array}{l} \Delta J_{298}^0 ...... \\ (\Delta J)_{298}^0 .... \end{array}\right\}$ are changes in the quantity J under standard conditions

If i is a component and α a phase:

J_i.........   is the quantity attributable to component i

J^α.........   the quantity attributable to phase α

J_i^α.........   the quantity attributable to component i in phase α

$\left.\begin{array}{l} \overline{J_i} .... \\ \overline{J_i^\alpha} .... \end{array}\right\}$ the partial molar quantity of component i

J_i^0.........   the molar quantity of pure component i

Symbols for thermodynamic quantities

Q.........   heat absorbed by system
W.........   work done on system
U.........   internal energy
F.........   Helmholtz function or free energy
H.........   enthalpy or heat function
G.........   Gibbs free energy or free enthalpy
μ.........   chemical potential
Φ.........   gravitational potential
σ.........   surface free energy
S..........   entropy
s..........   surface area
v..........   volume
V.........   molar volume
n..........   number of moles
c.........   molal concentration
x..........   mole fraction
a..........   activity
f.........   fugacity

γ . . . .   activity coefficient or fugacity coefficient
β . . . .   degree of excess or of supersaturation
P . . . .   total pressure
p . . . .   partial pressure
T . . . .   temperature
m . . . .   mass
M . . . .   molar mass
ρ . . . .   specific gravity
h . . . .   height

Constants and general symbols

ν . . . .   extent of reaction
α . . . .   coefficient of expansion
χ . . . .   coefficient of compressibility
C_P, C_v . . . . .   specific heat at constant pressure or constant volume
R . . . .   the gas constant
K . . . .   equilibrium constant
λ . . . .   any constant
φ . . . .   number of phases
$\mathfrak{C}$ . . . .   number of independent components
$\mathfrak{N}$ . . . .   number of components
$\mathfrak{R}$ . . . .   number of restrictions
f_{ext} . . . .   number of extensive parameters
f_{int} . . . .   number of intensive parameters
ln . . . .   Naperian (natural) logarithm
log . . . .   common (decadic) logarithm

2.   Units

Heat

The calorie, 1000 cal = 1 Kcal

In a reaction the enthalpy, internal energy, free energy, and free enthalpy are given in calories per gram (cal g^{-1}) or in calories per mole (cal $mole^{-1}$) with respect to a stated component.

Specific heat

   Cal g^{-1}deg^{-1} or cal mole^{-1}deg^{-1}

Entropy

   Cal deg^{-1}mole^{-1} = Clausius mole^{-1} (in European usage) = entropy
   unit (e.u.)

Work

   The erg = 1 dyne cm = 10^{-7} joule

Pressure

   The barye = 1 dyne cm^{-2} = 10^{-6} bars
   The kilogram cm^{-2}; 1 bar = 1.0197 Kg cm^{-2}
   The standard atmosphere = the pressure exerted by a column of
   Hg 760 mm in height, with a density of 13.595 g cm^{-3}, in a
   place where the acceleration due to gravity, g, has the value
   980.7 cm sec^{-2}.
   1 atm = 1.0133 bar
   1 atm = 1.0332 Kg cm^{-2}

Mechanical equivalent of heat

   1 cal = 4.186 joules
   1 cal = 41.8 bar cm^3
   1 cal = 42.6 Kg cm
   1 cal = 41.3 atm cm^3

3.   Constants

Absolute zero

   −273.16°C, but it is quite common to approximate t = 25°C to
   T = 298°K

Avogadro's number

   N = 6.023 × 10^{23} mole^{-1}

Gas constant

R = 8.315 joule deg^{-1}mole^{-1}

R = 1.987 cal deg^{-1}mole^{-1}

R = 82.06 atm cm^3 deg^{-1}mole^{-1}

R ln x = 4.576 log x for R measured in cal deg^{-1}mole^{-1}, since log x = 0.4343 ln x

III

Definitions and Conventions

At the start of every thermodynamic discussion it is necessary to define the matter to be studied: the astronomer may be interested in assemblages of stars or in the whole universe, while the geologist concerns himself only with the problems posed by the earth. The thermodynamicist has a restrained appetite and merely seeks to study some part, often a much restricted part of the earth, not restricted in any geographical sense, but in some more arbitrary manner: he describes his selection as a *system*.

1. The thermodynamic system

The thermodynamicist defines a *system* as an assemblage of materials (rocks, minerals, atoms), which he isolates in thought from the remainder of the universe. In particular he distinguishes, having chosen his system, the system in the strict sense, that is the *internal system*, from the *external system*. Geometrically a system is thus defined as a certain region of space.

The choice of a system depends on the use to which it is to be put and often poses delicate problems. Consider, for instance, a lens of marble included in a gneiss formation. Depending on the problem to be investigated, the system might be restricted to the lens and some part of its envelope, to the lens alone, or even to an arbitrarily selected part of it. In such a case it may be advantageous to define an *idealized system* composed for instance of an imaginary assemblage of calcite, phlogopite and forsterite in the same proportions as in the rock.

29

2.   Exchanges

A system may be imagined to undergo changes of a variety of kinds. For instance the internal system may change without making any demands on the external system; it is then an *isolated system* and there is no exchange of matter, nor of energy with the external system. Alternatively a *closed system* may be defined as one that changes only by exchanging energy with the external system. An *open system* may correspondingly be defined as the more general case, capable of exchanging matter and energy with the external system. And finally, a system may be said to be subjected to *adiabatic change* when it is incapable of exchanging heat with the external system.

In the example of paragraph 1, it may be supposed that the changes experienced by the marble lens in the course of its history were effected at constant composition. The system comprising the lens alone is then closed. On the other hand, if the substance of the envelope has reacted with the marble, the system comprised by the lens will be open, but the system marble + envelope may be regarded as closed.

An important example of a closed system is represented by the crystalline schists which have undergone what petrologists describe as *topochemical* metamorphism. *Metasomatic* rocks, on the contrary, constitute open systems, at least in so far as systems of limited geometrical extent are concerned.

3.   Phases

A phase is defined as a restricted portion of a system, homogeneous with respect to all its properties (that is to say the system possesses the same properties throughout this portion on the scale of the observations being discussed). Thus in the foregoing example the assemblage of calcite crystals constitutes a phase, and likewise the assemblage of forsterite crystals and so on. Under certain conditions alkali feldspars may form only a single phase, whose composition varies continuously from an essentially sodic to an essentially potassic end-member (solid solution). Under other conditions there may be separation into

of components i and j respectively. This equation corresponds for instance to the reaction

$$Mg_2SiO_4 + SiO_2 \rightarrow 2\ MgSiO_3$$

with $n_1 = 1$, $n_2 = 1$ initially and $n_1' = 2$ finally.

If this transformation is accompanied by a loss of heat Q it is written as $-Q$, but if heat is absorbed the heat change is written as $+Q$. Alternatively it could be said that logical application of the convention leads to a negative sign for exothermic and a positive sign for endothermic reactions.*

In general we shall adhere strictly to this convention for all changes, whatever they may be: thus if there is an increase in volume accompanying the change from 1 to 2, we shall attach to that change ΔV a positive sign (in other words we shall say that the system has received volume from the exterior during the change).

---

* It should be noted that this result is the exact opposite of the convention used by the early thermodynamicists, a convention that is still used in many elementary textbooks.

IV

The First Law

1. Equivalence of the various forms of energy

Every change that matter undergoes involves the intervention of energy, be it mechanical, thermal, magnetic, chemical, or some other form. All forms of energy are mutually interconvertible; that is simply what the First Law states: *The various forms of energy are equivalent and energy is indestructible.*[*]

Mechanical and thermal energy have often been distinguished and it was only in 1842 that Robert Mayer showed that these two forms of energy were related. If the former is expressed in units of work W and the latter in calories Q, they are related by

$$W = JQ,$$

where J is the *mechanical equivalent of heat.* In thermodynamics, the different forms of energy being equivalent, they are all expressed, without distinction of form, in calories. Consequently the factor J will scarcely ever be seen on the following pages.

2. The significance of the First Law

The First Law may be formulated in more explicit and useful terms by the following argument.

Suppose the system to be the site of successive changes

$$1 \rightarrow 2 \rightarrow 3 \rightarrow \cdots \rightarrow 1,$$

* Einstein has shown that the various forms of energy are not only equivalent but may be equated also to mass. In the field of chemical thermodynamics this extension of the First Law does not arise.

that is to say the system leaves an initial state 1 and returns to a final identical state 1. The total change is said to be closed, or in other words the system has traversed a *closed cycle* (fig. 1).

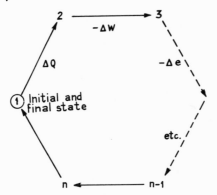

Fig. 1. Diagrammatic representation of a closed thermodynamic cycle in which the system exchanges energy in various forms before regaining its initial state.

In the course of this sequence of changes there may be exchanges of energy, say, thermal (ΔQ), mechanical $(-\Delta W)$, electrical $(-\Delta e)$, chemical, and so on. It follows from the equivalence of the various forms of energy that

$$\Delta Q - \Delta W - \Delta e + \cdots = 0,$$

since the system returns to its initial state and energy is indestructible. Whence the alternative statement of the First Law:

When a system undergoes any series of changes which leave it in a final state identical with its initial state, the algebraic sum of the energy exchanges measured in the same units is zero. [*] [†]

$$\sum_i \Delta E_i = 0.$$

By way of example, consider the closed system comprising a definite quantity of a sand-clay mixture at the mouth of a river at atmospheric pressure and temperature. Under the action of factors described as *external*, the mixture is carried toward the sea, is deposited

[*] The changes envisaged are quite distinct from those that will be envisaged in the exposition of the Second Law, isothermal, reversible, irreversible changes and so on.
[†] "Zero" is here used to translate the French *nulle*, since in American usage "nil" may be used to signify either "negligible" or zero.

as a sediment, and buried under newer sediments; these processes change the mechanical energy of the system. Subsequently, in the course of metamorphism, the system may become the site of reactions giving rise to changes in its chemical, thermal, and mechanical energy leading to the formation of a gneiss. Involved in an orogenic phase, the newly formed gneiss is carried up to a high level and again makes contact with the atmosphere. New reactions take place to produce once again the sand-clay mixture by weathering; and the mixture may finally be transported back toward its original site. The final state is identical with the initial state; the system has traversed a closed cycle; and by the First Law the algebraic sum of the energy exchanges is zero.

3. The first abstraction of thermodynamics: internal energy

Consider a system evolving from an initial state 1 toward a final state 2, different from the initial state, either passing directly from 1 to 2, or through the intermediate states $1'$, $1''$, etc. (fig. 2). In the

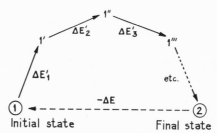

Fig. 2. Passage from an initial state 1 to a final state 2 by two different routes. The change in internal energy is independent of the path taken.

first case the algebraic sum of the energy exchanges is $\Delta E \neq 0$, in the second $\sum_i \Delta E'_i \neq 0$.

Imagine now that the system describes the closed cycle: $1 \rightarrow 1' \rightarrow 1'' \rightarrow \cdots 2 \rightarrow 1$. In order to pass from 1 to 2 through $1'$, $1''$, etc., $\ldots$ it exchanges $\sum_i \Delta E'_i$ and to pass directly from 2 to 1 it exchanges $-\Delta E$. Now, since the cycle is closed, the algebraic sum of the energy exchanges must be zero:

$$\sum_{i} \Delta E_i' - \Delta E = 0$$

$$\therefore \quad \sum_{i} \Delta E_i' = \Delta E.$$

The same would be true for all the other possible routes by which the system might pass from 1 to 2, *i.e.*,

$$\Delta E = \sum_{i} \Delta E_i' = \sum_{i} \Delta E_i'' \dots = \text{Constant.}$$

Whence the following statement: *When a system passes from a state 1 to a state 2 by any series of changes whatsoever, the algebraic sum of the energies exchanged, measured in the same units, depends only on the initial and the final state, and is independent of the sequence or path of the changes.*

One could therefore assign to each state a function U whose variation ΔU in the passage from state 1 to state 2 is given by

$$\Delta U = \Delta E = U_2 - U_1.$$

The function U is called *internal energy*. And it must be borne in mind that this function can be known only by its variation and never in absolute magnitude; in practice that restriction is of no consequence for what is measured in all energy exchanges is the variation in energy between two states of the system.

This deduction from the First Law is of the greatest practical significance.

4.   Mathematical properties of the function, internal energy*

The passage of a system from the initial state 1 to the final state 2 takes place under the influence of certain parameters (pressure, temperature, concentration, and so on). Since there can be assigned to each state, defined for example by the parameters $x, y, z \dots$, an internal energy function $U(x, y, z \dots)$, whose variation between the states $(x_1, y_1, z_1 \dots)$ and $(x_2, y_2, z_2 \dots)$ is

[1] $\Delta U = U(x_2, y_2, z_2 \dots) - U(x_1, y_1, z_1 \dots)$

* This paragraph might be studied in detail on a second reading of the book.

the fact that ΔU depends only on the initial and final states can be expressed mathematically quite simply.

Consider an initial state defined by the parameters $x, y, z \ldots$ and a final state infinitesimally separated from it, $x + dx, y + dy, z + dz \ldots$. Passage from the one to the other corresponds to a variation in internal energy dU for which one could write

[2] $\qquad dU = U(x + dx, y + dy, z + dz \ldots) - U(x, y, z \ldots)$

which corresponds* to

[3] $\qquad dU = \left(\dfrac{\partial U}{\partial x}\right)_{yz..} dx + \left(\dfrac{\partial U}{\partial y}\right)_{xz..} dy + \left(\dfrac{\partial U}{\partial z}\right)_{xy..} dz \ldots$

Each function in parentheses in equation (3) is a *partial derivative* of the function $U(x, y, z \ldots)$ with respect to one of the variables, the others remaining constant. The differential dU, sum of all the partial derivatives, is called a *perfect differential*.

Mathematical expression may be given to the First Law by writing that dU is a perfect differential or, what amounts to the same statement, that there exists a function $U(x, y, z \ldots)$ such that:

$$\int_1^2 dU = U(x_2, y_2, z_2 \ldots) - U(x_1, y_1, z_1 \ldots).$$

For instance take the function $U(x, y, z) = x^2y^3 + xz$. Its partial derivatives are:

$$\left(\frac{\partial U}{\partial x}\right)_{yz} = 2xy^3 + z; \qquad \left(\frac{\partial U}{\partial y}\right)_{xz} = 3x^2y^2; \qquad \left(\frac{\partial U}{\partial z}\right)_{xy} = x$$

and the perfect differential is:

$$dU = (2xy^3 + z) \, dx + 3x^2y^2 \, dy + x \, dz.$$

What then are the conditions for a differential to be perfect?

It can be proved, and we shall assume it to be true, that for a perfect differential

$$dU = \left(\frac{\partial U}{\partial x}\right)_{yz..} dx + \left(\frac{\partial U}{\partial y}\right)_{xz..} dy + \left(\frac{dU}{\partial z}\right)_{xy..} dz \ldots$$

---

* Assuming that the sum of the differentials of higher than first order is negligible, as it is in practice.

the following relations are true:*

[4] $\qquad \dfrac{\partial^2 U}{\partial x\, \partial y} = \dfrac{\partial^2 U}{\partial y\, \partial x};\qquad \dfrac{\partial^2 U}{\partial y\, \partial z} = \dfrac{\partial^2 U}{\partial z\, \partial y};\qquad \dfrac{\partial^2 U}{\partial z\, \partial x} = \dfrac{\partial^2 U}{\partial x\, \partial z}\, .\, .\, .\, .$

Conversely, consider the differential

$$dU = X\, dx + Y\, dy + Z\, dz\, .\, .\, .\, .$$

If this differential is perfect, there exists a function $U(x, y, z\, .\, .\, .)$ such that

$$X = \left(\dfrac{\partial U}{\partial x}\right)_{yz..};\qquad Y = \left(\dfrac{\partial U}{\partial y}\right)_{xz..};\qquad Z = \left(\dfrac{\partial U}{\partial z}\right)_{xy..}\, .\, .\, .$$

and therefore from equations (4) it follows that

[5] $\qquad\qquad \dfrac{\partial X}{\partial y} = \dfrac{\partial Y}{\partial x};\qquad \dfrac{\partial Y}{\partial z} = \dfrac{\partial Z}{\partial y};\qquad \dfrac{\partial Z}{\partial x} = \dfrac{\partial X}{\partial z}\, .\, .\, .\, .$

The set of equations (5) constitutes a necessary and sufficient condition for $dU = Xdx + Ydy + Zdz\, .\, .\, .$ to be a perfect differential; and furthermore these equations constitute a precise statement of the First Law.

Example: The function $(2xy^3 + z)\, dx + 3x^2y^2\, dy + x\, dz$ is a perfect differential, that is:

$$\dfrac{\partial(2xy^3 + z)}{\partial y} = 6xy^2;\qquad\qquad \dfrac{\partial(3x^2y^2)}{\partial x} = 6xy^2$$

$$\dfrac{\partial(3x^2y^2)}{\partial z} = 0;\qquad\qquad \dfrac{\partial(x)}{\partial y} = 0$$

$$\dfrac{\partial(x)}{\partial x} = 1;\qquad\qquad \dfrac{\partial(2xy^3 + z)}{\partial z} = 1.$$

The function $x^2y^4\, dx + x^3y^3\, dy$, on the contrary, is not a perfect differential, since:

$$\dfrac{\partial(x^2y^4)}{\partial y} = 4x^2y^3;\qquad \dfrac{\partial(x^3y^3)}{\partial x} = 3x^2y^3.$$

---

* It should be remembered that

$$\dfrac{\partial^2 U}{\partial y\, \partial x} = \dfrac{\partial\left(\dfrac{\partial U}{\partial x}\right)}{\partial y}\qquad \text{and}\qquad \dfrac{\partial^2 U}{\partial x^2} = \dfrac{\partial\left(\dfrac{\partial U}{\partial x}\right)}{\partial x}.$$

Example: Again for example suppose that the change in internal energy dU of a system be the sum of a change in mechanical energy dW and in thermal energy dQ and, putting (p. 31)

dW $= -$ P dV (P = pressure, dV = change in volume)

and dQ $=$ T dS (T = temperature, dS = change in entropy),

it follows that

$$d\text{U} = -\text{P}\,d\text{V} + \text{T}\,d\text{S}.$$

The First Law may thus be expressed by stating that dU is a perfect differential, so that

$$-\left(\frac{\partial \text{P}}{\partial \text{S}}\right)_{\text{v}} = \left(\frac{\partial \text{T}}{\partial \text{V}}\right)_{\text{s}}.$$

This example leads also to another important statement: *If dU is a perfect differential, the changes in mechanical (dW), thermal (dQ), electrical energy, etc., need not necessarily themselves be perfect differentials when taken separately.* In other words, the changes ΔW, ΔQ, etc., between the states 1 and 2 depend in general not only on the final and initial states, but also on the path by which the change from state 1 to state 2 takes place.

The integration of a perfect differential dU is theoretically a very simple operation. Since the integration

$$\int_{1}^{2} d\text{U} = \text{U}_2 - \text{U}_1$$

does not depend on the path taken between the two limiting states, a conveniently simple path may be chosen.

Let

$$d\text{U} = \text{X}(x, y, z \ldots)\,dx + \text{Y}(x, y, z \ldots)\,dy + \text{Z}(x, y, z \ldots)\,dz \ldots$$

be a perfect differential. It can be shown that

$$\text{U}(x, y, z \ldots) - \text{U}(x_0, y_0, z_0 \ldots) = \int d\text{U}$$

$$= \int_{x_0}^{x} \text{X}(x, y_0, z_0 \ldots)\,dx + \int_{y_0}^{y} \text{Y}(x, y, z_0 \ldots)\,dy + \int_{z_0}^{z} \text{Z}(x, y, z \ldots)\,dz.$$

It is apparent that $x, y, z \ldots$ are interchangeable and the integration could quite as well be begun with respect say to y, leaving x

and z constants equal respectively to x_0 and z_0. Thus for a function of the variables x and y:

$$U(x, y) - U(x_0, y_0) = \int_{x_0}^{x} X(x, y_0)\, dx + \int_{y_0}^{y} Y(x, y)\, dy$$

$$= \int_{y_0}^{y} Y(x_0, y)\, dy + \int_{x_0}^{x} X(x, y)\, dx.$$

Consider for example the differential,

$$dU = (2xy^3 + z)\, dx + 3x^2y^2\, dy + x\, dz$$

which has been shown to be a perfect differential:

$$U - U_0 = \int_{x_0}^{x} (2xy_0^3 + z_0)\, dx + \int_{y_0}^{y} 3x^2y^2\, dy + \int_{z_0}^{z} x\, dz$$

$$= y_0^3(x^2 - x_0^2) + z_0(x - x_0) + x^2(y^3 - y_0^3) + x(z - z_0)$$

whence

$$U(x, y, z) - U(x_0, y_0, z_0) = (x^2y^3 + xz) - (x_0^2y_0^3 + x_0z_0).$$

---

5. Heat of reaction, internal energy, and enthalpy

It has just been shown that although the change in internal energy of a system depends only on the initial and final states of the system, that is not in general the case for other forms of energy. However there are some kinds of change, including two that are of considerable practical significance, in which thermal energy depends uniquely on the initial and final states of the system.

The argument may be restricted, to start with, to thermomechanical changes, that is changes in the course of which the system exchanges only heat and mechanical energy (compression, or chemical reaction in a closed system for instance).

For an infinitesimal change of state, with heat change dQ and work done $dW = -P\, dV$,

[6] $$dU = dQ - P\, dV$$

$$\therefore \quad dQ = dU + P\, dV.$$

If the system passes by any path from state 1 to state 2:

$$\Delta Q = \int_1^2 dQ = \int_1^2 dU + \int_1^2 P\, dV$$

whence

[7]
$$\Delta Q = \Delta U + \int_1^2 P\, dV.$$

5.1. Changes at constant volume (isochoric changes).

In this case $dV = 0$ and equation (7) reduces to

[8]
$$(\Delta Q)_V = (\Delta U).$$

The heat of reaction of a thermomechanical change at constant volume is equal to the change in internal energy of the system and therefore depends only on the initial and final states.

5.2. Changes at constant pressure (isobaric changes). Enthalpy.

In this case equation (7) becomes

$$(\Delta Q)_P = (\Delta U) + P \int_1^2 dV$$

whence

$$(\Delta Q)_P = (\Delta U) + P(\Delta V) = (U_2 + PV_2) - (U_1 + PV_1).$$

$(\Delta Q)_P$ therefore depends only on states 1 and 2 and may in consequence be related to a function of state, called *enthalpy* and symbolized by the letter H*

[9]
$$H = U + PV.$$

It follows that $(\Delta Q)_P = (U_2 + PV_2) - (U_1 + PV_1) = H_2 - H_1$, whence

[10]
$$(\Delta Q)_P = (\Delta H).$$

The heat of reaction of a thermomechanical change at constant pressure is equal to the change in enthalpy of the system and depends only on the initial and final states.

It should be noticed that for an isobaric thermomechanical change

* The function enthalpy is merely an auxiliary function which could be omitted. It is introduced primarily for the sake of abbreviation.

the First Law can be expressed by stating that ΔH is a perfect differential.

In the case of laboratory experiments the choice of observing one or other of these two types of change amounts in essence to a choice of experimental method. However the choice is subject to certain considerations of experimental convenience. Thus in the open air, or at least at atmospheric pressure, reactions will obviously take place at constant pressure. At pressures other than atmospheric pressure there are technical difficulties involved in maintaining constant pressure during reaction and the experimenter finds it more convenient usually to work at constant volume, especially at high pressures (for instance in bomb calorimetry).

For the mineralogist the problem is rather different. Not only is he not at liberty to make a choice *a priori* of the type of change, but it is often difficult for him to establish with certainty the constancy of either pressure or volume during a reaction that has taken place in nature. Certain field observations and especially microscopical studies (by thin or polished sections) permit the demonstration of the constancy of volume in reaction. But in a general way, it is usually supposed that the majority of reactions which have taken place in the rocks have been effected at constant pressure. That is why in this book, attention will for the most part be focused on enthalpy rather than on internal energy.

6.   Some examples of enthalpy of reaction

The physical state of reactants and products will be specified by the following symbols: (g) = gas, (l) = liquid, (aq) = aqueous solution, (c) = crystals. All the changes listed take place at a pressure of one atmosphere. Temperatures are expressed in degrees on the Kelvin scale.

Homogeneous systems (i.e., single phase systems).
Enthalpy of reaction:

$$H_2(g) + I_2(g) \rightarrow 2\ HI(g)$$
$$(\Delta H)_{298} = +40\ Kcal\ per\ mole\ of\ HI\ formed.$$

Enthalpy of polymerization:

$$2\ NO_2(g) \rightarrow N_2O_4(g)$$
$(\Delta H)_{298} = +5$ Kcal per mole of N_2O_4 formed.

Enthalpy of neutralization in solution:

$$HCl(aq) + NaOH(aq) \rightarrow NaCl(aq) + H_2O(l)$$
$(\Delta H)_{291} = -13.7$ Kcal mole^{-1}.

Heterogeneous systems (i.e., polyphase systems).
Enthalpy of solution:

$$LiCl(c) + H_2O(l) \rightarrow LiCl(aq) + H_2O(l)$$
$(\Delta H)_{291} = -8.6$ Kcal mole^{-1}.

Enthalpy of crystallization:

$$LiCl(aq) + H_2O(l) \rightarrow LiCl(c) + H_2O(l)$$
$(\Delta H)_{291} = +8.6$ Kcal mole^{-1}.

Enthalpy of precipitation:

$$AgNO_3(aq) + NaCl(aq) \rightarrow AgCl(c) + NaNO_3(aq)$$
$(\Delta H)_{298} = -15.6$ Kcal mole^{-1}.

Enthalpy of reaction:

$$Mg_2SiO_4(c) + SiO_2(c) \rightarrow (MgSiO_3)_2(c)$$
$(\Delta H)_{298} = +2.3$ Kcal mole^{-1}.

Enthalpy of fusion*:

$$Cu(c) \rightarrow Cu(l)$$
$(\Delta H)_{1357} = +3.1$ Kcal mole^{-1}.

Enthalpy of vaporization:

$$Cu(l) \rightarrow Cu(g)$$
$(\Delta H)_{3120} = 72.2$ Kcal mole^{-1}.

Enthalpy of order—disorder transformation (for albite at 74.7°C):

$$Ab_{LT} \rightarrow Ab_{HT}$$
$(\Delta H)_{74.7} = -2.3$ Kcal mole^{-1}.

Enthalpy of polymorphic transformation:

$$SiO_2\ (low\ quartz) \rightarrow SiO_2\ (high\ quartz)$$
$(\Delta H)_{848} = 0.21$ Kcal mole^{-1}.

---

* Often called latent heat of fusion, and similarly of vaporization, etc.

7. Application of the First Law: the determination of enthalpies of reaction

Enthalpies of reaction are determinable by direct application of the First Law, either by consideration of closed cycles (the experimental method) or open cycles (the method of standard enthalpies).

7.1. The experimental method.

Certain reactions, among them the majority of geologically interesting reactions, are for a variety of reasons difficult to observe directly. The enthalpy changes that accompany such reactions can nevertheless be evaluated.

7.1.1. The polymorphic transformation graphite-diamond.—It is required to determine at 1500°C the enthalpy of the reaction

$$C \text{ (graphite)} \rightarrow C \text{ (diamond)}; (\Delta H_1).$$

The transformation in this direction is difficult to perform in the laboratory (the difficulties posed by the synthesis of diamond are well known). However the enthalpy changes on combustion can be measured at 1500°C.

$$C \text{ (graphite)} + O_2(g) \rightarrow CO_2(g); (\Delta H_2)$$
$$C \text{ (diamond)} + O_2(g) \rightarrow CO_2(g); (\Delta H_3).$$

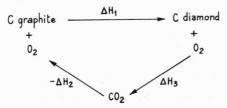

Fig. 3. Indirect evaluation of the enthalpy of the transformation from graphite to diamond by construction of an isothermal cycle making use of two well-known reactions.

Imagine the closed cycle represented by fig. 3. By virtue of the First Law,

$$(\Delta H_1) + (\Delta H_3) - (\Delta H_2) = 0$$

whence

$$(\Delta H_1) = (\Delta H_2) - (\Delta H_3).$$

However at 1500° the heats of combustion are still difficult to deter-

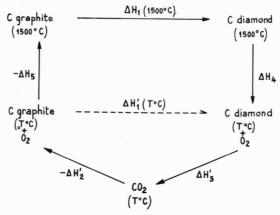

Fig. 4. Indirect enthalpy evaluation of the transformation from graphite to diamond by construction of a cycle at variable temperature again using well-known reactions.

mine and it is necessary to take the further step of imagining the more elaborate cycle shown in fig. 4.

$$C \text{ (graphite)} \rightarrow C \text{ (diamond) at } 1500°C; \ (\Delta H_1)$$
$$C \text{ (graphite) at } 1500°C \rightarrow C \text{ (graphite) at T}; \ (\Delta H_5),$$

where T is an easily accessible temperature at which the heat of combustion can be determined:

$$C \text{ (graphite)} + O_2(g) \rightarrow CO_2(g) \text{ at T}; \ (\Delta H'_3)$$

and likewise for diamond.

Let $C_{P(D)}$ and $C_{P(G)}$ be the molar specific heats at constant pressure of diamond and graphite respectively. It is known that $dQ_P = C_P \, dT$ and consequently

$$(\Delta H_5) = \int_{1500}^{T} C_{P(G)} \, dT; \qquad (\Delta H_4) = \int_{1500}^{T} C_{P(D)} \, dT.$$

The application of the First Law gives

$$(\Delta H_1) + (\Delta H_4) + (\Delta H'_2) - (\Delta H'_3) - (\Delta H_5) = 0$$

whence

$$(\Delta H_1) = (\Delta H'_3) - (\Delta H'_2) - \int_{1500}^{T} C_{P(D)}\, dT + \int_{1500}^{T} C_{P(G)}\, dT$$

and substituting

$$C_{P(D)} - C_{P(G)} = \Delta C_P$$

the expression becomes

$$(\Delta H_1) = (\Delta H'_3) - (\Delta H'_2) - \int_{1500}^{T} \Delta C_P\, dT.$$

The integration may be done graphically from experimental determinations of $C_{P(D)}$ and $C_{P(G)}$ at various temperatures.

It will be necessary to return later to this point, but it can be said now that the quantity $(\Delta H'_3) - (\Delta H'_2)$ represents the variation in enthalpy $(\Delta H'_1)$ of the transformation at the temperature T; whence

$$(\Delta H_1) = (\Delta H'_1) - \int_{1500}^{T} \Delta C_P\, dT.$$

This result is quite general, and can be written as:

$$(\Delta H)_{T_2} - (\Delta H)_{T_1} = \int_{T_1}^{T_2} \Delta C_P\, dT \text{ or } \frac{d(\Delta H)}{dT} = \Delta C_P.$$

7.1.2. The reaction forsterite + quartz → enstatite.—This reaction which can be written as

$$Mg_2SiO_4 + SiO_2 \rightarrow 2\ MgSiO_3;\ (\Delta H_1)$$

is not easily performed—on account of its high temperature, the slowness of reaction and other factors—under the restricted experimental conditions possible for calorimetry. However the three compounds are completely soluble in hydrofluoric acid at convenient temperatures and their enthalpies of solution can readily be measured at some moderate temperature. The process of solution may be formulated as

$$Mg_2SiO_4 + \infty\ HF \rightarrow A + B + \infty\ HF + \cdots.$$

Let (ΔH_2), (ΔH_3), (ΔH_4) be the heats of solution of forsterite,

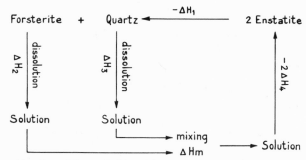

Fig. 5. Determination of the enthalpy of the reaction forsterite + quartz → enstatite by solution in hydrofluoric acid.

quartz, and enstatite in HF; and consider the imaginary cycle shown in fig. 5 and detailed below:

Solution of forsterite in HF: (ΔH_2).

Solution of quartz in HF: (ΔH_3).

Mixing of the two solutions: (ΔH_m), the enthalpy of mixing.

Formation of enstatite from the mixture: $-2(\Delta H_4)$.

Decomposition of enstatite into quartz and forsterite: $-(\Delta H_1)$.

The cycle is closed and it follows from the First Law that

$$\Sigma(\Delta H) = 0$$

which here becomes

$$(\Delta H_2) + (\Delta H_3) + (\Delta H_m) - 2(\Delta H_4) - (\Delta H_1) = 0.$$

If the solutions are dilute, ΔH_m is negligible and then

$$(\Delta H_1) = (\Delta H_2) + (\Delta H_3) - 2(\Delta H_4).$$

The values (ΔH_2), (ΔH_3), (ΔH_4) have been determined by Sahama and Torgeson (1949) by solution in 20.1% aqueous HF at 73.7°C as

$$(\Delta H_2) = -95.4 \text{ Kcal mole}^{-1}$$
$$(\Delta H_3) = -33.0 \text{ Kcal mole}^{-1}$$
$$(\Delta H_4) = -62.9 \text{ Kcal mole}^{-1}.$$

These data lead to $(\Delta H_1) = -2.6$ Kcal or -1.3 Kcal per mole of $MgSiO_3$ formed.

7.1.3. *The reaction olivine + quartz → orthopyroxene.*—This reaction is comparable to the previous one and may be formulated as

$$(Mg_xFe_{1-x})_2SiO_4 + SiO_2 \to 2(Mg_xFe_{1-x})SiO_3 \ (0 \leqslant x \leqslant 1).$$

The calculation of the heat of reaction $[\Delta H_1(x)]$ implies knowledge of the variation of the enthalpies of solution $[\Delta H_2(x)]$ and $[\Delta H_4(x)]$ as functions of the composition of the minerals. If it is assumed that the series forsterite (Mg_2SiO_4)—fayalite (Fe_2SiO_4) and enstatite ($MgSiO_3$)—orthoferrosilite ($FeSiO_3$) are ideal solid solutions, (ΔH_2) and (ΔH_4) are then linear functions of x. Knowledge of the heats of solution in HF of forsterite (-95.4 Kcal mole^{-1}), of fayalite (-81.3 Kcal mole^{-1}), of enstatite (-62.9 Kcal mole^{-1}), and of orthoferrosilite (-57.0 Kcal mole^{-1}), leads to the expressions:

$$[\Delta H_2(x)] = -81.3 - 14.2x, \text{ Kcal mole}^{-1}$$
$$[\Delta H_4(x)] = -57.0 - 5.9x, \text{ Kcal mole}^{-1}$$

and consequently to an expression for the heat of reaction,

$$[\Delta H_1(x)] = [\Delta H_2(x)] + (\Delta H_3) - [2\,\Delta H_4(x)] = -(0.3 + 2.3x) \text{ Kcal.}$$

For $x = 1$ the result already established (ΔH_1) = -2.6 Kcal is found again.

7.1.4. Solid solutions.—It was assumed at the start of the preceding example that the series forsterite—fayalite and enstatite—orthoferrosilite constitute true solid solutions, somewhat analogous to ideal solutions in the sense that the substitution of a Fe^{2+} ion for a Mg^{2+} ion, or *vice versa*, does not disturb the structure of the minerals. The calorimetric measurements of Sahama and Torgeson (1949) on intermediate olivines and pyroxenes (fig. 6) confirm this hypothesis. But it must be pointed out that this is not always so in the many mineral series that are commonly regarded as solid solutions.

Thus, the heat of solution of the plagioclase feldspars (Ab_xAn_{1-x}) in hydrofluoric acid is not a linear function of x (fig. 7), as the work of Kracek and Neuvonen (1952) has shown. These authors worked on feldspars separated from coarse-grained igneous rocks (anorthosites, pegmatites, and so on), which it is reasonable to suppose were of low temperature structural type (with the exception of a pure synthetic anorthite). The difference between the heat of solution of such a feldspar and that of the solid solution of the same composition (calculated from the heats of solution of pure albite and anorthite) may reach -5 Kcal mole^{-1} for a bytownite of composition An_{80}.* These

* It must be noted that Kracek and Neuvonen took as their reference the hypothetical solid solution between low–temperature albite (Ab_{LT}) and high–temperature

irregularities could be explained in the following manner (Buerger, 1948; Cole, Sorum and Taylor, 1951). At high temperature the plagioclases form a continuous solid solution. At low temperatures two series can be distinguished, one isomorphous with albite (An_0 to An_{30}) and the other isomorphous with anorthite (An_{70} to An_{100}). Be-

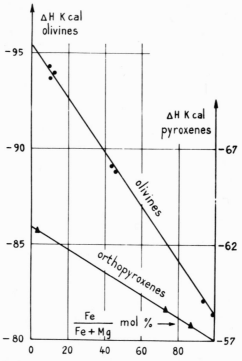

Fig. 6. Heats of solution of olivines and pyroxenes in HF (after Sahama and Torgeson, 1949).

tween An_{30} and An_{70} incipient unmixing and the formation of a complex composed of the two structural types, somewhat analogous

anorthite (An_{HT}). It would have been more logical to have compared the results obtained on natural low–temperature feldspars with the true solid solution between the high–temperature polymorphs, $Ab_{HT} - An_{HT}$. The authors have however measured the heat of solution of high–temperature albite in hydrofluoric acid, from which it may be deduced that at 74.7°C $(\Delta H_{Ab_{HT}}) - (\Delta H_{Ab_{LT}}) = -2.3$ Kcal mole^{-1} (this enthalpy evidently corresponds to the heat of transformation from ordered (low-temperature) to disordered (high–temperature) albite.)

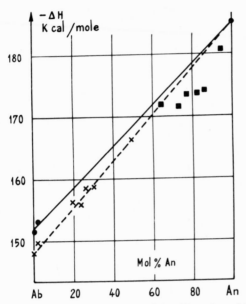

Fig. 7. Heats of solution of plagioclases in HF (after Kracek and Neuvonen, 1952).
  Crosses: pegmatites (low temperature).
  Squares: norites and anorthosites.
  Circles: synthetic or heated (high temperature).

to the cryptoperthites in the alkali feldspar series (see also Chapter XI–2) may be expected.

The indirect calculation of heats of reaction by construction of a cycle is described in some textbooks of thermodynamics as the application of Hess' Law. But no new law is involved, merely a simple application of the First Law.

7.2. The method of "standard" data.

7.2.1. *The principle of the method and some definitions.*—It is convenient to introduce the method by considering the now familiar reaction

$$\underset{\text{forsterite}}{Mg_2SiO_4} + \underset{\text{quartz}}{SiO_2} \rightarrow \underset{\text{enstatite}}{2\ MgSiO_3}.$$

The enthalpy of reaction (ΔH) may be expressed in the form

$$(\Delta H) = 2\,H_{en} - H_q - H_{fo}$$

it being supposed that the absolute enthalpies of the compounds involved are known. However only changes in enthalpy can be determined and moreover it is only the changes that are required for thermodynamic calculations. But it is possible by constructing more or less complicated cycles from various calorimetric measurements to calculate once and for all the enthalpies of formation of compounds from their elements. It is convenient to derive enthalpies of formation for 298.16°K and under certain other conditions that will be specified in due course.

$$2\,Mg(c) + Si(c) + 2\,O_2(g) \rightarrow Mg_2SiO_4(fo)\,;\,\Delta H^0_{298}(fo) = -508.1\ Kcal$$
$$Mg(c) + Si(c) + \tfrac{3}{2}\,O_2(g) \rightarrow MgSiO_3(en)\,;\,\Delta H^0_{298}(en) = -357.9\ Kcal$$
$$Si(c) + O_2(g) \rightarrow SiO_2(q)\,;\,\Delta H^0_{298}(q) = -205.4^*\ Kcal.$$

The enthalpy of reaction is derived directly as

$$(\Delta H)^0_{298} = 2\,\Delta H^0_{298}(en) - \Delta H^0_{298}(q) - \Delta H^0_{298}(fo) = -2.3\ Kcal.$$

The values $\Delta H^0_{298}(en)$, $\Delta H^0_{298}(q)$, $\Delta H^0_{298}(fo)$ are called the *standard enthalpies of formation* of enstatite, quartz, and forsterite respectively. The subscript 298 indicates the reference temperature (298.16°K = 25°C) and the whole suffix $^0_{298}$ describes the *reference state* or *standard conditions*.

Standard enthalpy, as an example of standard data, is defined as the change in enthalpy ΔH_i on formation of one mole of the substance i at 298.16°K in the reference state, which is defined, according to the case in question, in the following manner:

* These data are taken from Rossini *et al.* (1952) with the exception of the heat of formation of forsterite (for which Rossini gives $\Delta H^0_{298}(fo) = -488.2$), for which an improved value has been calculated in the following manner.

$$\Delta H^0_{298}(SiO_2,\ quartz) = -205.4\ Kcal\ mole^{-1}$$
(Rossini et al., 1952)

$$\Delta H^0_{298}(MgO,\ periclase) = -143.8\ Kcal\ mole^{-1}$$

$$SiO_2 + 2\,MgO \rightarrow Mg_2SiO_4;\ (\Delta H)^0_{298} = -15.1\ Kcal\ mole^{-1}$$
(Miyashiro, 1960).

The heat of formation of forsterite from its elements is then readily deducible as

$$\Delta H^0_{298}(fo) = -15.1 - 205.4 - 2(143.8) = -508.1\ Kcal\ mole^{-1}$$

Condensed phases: T = 298.16°K, P = 1 atm. The standard enthalpy of elements in their stable solid or liquid state is taken equal to zero.

Gaseous phases: T = 298.16°K, f = 1 atm (f = fugacity of the gas, that is the imaginary pressure at which the real gas would have the same properties as the corresponding perfect gas). The standard enthalpy of elements in their stable gaseous state is taken equal to zero.

Solute phases: T = 298.16°K, a = 1 mole liter^{-1}, the external pressure being 1 atm (a = activity of a substance in solution, that is the imaginary concentration at which the solution would have the same properties as the corresponding ideal solution). The standard enthalpy of the H^+ ion under these conditions is taken equal to zero.

The heat of reaction for a reaction written in the most generalized manner

$$\sum_i n_i M_i \rightarrow \sum_j n'_j M'_j,$$

is given by

$$(\Delta H)^0_{298} = \sum_j n'_j \Delta H^0_{298}(j) - \sum_i n_i \Delta H^0_{298}(i).$$

Standard enthalpies of formation could equally well be defined with reference to oxides; for forsterite and enstatite for instance:

$$2\ MgO + SiO_2 \rightarrow Mg_2SiO_4;\ \Delta H'^0_{298}(fo)$$
$$MgO + SiO_2 \rightarrow MgSiO_3;\ \Delta H'^0_{298}(en).$$

The stable oxides under the standard conditions (for SiO_2, quartz; for MgO, periclase) are assigned zero standard enthalpy. The use of this convention is not very widespread; but, for obvious reasons, some petrologists appear to prefer it to the more usual convention.

Standard data are very useful in practice and are consequently systematically collected and tabulated in a number of publications, which are regularly kept up to date; reference to some of these collections is made in the bibliography.

7.2.2. Examples of the use of standard data.—(a) Calculation of the heats of reaction at 298°K and 1 atm for the three reactions:

$$C\ (diamond) + \tfrac{1}{2}\ O_2(g) \rightarrow CO(g);\ (\Delta H)^0_{298}$$
$$C\ (graphite) + CO_2(g) \rightarrow 2\ CO(g);\ (\Delta H')^0_{298}$$
$$C\ (diamond) \rightarrow C\ (graphite);\ (\Delta H'')^0_{298}.$$

The standard enthalpies (in Kcal mole^{-1}) of the substances involved are given in Rossini *et al.* (1952) as:

Graphite	Diamond	$CO_2(g)$	$CO(g)$
0	+0.45	−94.05	−26.41

The standard enthalpy of formation of graphite is taken as zero since it is the stable form of carbon at 298°K under one atmosphere pressure. Likewise for oxygen. Therefore the three heats of reaction are given by:

$$(\Delta H)^0_{298} = -26.41 - 0.45 = -26.86 \text{ Kcal}$$
$$(\Delta H')^0_{298} = -2(26.41) - (-94.05) = +41.23 \text{ Kcal}$$
$$(\Delta H'')^0_{298} = -0.45 \text{ Kcal.}$$

(b) Calculation of the enthalpies of solution of calcite and aragonite in water and the heat of transformation of calcite to aragonite under the conditions, T = 298°K, P = 1 atm, ions in ideal solution of concentration molality equal to unity.

$$CaCO_3 \text{ (calcite)} \rightarrow Ca^{2+} + CO_3^{2-}; (\Delta H)^0_{298}$$
$$CaCO_3 \text{ (aragonite)} \rightarrow Ca^{2+} + CO_3^{2-}; (\Delta H')^0_{298}$$
$$CaCO_3 \text{ (calcite)} \rightarrow CaCO_3 \text{ (aragonite)}; (\Delta H'')^0_{298}.$$

Standard enthalpies of formation given in Rossini *et al.* (1952) are:

Calcite	Aragonite	Ca^{2+}	CO_3^{2-}
−288.45	−288.49	−129.77	−161.63

Therefore:

$$(\Delta H)^0_{298} = -129.77 - 161.63 - (-288.45) = -2.95 \text{ Kcal}$$
$$(\Delta H')^0_{298} = -129.77 - 161.63 - (-288.49) = -2.91 \text{ Kcal}$$
$$(\Delta H'')^0_{298} = -288.49 - (-288.45) = -0.04 \text{ Kcal.}$$

(c) Calculation of heats of reaction for the following reactions:

$$\underset{\text{nepheline}}{NaAlSiO_4} + \underset{\text{quartz}}{2\ SiO_2} \rightarrow \underset{\text{albite}}{NaAlSi_3O_8}; (\Delta H)^0_{298}$$
$$\underset{\text{leucite}}{KAlSi_2O_6} + \underset{\text{quartz}}{SiO_2} \rightarrow \underset{\text{orthoclase}}{KAlSi_3O_8}; (\Delta H')^0_{298}.$$

Standard enthalpies of formation from the oxides are given by Miyashiro (1960) as:

Nepheline	Leucite	Albite	Orthoclase
−36.2	−51.6	−41.2	−56.4

The standard enthalpy of formation of quartz is taken equal to zero since it is the stable polymorph of SiO_2 under the standard conditions. It is immediately evident that:

$$(\Delta H)^0_{298} = -41.2 - (-36.2) = -5.0 \text{ Kcal}$$
$$(\Delta H')^0_{298} = -56.4 - (-51.6) = -4.8 \text{ Kcal.}$$

These few examples should suffice to display the convenience and simplicity of the use of standard data. Regrettably the data of geological interest that are available are few indeed and many experimental measurements remain to be made in the future.

V

The Second Law

1. Direction of change

1.1. Preliminary.

The First Law asserts the equivalence of the various forms of energy and in particular of thermal and mechanical energy. The various relations derived from the First Law are of universal application, but they give no indication of whether the changes envisaged can actually take place.

Consider for instance a fragment of metallic sodium thrown into water; the First Law shows that, no matter what the physical form of the metal (sheet, granular, or powdered sodium) or how it is thrown into the water (slowly or rapidly), the energetic balance remains the same. The inverse change gives, again according to the First Law, the same overall balance with reversed sign. Experience shows however that under normal conditions the system $Na + H_2O$ changes spontaneously to $NaOH$ (or $Na^+ + OH^-$), while under the same conditions an aqueous solution of $NaOH$ can never change to $Na + H_2O$.

It is a completely general fact of observation that in nature changes have a definite sense, some are spontaneous (natural), others not so (unnatural).

These terms, which are due to Planck, are however not rigorous. For instance the melting of ice is a natural change above $0°C$ at atmospheric pressure and an unnatural change below that temperature. Is there then any thermodynamic criterion that can indicate the direction of a change and, if so, what is it? These are the questions that the Second Law answers.

1.2. A blind alley: affinity.

Thermodynamicists and chemists did not immediately find the answer; many hesitant steps intervened. The best known of these is that of Berthelot, the nineteenth century French chemist, who proposed the term *affinity* for the quantity characteristic of direction of change and put it equal to the heat loss in the change at constant pressure:

$$A = -(\Delta H).$$

According to Berthelot a reaction would take place spontaneously if $A > 0$, or in current terminology, if the reaction were exothermic.

This statement would be acceptable if it were generally true. Now, although under normal conditions the majority of exothermic reactions occur spontaneously, some do not and moreover some endothermic reactions do occur spontaneously. For instance, some salts dissolve with evolution and others with absorption of heat; in either case the process of solution takes place spontaneously. The example of the reaction water $\rightleftharpoons$ ice is equally instructive: below 0°C water changes to ice with evolution of heat, but above 0°C the inverse reaction, which is endothermic, occurs.

Berthelot did not ignore such observations, but attempted to separate such changes, which he qualified as *physical* and *chemical* changes. It must however be remembered that it is also very easy to change the sense of certain chemical reactions: the saponification of esters is one elementary example well-known to chemists.

---

2.   Statement of the Second Law, the second abstraction of thermodynamics: entropy

There are many ways of expressing the Second Law. We shall here follow our practice in the case of the First Law, by choosing a primary statement that is immediately understandable and common-sensical:

Two bodies which are at different temperatures exchange heat in such a manner that heat flows naturally from the hotter to the colder body.*

Just as, in order to express the First Law, the thermodynamic function internal energy was introduced, so it becomes necessary now to define a *function of evolution* to give quantitative expression and greater usefulness to the Second Law. This function has been named entropy† and is represented by the symbol S.

2.1. Isolated systems.

Consider an isolated system (that is a system exchanging neither heat nor matter with the external system) composed of two phases 1 and 2 at absolute temperatures T_1 and T_2 respectively such that $T_2 > T_1$. If dQ_1 is the heat gained by phase 1 and dQ_2 the heat gained by phase 2 in the course of their reaction (fig. 8), put

$$dS_1 = \frac{dQ_1}{T_1} \qquad \text{and} \qquad dS_2 = \frac{dQ_2}{T_2}.$$

The quantities dS_1 and dS_2 are, by definition, the changes in entropy of each phase respectively.

By definition then, the function S is an extensive property and the total change in entropy of the system is given by

$$dS = dS_1 + dS_2.$$

And by application of the First Law to an isolated system

$$dQ_1 + dQ_2 = 0$$

therefore

$$dS = dQ_1 \left(\frac{1}{T_1} - \frac{1}{T_2} \right).$$

Since phase 1 is the colder, it must, by the Second Law, receive heat, that is $dQ_1 > 0$. Therefore

$$\overline{dS > 0.}$$

In a natural change, the entropy of an isolated system can only increase.

---

* Clausius (1850) stated the Second Law as: heat cannot pass of its own accord from a colder to a hotter body.

† From the Greek word τροπή, meaning transformation.

2.2. *Closed systems.*

Consider a closed system (that is a system that does not exchange matter with the exterior) composed of two phases 1 and 2 at absolute temperatures T_1 and T_2, where $T_2 > T_1$ (fig. 9).

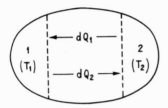

Fig. 8. Two phases 1 and 2 react with exchange of heat in an isolated system.

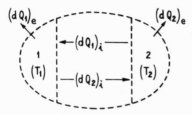

Fig. 9. In a closed system two phases 1 and 2 react with exchange of heat with one another and with the exterior.

Phase 1 exchanges an amount of heat $(dQ_1)_e$ with the exterior and an amount $(dQ_1)_i$ with phase 2:

$$dQ_1 = (dQ_1)_e + (dQ_1)_i$$

and likewise for phase 2

$$dQ_2 = (dQ_2)_e + (dQ_2)_i.$$

Again put

$$dS = \frac{dQ_1}{T_1} + \frac{dQ_2}{T_2}$$

so that

$$dS = \frac{(dQ_1)_e}{T_1} + \frac{(dQ_2)_e}{T_2} + \frac{(dQ_1)_i}{T_1} + \frac{(dQ_2)_i}{T_2}$$

and notice that

$$(dQ_1)_i + (dQ_2)_i = 0,$$

therefore

$$dS = \frac{(dQ_1)_e}{T_1} + \frac{(dQ_2)_e}{T_2} + (dQ)_i \left(\frac{1}{T_1} - \frac{1}{T_2} \right).$$

Put

$$(dS)_e = \frac{(dQ_1)_e}{T_1} + \frac{(dQ_2)_e}{T_2}$$

and

$$(dS)_i = (dQ)_i \left(\frac{1}{T_1} - \frac{1}{T_2}\right)$$

so that

$$dS = (dS)_e + (dS)_i.$$

The total change in entropy is thus split into the entropy exchanged internally and externally.

By the Second Law, since $T_2 > T_1$,

$$(dQ_1)_i > 0$$

whence

[1′] $\overline{(dS)_i > 0}$

and consequently

$$dS > (dS)_e$$

so that

[2] $dS > \frac{(dQ_1)_e}{T_1} + \frac{(dQ_2)_e}{T_2}.$

In a natural process, *the change in entropy resulting from internal heat exchanges in a closed system is always positive.* It should be noticed that the sign of the overall change in entropy dS does not give any information about the direction of evolution of the system.

2.3. Open systems.

In the preceding paragraphs it has not been found necessary to make any assumptions about the origin of the thermal exchanges. That the system exchanges or does not exchange matter is clearly not relevant and the results already established can be extended immediately to open systems, for which therefore

$$\overline{(dS)_i > 0},$$

$$dS > \frac{(dQ_1)_e}{T_1} + \frac{(dQ_2)_e}{T_2}.$$

3. General conditions for equilibrium or evolution

It has been shown that, in a very general way, the change in entropy of a system can be written as

$$dS = (dS)_e + (dS)_i$$

with

$$(dS)_i = (dQ_1)_i \left(\frac{1}{T_1} - \frac{1}{T_2}\right).$$

When the system is in equilibrium $T_1 = T_2$, therefore

$$(dS)_i = 0$$

so that

$$dS = (dS)_e$$

or

[3] $$\overline{dS = \frac{dQ}{T}}$$ (Equilibrium condition).

If the system is not in equilibrium, $(dS)_i > 0$ and consequently

[4] $$\overline{dS > \frac{dQ}{T}}$$ (Evolutionary condition).

4. Reversible and irreversible changes

So far only elementary changes have been discussed. Consider now a system evolving from an initial state 1 toward a final state 2. The change may occur in a single step or may be imagined to consist of an infinite sequence of infinitesimally close equilibrium states. This amounts to saying that if the state of the system is governed by the parameters $x, y, z \ldots$, then starting from state 1 $(x_1, y_1, z_1 \ldots)$ the parameters take on new, infinitesimally different values $(x_1 + dx, y_1 + dy, z_1 + dz \ldots)$ and a new equilibrium is established; further infinitesimal change in the parameters leads to yet another equilibrium state and so on. When a system evolves a finite amount in a single step it is said to undergo an *irreversible change;* when it evolves through an infinite succession of infinitesimally separated equilibrium states it is said to undergo a *reversible change.*

In a reversible process taking a system from state 1 to state 2

$$dS = \frac{dQ}{T}$$

for each of the intermediate equilibria; and for the total transformation (fig. 10):

[5]
$$\overline{\int_1^2 \frac{dQ}{T} = S_2 - S_1 = \Delta S} \qquad \text{(Reversible process).}$$

When a system passes from a state 1 to a state 2 by a series of reversible changes, the value of the integral

$$\int_1^2 \frac{dQ}{T}$$

is equal to the difference in the values of the function entropy in states 1 and 2.

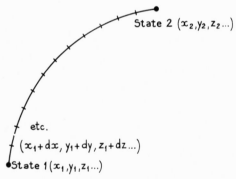

State 2 $(x_2, y_2, z_2 \ldots)$

etc.

$(x_1 + dx, y_1 + dy, z_1 + dz \ldots)$

State 1 $(x_1, y_1, z_1 \ldots)$

Fig. 10. Change from a state 1 to a state 2 by a sequence of reversible changes.

The integral depends only on the initial and final states and is independent of the path taken by the change from one state to the other. This is an interesting and significant attribute of reversible changes, which leads to a precise statement reminiscent of that used for the First Law: $dS = \frac{dQ}{T}$ *is a perfect differential for a reversible process.*

The relation $\int_1^2 \frac{dQ}{T} = \Delta S$, appropriate to a reversible change, becomes for an irreversible change:

[6] $$\overline{\int_1^2 \frac{dQ}{T} < \Delta S}$$ (Irreversible process).

5.   Isothermal changes: the auxiliary functions, free energy and free enthalpy

Equations (3) and (4) are completely general and are adequate for dealing with every thermodynamic problem, but the imposition of certain restrictive conditions leads to some equations of greater practical interest.

5.1. Conditions of equilibrium and of evolution for isothermal changes.

Consider the isothermal transformation that takes a system from state 1 to state 2. Since P is constant, equation (5) becomes

$$\Delta S = \frac{1}{T} \int_1^2 dQ = \frac{\Delta Q}{T}$$

whence

[7] $\Delta Q - T \Delta S = 0$.

It is known from the previous discussion of the First Law (see p. 42) that ΔQ has special properties in the case of thermomechanical changes (that is changes where work is done only against pressure) at constant volume or constant pressure:

$$V \text{ constant, } \Delta Q_V = \Delta U$$
$$P \text{ constant, } \Delta Q_P = \Delta H.$$

Substitution in equation (7) yields

[8]   T, V constant, $\Delta U - T \Delta S = 0$ ⎱
[8′]   T, P constant, $\Delta H - T \Delta S = 0$ ⎰
                                         (Equilibrium conditions).

These equations represent respectively the conditions for equilibrium in isothermal thermochemical changes at constant volume and constant pressure.

Similar reasoning applied to irreversible changes leads to the derivation from equation (8) of

[9]   T, V constant, $\Delta U - T \Delta S < 0$ ⎱
[9′]   T, P constant, $\Delta H - T \Delta S < 0$ ⎰
                                         (Evolutionary conditions).

5.2. *Free energy and free enthalpy.*

We have already defined three thermodynamic functions: U and H, which are necessary for the precise expression of the First Law and S which serves to give mathematical expression to the Second Law. These three functions are necessary and sufficient for all thermodynamic studies.* But for the sake of symmetry and convenience it is desirable to introduce two additional functions defined by the equations

[10]
$$F = U - TS$$
$$G = H - TS.\dagger$$

How can the conditions of equilibrium or of evolution of a reaction be expressed in terms of F and G?

Equations (8) and (8′) may be rewritten as

$$T, V \text{ constant, } (U_2 - TS_2) - (U_1 - TS_1) = 0$$
$$T, P \text{ constant, } (H_2 - TS_2) - (H_1 - TS_1) = 0$$

and taking equation (10) into account,

$$(U_2 - TS_2) - (U_1 - TS_1) = F_2 - F_1 = \Delta F$$
$$(H_2 - TS_2) - (H_1 - TS_1) = G_2 - G_1 = \Delta G$$

it follows that

[11]
$$T, V \text{ constant, } \Delta F = 0$$
$$T, P \text{ constant, } \Delta G = 0$$
(Equilibrium conditions).

It is thus possible to express very simply by use of the functions F and G *the equilibrium conditions for isothermal thermomechanical changes at constant volume or constant pressure.*

With the same definitions equations (9) and (9′) become

[12]
$$T, V \text{ constant, } \Delta F < 0$$
$$T, P \text{ constant, } \Delta G < 0$$
(Evolutionary conditions).

That is to say, when a system evolves naturally (that is, undergoes a

---

* Gibbs' treatment of thermodynamics made use only of U and S.
† The first, F, is called free energy (or Helmholtz function), the second, G, free enthalpy (or Gibbs' function).

H is not necessary

see p. 42 footnote

natural process) in an isothermal manner at constant volume or constant pressure, its free energy or free enthalpy always decreases.*

5.3. Properties of the functions F and G.

5.3.1. The defining equations (10).

$$F = U - TS$$
$$G = H - TS$$

show that since U, H, *and* S *are extensive properties, the functions* F *and* G *are so also.*

5.3.2.—On differentiation the defining equation for free energy $F = U - TS$ becomes

$$dF = dU - T\,dS - S\,dT$$

and if T is constant, $dT = 0$ so that

$$dF = dU - T\,dS.$$

Since dU and dS are perfect differentials, dF must be so likewise.

It is therefore possible to express simultaneously the two Laws for an isothermal reversible change in mathematical form by stating that dF *is a perfect differential.*

5.3.3.—On differentiation the defining equation for free enthalpy $G = H - TS$, or $G = U + PV - TS$ becomes

$$dG = dU + P\,dV + V\,dP - T\,dS - S\,dT$$

and if P, T are constant, $dP = 0$ and $dT = 0$ so that

$$dG = dU + P\,dV - T\,dS.$$

Since dU, dV, and dS are perfect differentials, so is dG.

It is therefore possible to express simultaneously the two Laws for an isothermal reversible change in mathematical form by stating that dG *is a perfect differential.*

---

* Equations (11) and (12) only indicate equilibrium or evolution in thermomechanical changes; when other modes of work, ΔW, are involved, the conditions are different (see the table on p. 66).

6.   Summary of conditions for equilibrium

Criterion		Conditions imposed			
Equilibrium	Evolution	Thermo-mechanical	Isothermal	V const.	P const.
$dS = dQ/T$	$dS > dQ/T$				
$\Delta S = \Delta Q/T$	$\Delta S > \Delta Q/T$		×		
$\Delta F = \Delta W$	$\Delta F < \Delta W$		×	×	
$\Delta G = \Delta W$	$\Delta G < \Delta W$		×		×
$\Delta F = 0$	$\Delta F < 0$	×	×	×	
$\Delta G = 0$	$\Delta G < 0$	×	×		×

7.   Applications of the Second Law

7.1. The functions S, F, *and* G *for a reaction.*

Consider the generalized reaction (p. 32),

$$\overset{1}{\underset{i}{\sum}} n_i M_i \rightarrow \overset{2}{\underset{j}{\sum}} n_j' M_j'.$$

The reaction is accompanied by changes in magnitude of the thermodynamic functions U, H, S, F, and G. Each of the changes (ΔU), (ΔH), etc. is clearly a function of the parameters of state $x, y, z \ldots$.

It has already been shown that if certain restrictions are applied to the manner in which the reaction takes place (constant temperature, pressure, or volume, etc.), the study of (ΔG) or of (ΔF) will yield information about the conditions of equilibrium or evolution. In particular, it now becomes possible to predict the sense of a reaction, for which state 1 or state 2 is stable, under any given conditions $x_0, y_0, z_0 \ldots$. Suppose for instance that the reaction takes place isothermally at constant pressure. Then if (ΔG) $(x_0, y_0, z_0 \ldots) < 0$, the reaction would evolve naturally from left to right, that is state 2 would be stable. If, on the contrary, (ΔG) $(x_0, y_0, z_0 \ldots) > 0$, then state 1 would be stable. Or if (ΔG) $(x_0, y_0, z_0 \ldots) = 0$, the two states would be in equilibrium.

The functions (ΔF) and (ΔG) could be determined either directly by experimental observation of an isothermal process, or by some indirect means. The application of the method of standard data will be discussed to start with.

Since S, F, and G are extensive properties, expressions analogous to those already developed (p. 51) for H and U apply to these functions also:

$$(\Delta S)_{298}^0 = \sum_j n'_j (S'_j)_{298}^0 - \sum_i n_i (S_i)_{298}^0$$

$$(\Delta F)_{298}^0 = \sum_j n'_j (F'_j)_{298}^0 - \sum_i n_i (F_i)_{298}^0$$

$$(\Delta G)_{298}^0 = \sum_j n'_j (G'_j)_{298}^0 - \sum_i n_i (G_i)_{298}^0$$

where $(S)_{298}^0$, $(F)_{298}^0$, and $(G)_{298}^0$ are the standard entropy, free energy, and free enthalpy of the substances involved. And, further, the defining equations (10) become

$$(\Delta F)_{298}^0 = (\Delta U)_{298}^0 - T(\Delta S)_{298}^0$$

$$(\Delta G)_{298}^0 = (\Delta H)_{298}^0 - T(\Delta S)_{298}^0.$$

These equations enable (ΔF) and (ΔG) to be calculated for any given reaction under the conditions of the standard state.

Standard enthalpy changes ΔH_{298}^0, have already been discussed in the chapter on the First Law (p. 51); standard entropies S_{298}^0 are obtained from specific heat measurements by the following reasoning:

$$dQ = C\,dT$$

and

$$dQ = T\,dS,$$

at constant pressure $dH = C_P\,dT$

and

$$dH = T\,dS$$

whence $dS = C_P \dfrac{dT}{T}$

and for $T = 298°K$

$$S_{298}^0 = S_0^0 + \int_0^{298} dS = S_0^0 + \int_0^{298} C_P \frac{dT}{T} = S_0^0 + \int_0^{298} C_P\,d(\ln T).$$

The integration may be performed graphically by tracing the curve of $C_P = f(\ln T)$ and evaluating the area beneath the curve.

To evaluate the constant of integration S_0^0 (entropy at absolute zero) a supplementary hypothesis (due to Planck and sometimes called the Third Law of Thermodynamics) is required:

The entropy of all crystalline substances at absolute zero has a finite value which is in many cases zero.

The calculation of S_0^0 by statistical methods from data furnished by direct measurements of entropy is theoretically possible.

However the results are few in number, but, if certain organic compounds are omitted, it is fair to say that they deviate little from the value zero. In the absence of further information it is therefore reasonable to put

$$S_0^0 = 0$$

whence

$$S_{298}^0 = \int_0^{298} C_P \, d(\ln T).$$

Clearly this equation is only applicable if no change of state intervenes between absolute zero and 298°K.

If, however, there are changes of state between 0°K and 298°K the integral will be split into separate integrals for each state and the latent heat of each change of state must be taken into account. For instance consider a substance that undergoes the transformations shown below between 0° and 298°K at 1 atmosphere:

Temperature	States and transformations	C_P	H
0°K	crystalline state α	C_{P_1}	
T_t	polymorphic transformation		$(\Delta H)_t$
	crystalline state β, low–temperature modification	C_{P_2}	
T_c	second order transformation		$(\Delta H)_c$
	crystalline state β, high–temperature modification	C_{P_3}	
T_f	fusion		$(\Delta H)_f$
	liquid	C_{P_4}	
T_v	vaporization		$(\Delta H)_v$
298°K	vapor	C_{P_5}	

S_{298}^0 is then evaluated from the equation:

$$S_{298}^0 = \int_0^{T_t} C_{P_1} d(\ln T) + \frac{(\Delta H)_t}{T_t} + \int_{T_t}^{T_e} C_{P_2} d(\ln T)$$

$$+ \frac{(\Delta H)_e}{T_e} + \int_{T_e}^{T_f} C_{P_3} d(\ln T) + \frac{(\Delta H)_f}{T_f}$$

$$+ \int_{T_f}^{T_v} C_{P_4} d(\ln T) + \frac{(\Delta H)_v}{T_v} + \int_{T_v}^{298} C_{P_5} d(\ln T).$$

7.2. Numerical examples.

In general entropies are evaluated from the equation $dS = \dfrac{dQ}{T}$ in cal mole^{-1} deg^{-1}; this unit is alternatively called the *entropy unit* (e.u.) or *clausius mole*$^{-1}$.

7.2.1.—Returning to the Solution of Calcite and Aragonite in Water and the Calcite-Aragonite Transformation (p. 54):

$$CaCO_3 \text{ (calcite)} \rightarrow Ca^{2+} + CO_3^{2-}; (\Delta G)_{298}^0$$
$$CaCO_3 \text{ (aragonite)} \rightarrow Ca^{2+} + CO_3^{2-}; (\Delta G')_{298}^0$$
$$CaCO_3 \text{ (calcite)} \rightarrow CaCO_3 \text{ (aragonite)}; (\Delta G'')_{298}^0.$$

The standard data are:

	Ca^{2+}	CO_3^{2-}	Calcite	Aragonite
ΔH_{298}^0 Kcal mole^{-1}	−129.77	−161.63	−288.45	−288.49
S_{298}^0 cal deg^{-1} mole^{-1}	−13.2	−12.7	+22.2	+21.2

The free enthalpy $(\Delta G)_{298}^0 = \Delta H_{298}^0 - T\Delta S_{298}^0$ of the first reaction is given by:

$(\Delta G)_{298}^0$
$\quad = -129{,}770 - 161{,}630 - (-288{,}450) - 298(-13.2 - 12.7 - 22.2)$
$\quad = +11{,}384$ cal mole^{-1}.

Likewise for the second reaction

$$(\Delta G')_{298}^0 = +11{,}126 \text{ cal mole}^{-1}.$$

It will be shown in the next chapter how these data can be extended to temperatures other than 298°K and used to calculate in a very simple manner the solubility of calcite and of aragonite. But for the present these results can be used to indicate which phase, calcite or aragonite, is stable at 298°K.

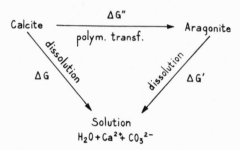

Fig. 11. Evaluation of the free enthalpy of the transformation from calcite to aragonite by construction of an imaginary cycle.

Consideration of the cycle displayed in fig. 11 leads immediately to the conclusion:

$$(\Delta G'')^0_{298} = (\Delta G)^0_{298} - (\Delta G')^0_{298}$$

that is

$$(\Delta G'')^0_{298} = 11,384 - 11,126 = +258 \text{ cal mole}^{-1}.$$

Thus the reaction calcite → aragonite takes place with increase in free enthalpy and it is therefore calcite that is stable under the standard conditions.

This conclusion can be arrived at directly simply by use of the standard data for calcite and aragonite:

$$(\Delta G'')^0_{298} = (\Delta H'')^0_{298} - T(\Delta S'')^0_{298}$$

that is

$(\Delta G'')^0_{298}$

$$= -288,490 - (-288,450) - 298(21.2 - 22.2) = +258 \text{ cal mole}^{-1}.$$

7.2.2. *Stability of jadeite at ordinary temperature and pressure.*—All attempts to synthesize jadeite, $NaAlSi_2O_6$, were unsuccessful for a number of years and so thermochemical experimentation and reasoning have been used by petrologists to establish its stability field. On heating jadeite goes to a glass, which can be recrystallized at 900 or 1000°C to produce a crystalline mixture of albite $NaAlSi_3O_8$ and nepheline $NaAlSiO_4$. The reverse, or jadeite producing, reaction is then

$$\tfrac{1}{2} \text{NaAlSiO}_4 + \tfrac{1}{2} \text{NaAlSi}_3\text{O}_8 \rightarrow \text{NaAlSi}_2\text{O}_6.$$

nepheline   albite   jadeite

Kracek, Neuvonen, and Burley (1951) have determined the enthalpies of solution in HF of the three phases and have found, by direct application of the First Law, that the heat of reaction at 20°C is:

$$(\Delta H)^0_{293} = -6200 \text{ cal mole}^{-1}.$$

From specific heat measurements Kelley and King (1961) have calculated the standard entropies of the three phases and thence the entropy change for the reaction is

$$(\Delta S)^0_{298} = -14.7 \text{ cal deg}^{-1} \text{ mole}^{-1}.$$

Assuming that $(\Delta H)^0_{298} \sim (\Delta H)^0_{293}$, the free enthalpy of reaction at 25°C is given by:

$$(\Delta G)^0_{298} = -6200 - 298(-14.7) = -1820 \text{ cal mole}^{-1}.$$

The change nepheline + albite → jadeite is thus accompanied at 25°C and 1 atmosphere by a decrease in free enthalpy. It is therefore jadeite that is stable under the standard conditions rather than the mixture nepheline + albite. We shall revert to this problem on p. 124.

VI

Dependence of Thermodynamic Functions on Parameters of State

This chapter is in the nature of an introduction to the succeeding chapters, though these should be readable without preliminary close study of this introduction. The various explicit values of the partial derivatives that are established here can be used quite effectively without thorough understanding of their derivation.

1. Introduction

We know that the thermodynamic functions U, H, S, F, and G are functions of the parameters of state x, y, z .... Let J represent any one of the functions. For certain values x, y, z ... of the parameters of state, the function J will then assume a value $J(x, y, z \ldots)$ and for the values $x + dx, y + dy, z + dz$ ... :

$$J + dJ = J(x + dx, y + dy, z + dz \ldots).$$

Thus for the increments dx, dy, dz ... of the parameters of state, there corresponds an increment dJ of the function under consideration, which can be expressed as:

[1] $$dJ = \left(\frac{\partial J}{\partial x}\right)_{y,z\ldots} dx + \left(\frac{\partial J}{\partial y}\right)_{x,z\ldots} dy + \left(\frac{\partial J}{\partial z}\right)_{x,y\ldots} dz \ldots$$

which amounts in practical terms to saying that the variation of J may be investigated by causing the parameters of state to vary, not all simultaneously, but one at a time. Thus the variation dJ of J as a function of x may be determined, all the parameters save x being maintained constant; then the variation dJ as a function of y, and so on. With complete generality the increment dJ is given by the sum of all such increments:

[2] $$dJ = X \, dx + Y \, dy + Z \, dz \ldots.$$

If the necessary conditions for dJ to be a perfect differential are fulfilled and not otherwise, then equations (1) and (2) become equivalent, and therefore:

$$\left(\frac{\partial J}{\partial x}\right)_{y,z\ldots} = X; \qquad \left(\frac{\partial J}{\partial y}\right)_{x,z\ldots} = Y; \quad \text{etc.}$$

It may be helpful at this stage to recapitulate the conditions under which dJ is a perfect differential:

J		Conditions	Reference
U	Internal energy	No restriction	Ch. IV, p. 37
H	Enthalpy	Constant pressure	Ch. IV, p. 42
S	Entropy	Reversible change	Ch. V, p. 62
F	Free energy	Isothermal reversible change	Ch. V, p. 65
G	Free enthalpy	Isothermal, isobaric reversible change	Ch. V, p. 65

The purpose of this chapter is to make the partial differentials explicit. It must be emphasized that this is primarily a matter of mathematical manipulation and not at all of physical understanding; the amount of attention devoted to this topic is entirely justified by the practical importance of the results obtained.

The parameters that are of interest and are more or less directly accessible to experimental observation are temperature T, pressure P, volume V, and number of moles n_1, n_2, n_3 . . . of the components 1, 2, 3 . . . of the system. To these it is necessary to add, when the occasion arises, surface tension between adjacent phases, intensity of a magnetic, electrical, or gravitational field, and so on. Thus,

$$dJ = \left(\frac{\partial J}{\partial T}\right)_{P,V,n_1,n_2\ldots} dT + \left(\frac{\partial J}{\partial P}\right)_{T,V,n_1,n_2\ldots} dP + \left(\frac{\partial J}{\partial V}\right)_{T,P,n_1,n_2\ldots} dV$$

$$+ \cdots + \left(\frac{\partial J}{\partial n_1}\right)_{T,P,V,n_2\ldots} dn_1 + \left(\frac{\partial J}{\partial n_2}\right)_{T,P,V,n_1\ldots} dn_2 + \cdots.$$

The expression may be simplified by grouping the terms due to variation of composition under the symbol

$$\sum_i \left(\frac{\partial J}{\partial n_i}\right)_{T,P,V,n_j} dn_i,$$

whence

$$[3] \quad dJ = \left(\frac{\partial J}{\partial T}\right)_{P,V,n_i} dT + \left(\frac{\partial J}{\partial P}\right)_{T,V,n_i} dP + \left(\frac{\partial J}{\partial V}\right)_{T,P,n_i} dV$$

$$+ \cdots + \sum_i \left(\frac{\partial J}{\partial n_i}\right)_{T,P,V,n_i} dn_i.$$

Consideration of the dependence of the thermodynamic functions on composition will be postponed until a later chapter (Chapter IX); in what follows it will be assumed that

$$\Sigma \left(\frac{\partial J}{\partial n_i}\right)_{T,P,V,n_j} dn_i = 0.$$

2.   Dependence of the thermodynamic functions on T, P, and V

It will be supposed in this section that not only composition, but all parameters other than T, P, and V remain constant. Equation (3) can then be rewritten

$$dJ = \left(\frac{\partial J}{\partial T}\right)_{P,V} dT + \left(\frac{\partial J}{\partial P}\right)_{T,V} dP + \left(\frac{\partial J}{\partial V}\right)_{T,P} dV.$$

2.1. Dependence of U, F, and S on T and V.

The study of the variation of U and F as functions of P is of little interest for the simple reason that other functions, H and G, have been specially created for just such a purpose.

Internal energy is defined by the equation

$$dU = dQ + dW.$$

And since all parameters other than T, P, and V are kept constant, work can only be done by pressure; therefore

$$dW = -P\,dV$$

and

$$[4] \qquad\qquad dU = dQ - P\,dV.$$

Moreover at constant volume

$$(dU)_V = (dQ)_V$$

and since by definition

$$dQ_V = C_V \, dT,$$

it follows that

[5]
$$\boxed{\left(\frac{\partial U}{\partial T}\right)_V = C_V.}$$

Since $dQ = T \, dS$ for a reversible change, equation (4) becomes:

[6]
$$dU = T \, dS - P \, dV.$$

But

$$dS = \left(\frac{\partial S}{\partial T}\right)_V dT + \left(\frac{\partial S}{\partial V}\right)_T dV;$$

and from (6):

[7]
$$dU = T\left(\frac{\partial S}{\partial T}\right)_V dT + \left[T\left(\frac{\partial S}{\partial V}\right)_T - P\right] dV$$

which on comparison with

[8]
$$dU = \left(\frac{\partial U}{\partial T}\right)_V dT + \left(\frac{\partial U}{\partial V}\right)_T dV$$

leads to

$$T\left(\frac{\partial S}{\partial T}\right)_V = \left(\frac{\partial U}{\partial T}\right)_V$$

and taking equation (5) into account

[9]
$$\boxed{\left(\frac{\partial S}{\partial T}\right)_V = \frac{C_V}{T}.}$$

Comparison of equations (7) and (8) also yields

[10]
$$\left(\frac{\partial U}{\partial V}\right)_T = T\left(\frac{\partial S}{\partial V}\right)_T - P.$$

Free energy F is defined by the equation

$$F = U - TS$$

which differentiates to

$$dF = dU - T \, dS - S \, dT;$$

substitution in equation (6) then leads to

$$dF = -S \, dT - P \, dV.$$

It suffices to compare this with the equation

$$dF = \left(\frac{\partial F}{\partial T}\right)_V dT + \left(\frac{\partial F}{\partial V}\right)_T dV$$

to obtain immediately:

[11]
$$\left(\frac{\partial F}{\partial T}\right)_V = -S$$

[12]
$$\left(\frac{\partial F}{\partial V}\right)_T = -P.$$

Supplementary equations may be obtained by recalling that dF is a perfect differential and that therefore

$$\frac{\partial \left(\frac{\partial F}{\partial T}\right)}{\partial V} = \frac{\partial \left(\frac{\partial F}{\partial V}\right)}{\partial T}.$$

Substitution of the values given by equations (11) and (12), for $\left(\frac{\partial F}{\partial T}\right)$ and $\left(\frac{\partial F}{\partial V}\right)$ yields

[13]
$$\left(\frac{\partial S}{\partial V}\right)_T = \left(\frac{\partial P}{\partial T}\right)_V.$$

Finally, substitution of equation (13) into equation (10), leads to

[14]
$$\left(\frac{\partial U}{\partial V}\right)_T = T \left(\frac{\partial P}{\partial T}\right)_V - P.$$

2.2. Dependence of H, G, and S on T and P.

Adopting a course precisely similar to that of VI–2.1, equations (5'), (11'), (9'), (14'), (12'), (13') analogous to those of VI–2.1 are obtained; they are displayed in the table below.

2.3. Recapitulation.

The table gathers together all the explicit expressions for the partial derivatives of the thermodynamic functions. Evaluation of the functions reduces in practice to the measurement of a few coefficients (see Chapter II):

$$C_V, \; C_P, \; \alpha, \; \chi.$$

The coefficients α and χ are defined by:

[15]
$$\alpha = \frac{1}{V} \left(\frac{\partial V}{\partial T}\right)_P$$

(coefficient of isobaric thermal expansion)

[16]
$$x = -\frac{1}{V}\left(\frac{\partial V}{\partial P}\right)_T$$

(coefficient of isothermal compressibility)

and equations (13′) and (14′) can then be rewritten as

$$\left(\frac{\partial H}{\partial P}\right)_T = V(1 - T\alpha) \quad \text{and} \quad \left(\frac{\partial S}{\partial P}\right)_T = -V\alpha.$$

To couch equations (13) and (14) in terms of α and χ it is necessary to write down the differential

$$dV = \left(\frac{\partial V}{\partial T}\right)_P dT + \left(\frac{\partial V}{\partial P}\right)_T dP$$

whence

$$\frac{dV}{dT} = \left(\frac{\partial V}{\partial T}\right)_P + \left(\frac{\partial V}{\partial P}\right)_T \frac{dP}{dT}$$

which leads at constant volume ($dV = 0$) from the definitions (15) and (16) to:

[17]
$$\left(\frac{\partial P}{\partial T}\right)_V = \frac{\alpha}{\chi}.$$

[5]	$\left(\frac{\partial U}{\partial T}\right)_V = C_V$	$\left(\frac{\partial U}{\partial V}\right)_T = T\left(\frac{\partial P}{\partial T}\right)_V - P = T\frac{\alpha}{\chi} - P$	[14]
[11]	$\left(\frac{\partial F}{\partial T}\right)_V = -S$	$\left(\frac{\partial F}{\partial V}\right)_T = -P$	[12]
[9]	$\left(\frac{\partial S}{\partial T}\right)_V = C_V/T$	$\left(\frac{\partial S}{\partial V}\right)_T = \left(\frac{\partial P}{\partial T}\right)_V = \frac{\alpha}{\chi}$	[13]
[5′]	$\left(\frac{\partial H}{\partial T}\right)_P = C_P$	$\left(\frac{\partial H}{\partial P}\right)_T = V - T\left(\frac{\partial V}{\partial T}\right)_P = V(1 - T\alpha)$	[14′]
[11′]	$\left(\frac{\partial G}{\partial T}\right)_P = -S$	$\left(\frac{\partial G}{\partial P}\right)_T = V$	[12′]
[9′]	$\left(\frac{\partial S}{\partial T}\right)_P = C_P/T$	$\left(\frac{\partial S}{\partial P}\right)_T = -\left(\frac{\partial V}{\partial T}\right)_P = -V\alpha$	[13′]

In the table the readily measurable physical quantities are the parameters of state P, V, T and the thermodynamic coefficients C_P, α, χ.

It should be noticed that knowledge of these is sufficient to determine all the partial derivatives in the table. In fact α and χ are tied, as has been seen, by equation (17) and C_V is dependent on C_P, α, and χ by an equation that can quite simply be derived:

[18]
$$C_P - C_V = TV \, \alpha^2/\chi.$$

2.4. The Gibbs-Helmholtz equations.

Substitution of the expressions for entropy from the table above in the defining equations for free energy and free enthalpy,

$$F = U - TS$$
$$G = H - TS$$

leads to

[19]
$$F = U + T \left(\frac{\partial F}{\partial T}\right)_V$$

[20]
$$G = H + T \left(\frac{\partial G}{\partial T}\right)_P.$$

Equations (19) and (20) are called the *Gibbs-Helmholtz equations*. It is also of some interest to evaluate the partial differentials

$$\left[\frac{\partial(F/T)}{\partial T}\right]_V \quad \text{and} \quad \left[\frac{\partial(G/T)}{\partial T}\right]_P.$$

The former may be rewritten as

$$\left[\frac{\partial(F/T)}{\partial T}\right]_V = \frac{T(\partial F/\partial T) - F}{T^2}$$

which, on substitution of equation (19) leads to

[21]
$$\left[\frac{\partial(F/T)}{\partial T}\right]_V = -\frac{U}{T^2}.$$

The equation

[22]
$$\left[\frac{\partial(G/T)}{\partial T}\right]_P = -\frac{H}{T^2}$$

can be established in an exactly analogous manner.

3. Dependence of the thermodynamic coefficients on the parameters of state

In contrast with what has been done in VI–2 for the thermodynamic functions, it must be admitted at once that classical thermodynamics is ill equipped for discussion of the dependence of such coefficients as C_P, α, χ on P, V, T (see I–2). It is usual in classical thermodynamics to accept experimental determinations of such coefficients or to fit them into various empirical formulae, or even to ignore them.

3.1.—Thus for specific heat as a function of temperature there are good grounds for assuming equations of the type

[23]
$$\begin{cases} C_P = C_0 + aT \\ \text{or } C_P = C_0 + a'T + b'T^2 \\ \text{or } C_P = C_0 + a''T - b''/T^2 \end{cases}$$

which conveniently represent the experimental data; a, a', a'', b', b'' are constants characteristic of each substance and the formulae apply within a restricted range of temperature that must be specified.

3.2.—The dependence of specific heats on P and V is, as will be shown, a relatively unimportant matter. The relation

$$\left(\frac{\partial C_V}{\partial V}\right)_T = \frac{\partial(\partial U/\partial T)_V}{\partial V} = \frac{\partial(\partial U/\partial V)_T}{\partial T}$$

leads, when equation (14) is substituted, to

$$\left(\frac{\partial C_V}{\partial V}\right)_T = \frac{\partial[T(\partial P/\partial T)_V - P]}{\partial T}$$

which simplifies to:

$$\left(\frac{\partial C_V}{\partial V}\right)_T = T\left(\frac{\partial^2 P}{\partial T^2}\right)_V$$

and on substitution of equation (17) becomes

[24]
$$\left(\frac{\partial C_V}{\partial V}\right)_T = T\left(\frac{\partial\left(\frac{\alpha}{\chi}\right)}{\partial T}\right)_V.$$

An analogous argument leads to

[25]
$$\left(\frac{\partial C_P}{\partial P}\right)_T = -T\left(\frac{\partial(V\alpha)}{\partial T}\right)_P.$$

It is apparent that these partial derivatives will usually be negligible; thus the second term in (25) becomes, on substitution of (15),

$$\left(\frac{\partial C_P}{\partial P}\right)_T = -T\left(\frac{\partial^2 V}{\partial T^2}\right)_P$$

which is clearly a second order quantity and therefore usually extremely small.

3.3.—The partial derivatives of α and χ as functions of P, V, T are likewise negligible in magnitude and no expressions will be derived for them.

4.   Simplifying hypotheses

The equations that have just been established assume a very simple form when certain hypotheses of state are applicable.

4.1. Perfect gases.

The hypothesis that is usually proposed to define a perfect gas is the well-known equation:

[26]
$$PV = RT$$

referring to one mole of the substance concerned. R is a constant independent of the nature of the gas and is equal to 1.987 cal deg^{-1} mole^{-1}. Equation (26) is called the *equation of state* since it interrelates certain parameters of state.

From (26) the partial derivatives may be evaluated as

[27]
$$\left(\frac{\partial V}{\partial T}\right)_P = \frac{R}{P}; \qquad \left(\frac{\partial P}{\partial T}\right)_V = \frac{R}{V}$$

whence the explicit evaluation of α and χ as

[28]
$$\alpha = \frac{R}{PV} = \frac{1}{T} \quad \text{and} \quad \chi = \frac{1}{P}$$

from (15) and (17).

The table of partial derivatives in VI–2.3 is thus simplified: the left hand column remains unchanged, while the right hand column becomes

$$\left(\frac{\partial U}{\partial V}\right)_T = 0; \qquad \left(\frac{\partial H}{\partial P}\right)_T = 0$$

from (14) and (14')

$$\left(\frac{\partial F}{\partial V}\right)_T = -\frac{RT}{V}; \qquad \left(\frac{\partial G}{\partial P}\right)_T = \frac{RT}{P}$$

from (12) and (12')

$$\left(\frac{\partial S}{\partial V}\right)_T = \frac{R}{V}; \qquad \left(\frac{\partial S}{\partial P}\right)_T = -\frac{R}{P}$$

from (13) and (13').

It is evident that internal energy and enthalpy become respectively independent of V and P at constant temperature.

Explicit expressions for F, G, and S may likewise be obtained from the modified table as

[29]	$dT = 0$	$dF = -RT\,d(\ln V)$	and	$F = F^0 - RT \ln V$
[29']		$dG = +RT\,d(\ln P)$	and	$G = G^0 + RT \ln P$
[30]	$dT = 0$	$dS = +R\,d(\ln V)$	and	$S = S^0 + R \ln V$
[30']		$dS = -R\,d(\ln P)$	and	$S = S'^0 - R \ln P$

F^0, G^0, S^0, and S'^0 are the energies and entropies corresponding respectively to unit volume and unit pressure at the temperature under consideration.

And the expressions for the derivatives of the thermodynamic coefficients (p. 79) are correspondingly simplified. Substitution of (27) into (24) and (25) yields

$$\left(\frac{\partial C_V}{\partial V}\right)_T = 0; \qquad \left(\frac{\partial C_P}{\partial P}\right)_T = 0.$$

On the other hand the perfect gas equation does not lead to any relationship between specific heat and temperature. The supplementary hypotheses of statistical thermodynamics must be introduced before any such relationship can be obtained.

4.2. Real gases. The concept of fugacity.

4.2.1.—Equation (29') is valid only for perfect gases. However the practical convenience of the equation is such that attempts have been made to generalize it for non-perfect gases. One such attempt, that of G. N. Lewis (1901) involves the introduction of the concept of *fugacity*. The fugacity of a real gas is defined as a function such that at a given temperature T°K

[31] $$dG = RT \, d \ln f.$$

It is obvious that fugacity will be measured in the same units as pressure.

For perfect gases equations (29′) and (31) must be equivalent, whence

$$d \ln f = d \ln P,$$

that is $\frac{f}{P}$ = constant. G. N. Lewis completed the definition of fugacity by stating that $f = P$ for perfect gases.

For non-ideal gases, the relationship between fugacity and pressure may be expressed as

[32] $$f = \gamma P$$

where γ is the *coefficient of fugacity*. Since all gases approach ideality at very low pressures, the coefficient of fugacity γ tends toward unity as P tends to zero.

4.2.2.—Substituting the value of dG obtained from (31) in the equation

$$\left(\frac{\partial G}{\partial P}\right)_T = V$$

the variation of fugacity with pressure is obtained as:

[33] $$\left(\frac{\partial \ln f}{\partial P}\right)_T = \frac{V}{RT}.$$

Substituting γP for f, this equation becomes

$$\left(\frac{\partial \ln \gamma}{\partial P}\right)_T = \frac{V}{RT} - \frac{1}{P}$$

and at a given temperature T°K

[34] $$RT \, d \ln \gamma = \left(V - \frac{RT}{P}\right) dP.$$

The two equations (33) and (34) provide a means of calculating the fugacity of a gas as a function of pressure at any temperature. The simplest way is to plot the curve $\alpha = f(\mathrm{P})$ for the deviation from the perfect gas equation, where

$$\alpha = \frac{RT}{P} - V \qquad \text{(fig. 12)}.$$

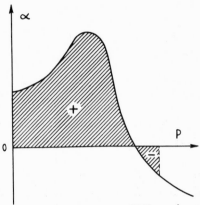

Fig. 12. Deviation from the perfect gas equation $\left(\dfrac{RT}{P} - V\right)$ as a function of pressure.

Equation (34) may then be rewritten as

$$RT\, d \ln \gamma = -\alpha\, dP$$

and integrated at constant temperature to give*

$$RT \ln \gamma = -\int_0^P \alpha\, dP.$$

The integral is evaluated by measuring the hachured area under the curve of fig. 12.

Alternatively it is possible to start from an equation of state, such as the Van der Waals equation:

[35] $$\left(P + \frac{a}{V^2}\right)(V - b) = RT$$

from which it can be shown that, neglecting second order small quantities,

---

* The constant of integration is zero since $\gamma = 1$ at $P = 0$.

[36] $$\ln f = \ln \frac{RT}{V - b} + \frac{b}{V - b} - \frac{2a}{RTV}.$$

And so the fugacity of a gas that obeys Van der Waals equation may be evaluated at any temperature.

By way of example the fugacity (in atmospheres) and the fugacity coefficient are shown below for CO_2 at various pressures (in atmospheres) at 60°C:

P	25	50	100	200	300
f	23.2	42.8	70.4	91	112
γ	0.928	0.856	0.704	0.455	0.373

5.   Examples of the dependence of G on other parameters of state

It is convenient to take as examples the calculation of the dependence of dG variously on surface area and on gravitational field strength. Free enthalpy has been chosen because it is the most commonly used function, but the calculation is exactly analogous for any other thermodynamic function.

It must be noticed at once that when the system exchanges work dW' other than that due to the effect of pressure, the expression for free enthalpy must be written for a closed system as:

$$dG = -S\,dT + V\,dP + dW'.$$

Now

$$dU = dQ + dW$$
$$dQ = T\,dS$$

and

$$dW = -P\,dV + dW',$$

therefore

[37] $$dU = T\,dS - P\,dV + dW'.$$

However

$$G = U - TS + PV,$$

which differentiates to

$$dG = dU - T\,dS - S\,dT + P\,dV + V\,dP$$

and therefore, taking (37) into account,

[38] $$dG = -S\,dT + V\,dP + dW'.$$

5.1. Effect of the interfacial surface between adjacent phases.

When the surface area s between two phases is changed, an amount of work dW' given by

$$dW' = \sigma\,ds$$

must be done. The coefficient σ is called the *surface tension* of the interface. The change in free enthalpy is then given by

$$dG = -S\,dT + V\,dP + \sigma\,ds,$$

which on comparison with

$$dG = \left(\frac{\partial G}{\partial T}\right)_{P,s} dT + \left(\frac{\partial G}{\partial P}\right)_{T,s} dP + \left(\frac{\partial G}{\partial s}\right)_{T,P} ds$$

yields immediately

[39] $$\boxed{\left(\frac{\partial G}{\partial s}\right)_{T,P} = \sigma.}$$

The surface tension σ thus represents also the *surface free enthalpy* per unit area under the given conditions of temperature and pressure; it is in consequence sometimes called the surface free enthalpy (or surface free energy).

In what follows it will never be necessary to consider the partial derivative (39) as its value is quite negligible for systems or phases that are commonly extended, that is for phases or systems that are not dispersed. It is common for σ to have a value of the order of 50 erg cm^{-2} or $\dfrac{50}{4.19} \times 10^{-7}$ cal cm^{-2}. In order that one mole of matter should make a *surface contribution* of the order of 10^3 calories, that is, of the same order as is usual for *volume contributions*, it would be necessary for it to have a surface area of the order of 10^9 cm^2. This carries the implication that the substance is exceedingly finely divided, since for an ordinary molar volume of about 30 cm^3, the particles would have to be of the order of 10^{-7} cm in radius.

5.2. Effect of gravitational field.

5.2.1.—Consider a system composed of i constituents of molar mass M_i and let n_i be the number of moles of constituent i. Use Φ to denote the most general expression of the gravitational field. If the field varies by an amount $d\Phi$, the work done on the system will be

$$dW' = \left(\sum_i n_i M_i\right) d\Phi$$

and the consequent free enthalpy change will be

[40] $$dG = -S\, dT + V\, dP + \left(\sum_i n_i M_i\right) d\Phi.$$

Whence

[41] $$\left(\frac{\partial G}{\partial \Phi}\right)_{T,P} = \sum_i n_i M_i.$$

5.2.2.—Suppose for instance that the height h of the system above the terrestrial surface is caused to vary by an amount dh. It is known that the gravitational potential is given by

$$\Phi = \theta\, \frac{M_T}{(r_T + h)^2}$$

where θ is a constant (66.7×10^{-9} c.g.s. units),

$$M_T = \text{mass of the Earth}$$
$$r_T = \text{radius of the Earth.}$$

Therefore

$$d\Phi = -2\theta\, \frac{M_T}{(r_T + h)^3}\, dh$$

whence

[42] $$\left(\frac{\partial G}{\partial h}\right)_{T,P} = -\frac{2\theta M_T}{(r_T + h)^3} \sum_i n_i M_i.$$

5.2.3.—Similarly if the depth h below the surface of the earth is made to vary by an amount dh, the field strength Φ being then given by

$$\Phi = \theta\, \frac{M_i}{(r_T - h)^2}$$

where M_i is the mass of the sphere of radius $r_T - h$, so that

$$M_i = M_T\, \frac{(r_T - h)^3}{r_T^3},$$

then

$$\Phi = \frac{\theta M_T}{r_T^3}\, (r_T - h),$$

therefore

$$d\Phi = -\frac{\theta M_T}{r_T^3} \, dh$$

and finally

[43]
$$\left(\frac{\partial G}{\partial h}\right)_{T,P} = -\frac{\theta M_T}{r_T^3} \sum_i n_i M_i.$$

5.2.4.—Suppose now that the system is the site of a reaction

$$\overbrace{\sum_i n_i M_i}^{1} \rightarrow \overbrace{\sum_j n'_j M'_j}^{2}.$$

A change $d\Phi$ in the gravitational field corresponds to a change in the free enthalpy of each of the states 1 and 2 such that

$$\left(\frac{\partial G_1}{\partial \Phi}\right)_{P,T} = \sum_i n_i M_i \qquad \text{and} \qquad \left(\frac{\partial G_2}{\partial \Phi}\right)_{P,T} = \sum_j n'_j M'_j$$

therefore

$$\left[\frac{\partial(\Delta G)}{\partial \Phi}\right]_{P,T} = \left(\frac{\partial G_2}{\partial \Phi}\right)_{P,T} - \left(\frac{\partial G_1}{\partial \Phi}\right)_{P,T} = \sum_j n'_j M'_j - \sum_i n_i M_i.$$

If the system is closed, that is at constant composition,

$$\sum_j n'_j M'_j = \sum_i n_i M_i$$

and therefore

[44]
$$\left[\frac{\partial(\Delta G)}{\partial \Phi}\right]_{P,T} = 0 \qquad (\Sigma \, dn_i = 0).$$

In a closed system the position of equilibrium of a chemical reaction is independent of the strength of the gravitational field.

VII

Influence of Temperature and Pressure on Equilibrium Conditions

1. Preliminary remarks

In this chapter only isothermal changes at constant pressure will be discussed. The relations for isothermal changes at constant volume may very easily be deduced from the expressions developed here by inserting internal energy and free energy in place of enthalpy and free enthalpy. Two additional restrictions will be imposed:

(1) that the composition of the system or of its constituent phases remains constant ($dn_i = 0$).

(2) that the influence of parameters other than T, P, and V is negligible; in particular surface tension at the interfaces between adjacent phases* will be neglected.

Considering in these terms the reaction,

$$\overbrace{\sum_i n_i M_i}^{1} \to \overbrace{\sum_j n'_j M'_j}^{2}$$

the accompanying changes in volume, specific heat, enthalpy, entropy, and free enthalpy will be given by

$$(\Delta V) = \overbrace{\sum_j n'_j V'_j}^{2} - \overbrace{\sum_i n_i V_i}^{1}$$

$$(\Delta C_P) = \sum_j n'_j C'_{Pj} - \sum_i n_i C_{Pi}$$

---

* Very little attention has been paid to this point in the earth sciences; De Vore (1959) has however made some relevant comments.

$$(\Delta H) = \sum_j n'_j H'_j - \sum_i n_i H_i$$

$$(\Delta S) = \sum_j n'_j S'_j - \sum_i n_i S_i$$

$$(\Delta G) = \sum_j n'_j G'_j - \sum_i n_i G_i.$$

Each change is a function of the parameters of state, which in this case are P and T. Consider for instance the change in enthalpy (ΔH), which may be rewritten in abbreviated form as

$$(\Delta H) = H_2 - H_1.$$

Now if temperature is varied at constant pressure,

$$\left(\frac{\partial \Delta H}{\partial T}\right)_P = \left[\frac{\partial(H_2 - H_1)}{\partial T}\right]_P = \left(\frac{\partial H_2}{\partial T}\right)_P - \left(\frac{\partial H_1}{\partial T}\right)_P$$

and since

$$\left(\frac{\partial H}{\partial T}\right)_P = C_P \qquad \text{(see Chapter VI),}$$

it follows that

$$\left(\frac{\partial \Delta H}{\partial T}\right)_P = C_{P_2} - C_{P_1} = (\Delta C_P).$$

Thus all the equations established in the preceding chapter remain valid for differences in thermodynamic functions due to reaction, provided the absolute values of the extensive parameters involved are replaced by their differences due to the reaction.

It is consequently possible, at least theoretically, to calculate the value of (ΔG) at any temperature and pressure: (1) At given P and T,

$$\text{if } (\Delta G)^P_T = 0 \quad \text{equilibrium obtains,}$$
$$\text{if } (\Delta G)^P_T < 0 \quad \text{state 2 is stable,}$$
$$\text{and if } (\Delta G)^P_T > 0 \quad \text{state 1 is stable.}$$

(2) Conversely, the equation $\Delta G_{(P,T)} = 0$ provides the general relationship between P and T at equilibrium.

2. Temperature and pressure in geology

2.1. Temperature.

The range of temperatures that interests the geologist is restricted, running from 0°C (the mean temperature of the surface of the earth) to about 1200°C. The temperature increases more or less uniformly toward the center of the earth, rising on average by about 1° every 30 meters. This quantity is known as the *normal geothermal gradient*. The observed geothermal gradient may however exceed 1° per 20 meters in certain unstable regions of the terrestrial crust, or conversely, it may be as little as 1° per 100 meters in the ancient shield areas. It has been suggested by some geophysicists that the geothermal gradient decreases with depth: for instance Birch (1955) considered that the maximum normal temperature reached at 30 km is only about 600°C, although a uniform gradient of 1° per 30 meters would correspond to a temperature of 1000°C. This and similar hypotheses remain controversial, especially for the crystalline rocks. Some of the gradients that have been proposed by various authors are shown in fig. 13.

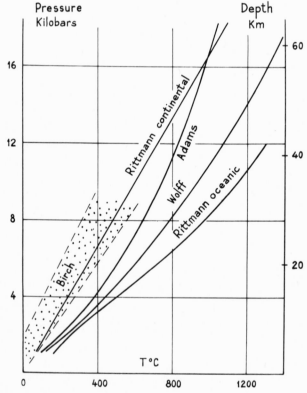

Fig. 13. Dependence of temperature on depth and pressure in the crust: geothermal gradients proposed by various authors.

Various methods, all more or less approximate, have been proposed for the determination of the temperatures of formation of rocks. Some of these, for instance, make use of the distribution of an element between several minerals: Barth's *geological thermometer* depends on the study of the partition of sodium between alkali feldspar and plagioclase, the theoretical basis of which will be discussed in Chapter XI–*2.1.* (p. 217).

It remains to comment on the geothermal gradients found in the vicinity of magmatic, or supposedly magmatic, rocks. Lafitte (1958) has shown that for intrusions of large size the gradients must be very small and that for minor intrusions, more or less independent of the *magma reservoir*, the gradients may be very steep at the time of emplacement, but very rapidly become negligible. And *a fortiori* likewise for volcanic, that is shallow, intrusions.

2.2. Pressure.

2.2.1.—It is impossible rigorously to evaluate the pressure within the rocks in terms of a single variable, as can be done for fluid systems, since the *stresses* due to the elasticity of the material must be taken into account. In the case of a fluid, one knows that the pressure has a value that is constant, whatever its direction may be. One then speaks of isotropic or hydrostatic pressure. On the contrary a general stress is characterized by the fact that the pressure has different values for different directions. Stated otherwise, it is necessary to represent such a state of stress by a mathematical function that is more complicated that that of a simple scalar, which is adequate for the description of a hydrostatic pressure.

The theoretical treatment of thermodynamic equilibrium under stress does not *a priori* present any major difficulty. Such a study however goes outside the scope of this work and it will always be supposed here that the pressure within the rocks is isotropic. This is not a completely arbitrary hypothesis and it is indeed quite often appropriate, especially when applied to a localized system for which there is supporting petrographic evidence. It must always, however, be borne in mind that the effect of constraints may be very significant. Apart from such obvious features as faults and mylonites (the result of particularly intense shearing), the oriented textures of metamorphic rocks are surely attributable, at least in part, to the operation of directed stresses (Kamb, 1959). Moreover, directed stresses may displace the position of equilibrium between minerals and thus give rise to the appearance of parageneses that are incapable of interpretation in terms of the operation of hydrostatic pressure. It is for this reason that *stress* and *anti-stress* minerals have been distinguished; this hypothesis, made most plausible by the thermodynamic analyses of Verhoogen (1951) and MacDonald (1957) has, however, remained inadequately investigated.

If the real situation is simplified by reduction to a single average pressure—supposedly isotropic and equated, as a first approximation, to the weight of the superimposed column of rock of 1 cm² cross-section at a depth h below the surface—the lithostatic pressure will be given by

$$P_S = \rho h.$$

2.2.2.—Fluids, such as water and carbon dioxide, are however commonly present in the rocks and it may be necessary to know their pressure. This *fluid pressure* may *a priori* be different from the rock pressure. This at first sight somewhat abstract notion may be related to reality by consideration of the system represented in figure 14, where a perforated piston transmits a pressure P_S to the solids while a second, impermeable, piston maintains the fluids at the pressure P_F, different from P_S. In earth-zones relatively close to the surface, experiment shows that the fluid pressure is equal to the hydrostatic pressure, that is to the weight of the column of water of 1 cm² cross-section between the surface and the depth h

$$P_F = 0.1h,$$

where h is in meters and P_F in Kg cm⁻². As the mean lithostatic pressure P_S can in general be expressed as a function of depth h and specific gravity ρ of the rocks ($P_S = 0.1 \rho h$), it is related to the hydrostatic pressure by the equation $P_F = P_S/\rho$, which in general approximates to

$$P_F \sim 0.3 P_S$$

or

$$P_S \sim 3 P_F.$$

Often, however, the fluid pressure differs from this simple hydrostatic

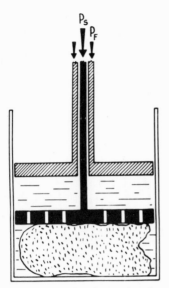

Fig. 14. Diagrammatic illustration of the distinction between hydrostatic pressure (P_F) and lithostatic pressure (P_S).

pressure, but it is nevertheless still true to write an equation of the form

$$P_F = \lambda P_S,$$

where λ is a coefficient of proportionality, usually between 0 and 1, and about 0.3 or 0.4 for zones close to the surface; λ may become equal to 1 for closed systems, where fluid pressure is equal to rock pressure; or λ may become negligible for a system whose fluid phase is completely free, for instance when the fluid phase is a gas in free communication with the external atmosphere at the surface.

2.3. Temperature-pressure relations.

It must be evident from what has already been said that temperature-pressure relations within the earth's crust must be exceedingly complex. For a normal geothermal gradient one or other of the curves shown on figure 13 is usually considered to be an adequate first approximation, with the additional assumption that the mean density of rocks is approximately equal to 2.7, so that $P = 0.27h$, where P is in bars and h in meters.

Finally, by way of example, the hypothetical pressure-temperature

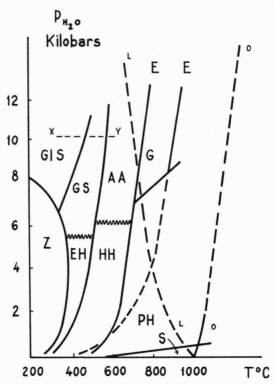

Fig. 15. Schematic representation of possible pressure-temperature fields of metamorphic facies and of granitic magmas (migmatites); all curves hypothetical.

   AA = almandine amphibolite. CG = cordierite granulites. E = eclogite.
EH = albite-epidote hornfels. G = granulite. GS = greenschist. GlS = glauco-
phane schist. HH = hornblende hornfels facies. PH = pyroxene hornfels. S =
sanidinite. Z = zeolite facies. LL, OO are curves of fusion of water-saturated
and anhydrous granite, respectively.

   XY is the possible range of temperature at 30 km depth for normal thermal
gradients according to Birch (1955).

   After Turner (in Fyfe, Turner, and Verhoogen, 1958).

relations that have been proposed for various types of metamorphism
may be quoted: those proposed by F. J. Turner (in Fyfe, Turner,
and Verhoogen, 1958) are shown in figs. 15 and 16, and those of A.
Miyashiro (1961) in fig. 17.

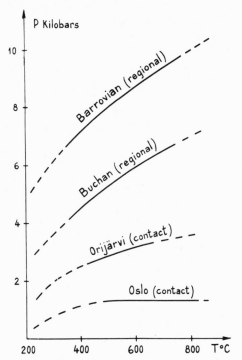

Fig. 16. Temperature-pressure relations within the crust during metamorphism according to Turner (in Fyfe, Turner, and Verhoogen, 1958).

3.   Calculation of ΔG at any pressure and temperature

3.1. *Effect of temperature.*

Suppose that pressure remains constant and equal, say, to one atmosphere. The free enthalpy of reaction at temperature T is denoted by $(\Delta G)_T^0$. Since

[1] $$(\Delta G)_T^0 = (\Delta H)_T^0 - T(\Delta S)_T^0,$$

$$\left(\frac{\partial \Delta H}{\partial T}\right)_P = (\Delta C_P) \quad \text{and} \quad \left(\frac{\partial \Delta S}{\partial T}\right)_P = \frac{(\Delta C_P)}{T},$$

it can immediately be deduced that:

[2] $$(\Delta H)_T^0 = (\Delta H)_{T_0}^0 + \int_{T_0}^{T} (\Delta C_P)^0 \, dT$$

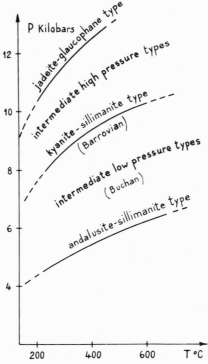

Fig. 17. Temperature-pressure relations within the crust during metamorphism according to Miyashiro (1961).

[3] $$(\Delta S)^0_T = (\Delta S)^0_{T_0} + \int_{T_0}^{T} \frac{(\Delta C_P)^0}{T} \, dT.$$

Equations (2) and (3) are sometimes called Kirchoff's Laws, but clearly they are simply logical consequences of the two Laws of Thermodynamics.

Substitution of (2) and (3) into (1) leads to:

[4] $$(\Delta G)^0_T = (\Delta H)^0_{T_0} - T(\Delta S)^0_{T_0} + \int_{T_0}^{T} (\Delta C_P)^0 \, dT - T \int_{T_0}^{T} \frac{(\Delta C_P)^0}{T} \, dT.$$

This expression could alternatively have been derived from

$$\left[\frac{\partial(\Delta G/T)}{\partial T} \right]_P = -\frac{(\Delta H)^0_T}{T^2}$$

$$i.e., \quad d\left(\frac{\Delta G}{T} \right) = -\frac{(\Delta H)^0_T}{T^2} \, dT \qquad \text{at constant pressure.}$$

Substituting for ΔH its value given by (2),

$$d\left(\frac{\Delta G}{T}\right) = -\frac{dT}{T^2}\int_{T_0}^{T}(\Delta C_P)^0\, dT - \frac{(\Delta H)^0_{T_0}}{T^2}\, dT$$

and integrating

[4'] $\qquad \dfrac{(\Delta G)^0_T}{T} = -\displaystyle\int_{T_0}^{T}\dfrac{dT}{T^2}\int_{T_0}^{T}(\Delta C_P)^0\, dT + \dfrac{(\Delta H)^0_{T_0}}{T} + \text{constant.}$

By putting the constant of integration equal to $-(\Delta S)^0_{T^0}$, it can readily be shown that equations (4) and (4') are mathematically equivalent.

An even simpler derivation starts with the equation

$$\left(\frac{\partial \Delta G}{\partial T}\right)_P = -(\Delta S)^0_T$$

$i.e.,\quad d(\Delta G) = -(\Delta S)^0_T\, dT \qquad$ at constant pressure,

and if (ΔS) is replaced by its value given by (3)

$$d(\Delta G) = -dT\int_{T_0}^{T}\frac{(\Delta C_P)^0}{T}\, dT - (\Delta S)^0_{T_0}\, dT$$

and integrating

[4''] $\qquad (\Delta G)^0_T = -\displaystyle\int_{T_0}^{T}dT\int_{T_0}^{T}\frac{(\Delta C_P)^0}{T}\, dT - T(\Delta S)^0_{T_0} + \text{constant.}$

And again it can be shown that equations (4) and (4'') are equivalent provided the constant of integration is put equal to $(\Delta H)^0_{T_0}$.

The use of equation (4), (4') or (4'') presupposes that the substances taking part in the reaction under consideration at a given pressure do not undergo any change of state in the temperature interval from T_0 to T. In general if the enthalpy change at the temperature T_1, $(\Delta H)^0_{T_1}$ and the entropy change at the temperature T_2, $(\Delta S)^0_{T_2}$ are known,

[5] $\quad (\Delta G)^0_T = (\Delta H)^0_{T_1} - T(\Delta S)^0_{T_2} + \displaystyle\int_{T_1}^{T}(\Delta C_P)^0\, dT - T\int_{T_2}^{T}\frac{(\Delta C_P)^0}{T}\, dT.$

Two situations are worth considering in detail:

(1) The values of the standard enthalpies and entropies of the substances involved in the reaction are known and from them it is a simple matter to calculate $(\Delta H)^0_{298}$ and $(\Delta S)^0_{298}$. Equations (4), (4'), and (4'') may then be written

[6] $(\Delta G)^0_T = (\Delta H)^0_{298} - T(\Delta S)^0_{298} + \int_{298}^{T} (\Delta C_P)^0 \, dT - T \int_{298}^{T} \frac{(\Delta C_P)^0}{T} \, dT$

[6'] $(\Delta G)^0_T = (\Delta H)^0_{298} - T(\Delta S)^0_{298} - T \int_{298}^{T} \frac{dT}{T^2} \int_{298}^{T} (\Delta C_P)^0 \, dT$

[6''] $(\Delta G)^0_T = (\Delta H)^0_{298} - T(\Delta S)^0_{298} - \int_{298}^{T} dT \int_{298}^{T} \frac{(\Delta C_P)^0}{T} \, dT.$

(2) The values of the standard entropies of the substances involved in reaction are not known, but since the entropy of a crystalline substance at absolute zero S_0 can be put equal to zero, $(\Delta S)_0 = 0$ (see p. 67). If $(\Delta H)^0_0$ is the heat of reaction at absolute zero, it follows that

[7] $(\Delta G)^0_T = (\Delta H)^0_0 + \int_0^T (\Delta C_P)^0 \, dT - T \int_0^T \frac{(\Delta C_P)^0}{T} \, dT$

[7'] $(\Delta G)^0_T = (\Delta H)^0_0 - T \int_0^T \frac{dT}{T^2} \int_0^T (\Delta C_P)^0 \, dT$

[7''] $(\Delta G)^0_T = (\Delta H)^0_0 - \int_0^T dT \int_0^T \frac{(\Delta C_P)^0}{T} \, dT$

Since it has been assumed that all the substances involved are in the crystalline state at absolute zero equations (7), (7'), and (7'') can only be made use of if all the substances remain in the same crystalline state between 0° and T°K.

In practice the evaluation of the temperature dependence of ΔC_P may be a matter of some difficulty. If simple empirical functions for $C_P(T)$ valid between T_0 and T are known, immediate integration is possible. If experimental measurements of C_P at various temperatures are available, the integrations may be done graphically better than by use of equations (6'') or (7''). Sometimes it is permissible to put $(\Delta C_P) = 0$ or $(\Delta C_P) = $ constant in the temperature interval under consideration, whence

[8]   if $(\Delta C_P) = 0$ between T_0 and T: $(\Delta G)^0_T = (\Delta H)^0_{T_0} - T(\Delta S)^0_{T_0}$

[9]   if (ΔC_P) = constant between T_0 and T:

$$(\Delta G)^0_T = (\Delta H)^0_{T_0} - T(\Delta S)^0_{T_0} - T(\Delta C_P)^0\left(\ln \frac{T}{T_0} + \frac{T_0}{T} - 1\right).$$

3.2. Effect of pressure.

3.2.1.—It will be supposed that temperature remains constant and equal, say, to T_0. The free enthalpy of reaction at pressure P will be denoted by $(\Delta G)^P_{T_0}$. Starting from the equation $\left(\dfrac{\partial(\Delta G)}{\partial P}\right) = (\Delta V)$, it follows that $d(\Delta G) = (\Delta V)\,dP$ at constant temperature; and integrating from $P = 1$ atm to P atm,

[10] $$(\Delta G)^P_{T_0} = (\Delta G)^0_{T_0} + \int_1^P (\Delta V)_{T_0}\,dP.$$

$(\Delta G)^0_{T_0}$ is the free enthalpy of reaction at $T_0°K$ and 1 atm. The evaluation of the integral implies knowledge of the function $(\Delta V) = f(P)$ and therefore of the compressibility χ. For gaseous substances there is no problem, since χ can be expressed very simply either as a function of pressure for perfect gases or as a function of fugacity for real gases. For condensed phases the dependence of volume on pressure can in general be neglected, that is:

$$\chi = -\frac{1}{V}\left(\frac{\partial V}{\partial P}\right)_T = 0.$$

Equation (10) then becomes

[11] $$\overline{(\Delta G)^P_{T_0} = (\Delta G)^0_{T_0} + (\Delta V)_{T_0}(P - 1).}$$

It follows that if the change of volume in reaction is zero $(\Delta V = 0)$, pressure has no effect on the equilibrium; if $\Delta V < 0$ (*i.e.*, the volume of the products of reaction is less than the volume of the reactants), pressure favors the reaction, since an increase in P results in a decrease in ΔG; and if $\Delta V > 0$, increase of pressure inhibits the reaction. It must be kept in mind that the pressures involved in geological processes are very large in relation to one atmosphere and so it is appropriate to regard $P = 0$ and $P = 1$ atm as sensibly equivalent in this context. It follows that if $P = 1$ can be approximated to P, equation (11) becomes

[11'] $$(\Delta G)^P_{T_0} = (\Delta G)^0_{T_0} + P(\Delta V)_{T_0}.$$

3.2.2.—Hitherto it has been supposed that fluids and solids are sub-jected to the same pressure P. In petrology this amounts to saying that the *lithostatic* and *hydrostatic pressures* are equal; but it has already been shown that there is no *a priori* reason why that should be so. Now, there are a great many petrologically significant systems that involve both fluid as well as solid phases, especially the presence of water or carbon dioxide, in the liquid or gaseous state. How will the equations that have been established above be affected?

Consider a system composed of solid phases (volume V_S) and fluid phases (volume V_F) and suppose that the composition of the phases remains constant (a closed system). Let P_S be the pressure applied to the solid phases and P_F be the pressure applied to the fluid phases. Then at constant composition and temperature:

$$dG_S = V_S \, dP_S$$
$$dG_F = V_F \, dP_F$$

and for the system

[12] $$dG = V_S \, dP_S + V_F \, dP_F.$$

The variation of free enthalpy of reaction is then given by

[13] $$d(\Delta G) = (\Delta V_S) \, dP_S + (\Delta V_F) \, dP_F$$

where (ΔV_S) and (ΔV_F) are the volume changes in reaction of the solids and fluids respectively. Integration of equation (13) yields:

[14] $$(\Delta G)_{T_0}^{P_S, P_F} = (\Delta G)_{T_0}^{0,0} + \int_1^{P_S} (\Delta V_S) \, dP_S + \int_1^{P_F} (\Delta V_F) \, dP_F,$$

where $(\Delta G)_{T_0}^{0,0}$ represents the free enthalpy of reaction at temperature T_0 and pressure $P_S = P_F = 1$ atm.

In practice three cases are important:

(1) $P_F = P_S = P$. This has already been dealt with and the result is given by equation (10):

[10] $$(\Delta G)_{T_0}^{P} = (\Delta G)_{T_0}^{0} + \int_1^{P} (\Delta V) \, dP \quad \text{with} \quad (\Delta V) = (\Delta V_S) + (\Delta V_F).$$

(2) $P_F = $ constant, $dP_F = 0$. Equation (14) now becomes

[15] $$(\Delta G)_{T_0}^{P_S} = (\Delta G)_{T_0}^{0} + \int_1^{P_S} (\Delta V_S) \, dP_S.$$

(3) $P_F = \lambda P_S$, where λ is a constant factor (see *2.2.2* and *2.2.3*). Equation (13) now becomes

[16] $$d(\Delta G) = [(\Delta V_S) + \lambda(\Delta V_F)] \, dP_S$$

which integrates to give

[17] $(\Delta G)_{T_0}^{P_S} = (\Delta G)_{T_0}^0 + \int_1^{P_S} [(\Delta V_S) + \lambda(\Delta V_F)] \, dP_S.$

3.3. The general case.

The free enthalpy of reaction $(\Delta G)_T^P$ at a temperature T and pressure P is given by equation (10),

$$(\Delta G)_T^P = (\Delta G)_T^0 + \int_1^P (\Delta V)_T \, dP.$$

But $(\Delta G)_T^0$ can be calculated from equations (4), (4') or (4''). It will be recalled that equation (4) is

$$(\Delta G)_T^0 = (\Delta H)_{T_0}^0 - T(\Delta S)_{T_0}^0 + \int_{T_0}^T (\Delta C_P)^0 \, dT - T \int_{T_0}^T \frac{(\Delta C_P)^0}{T} \, dT$$

which on substitution in the expression for $(\Delta G)_T^P$ yields

[18] $(\Delta G)_T^P = (\Delta H)_{T_0}^0 - T(\Delta S)_{T_0}^0 + \int_{T_0}^T (\Delta C_P)^0 \, dT$

$$- T \int_{T_0}^T \frac{(\Delta C_P)^0}{T} \, dT + \int_1^P (\Delta V)_T \, dP$$

where,

$(\Delta H)_{T_0}^0$ = enthalpy of reaction at $T = T_0$ and $P = 1$ atm,

$(\Delta S)_{T_0}^0$ = entropy of reaction at $T = T_0$ and $P = 1$ atm,

$(\Delta C_P)^0$ = change of specific heat at $P = 1$ atm (a function of T),

$(\Delta V)_T$ = change of volume (a function of P and T).

This is the general expression for the dependence of free enthalpy of reaction on temperature and pressure.

If condensed phases only are involved $(\Delta V)_T = (\Delta V)_T^0$, since ΔV is then independent of pressure, and equation (18) becomes

[19] $(\Delta G)_T^P = (\Delta H)_{T_0}^0 - T(\Delta S)_{T_0}^0 + \int_{T_0}^T (\Delta C_P)^0 \, dT$

$$- T \int_{T_0}^T \frac{(\Delta C_P)^0}{T} \, dT + P(\Delta V)_T^0.$$

(ΔV) is still temperature dependent and the solution of equation (19) will always require knowledge of the coefficients of thermal expansion $\alpha = \dfrac{1}{V}\left(\dfrac{\partial V}{\partial T}\right)_P$ for each substance involved. Taking $\alpha = 0$ as a first approximation, equation (19) simplifies to

[20] $(\Delta G)_T^P = (\Delta H)_{T_0}^0 - T(\Delta S)_{T_0}^0 + \displaystyle\int_{T_0}^T (\Delta C_P)^0\, dT$

$$- T \int_{T_0}^T \frac{(\Delta C_P)^0}{T}\, dT + P(\Delta V)_T^0.$$

If, further, the variation of (ΔC_P) with temperature can be neglected, the expression becomes

[21] $(\Delta G)_T^P$

$$= (\Delta H)_{T_0}^0 - T(\Delta S)_{T_0}^0 - T(\Delta C_P)_{T_0}^0 \left(\ln \frac{T}{T_0} + \frac{T_0}{T} - 1\right) + P(\Delta V)_{T_0}^0.$$

Ultimate simplification is obtained when (ΔC_P) is put equal to zero:

[22] $(\Delta G)_T^P = (\Delta H)_{T_0}^0 - T(\Delta S)_{T_0}^0 + P(\Delta V)_{T_0}^0.$

It must be remembered however that, if the pressure on the solid phases differs from that on the fluids, equations (18) to (22) will have to be modified in the light of the results obtained in paragraph *3.2.2.*

4.   Clapeyron's relation

4.1. The general expression.

Consider once again the generalized reaction

$$\overbrace{\sum_i n_i M_i}^{1} \to \overbrace{\sum_j n'_j M'_j}^{2}$$

and suppose that equilibrium obtains under the conditions defined by P and T, where $(\Delta G) = 0$. If now pressure and temperature vary by amounts dP and dT, the free enthalpy of reaction will vary by $d(\Delta G)$ and the new equilibrium condition will be:

$$(\Delta G) + d(\Delta G) = 0$$

and since $(\Delta G) = 0$

[23] $\underline{d(\Delta G) = 0.}$

This expresses the general condition for equilibrium in a differential form which may be expressed explicitly as a function of dP and dT. From the equation

$$dG = \left(\frac{\partial G}{\partial T}\right)_P dT + \left(\frac{\partial G}{\partial P}\right)_T dP$$

it follows immediately that

[24] $dG = -S\,dT + V\,dP$

since $\left(\frac{\partial G}{\partial T}\right)_P = -S$ and $\left(\frac{\partial G}{\partial P}\right)_T = V$

(equations (11'), (12') on p. 77).

Therefore

$$dG_1 = -S_1\,dT + V_1\,dP,$$
$$dG_2 = -S_2\,dT + V_2\,dP,$$

and $d(\Delta G) = dG_2 - dG_1 = -(S_2 - S_1)\,dT + (V_2 - V_1)\,dP$

so that

[25] $d(\Delta G) = -(\Delta S)\,dT + (\Delta V)\,dP.$

The equilibrium condition therefore becomes:

[26] $\overline{\underline{-(\Delta S)\,dT + (\Delta V)\,dP = 0}}$ or $\overline{\underline{\frac{dP}{dT} = \frac{(\Delta S)}{(\Delta V)}.}}$

Now, since

$$(\Delta G) = (\Delta H) - T(\Delta S)$$

and since $(\Delta G) = 0$ at equilibrium it follows that

$$(\Delta S) = \frac{(\Delta H)}{T}.$$

Therefore equation (26) can be written in alternative form as:

[27] $\overline{\underline{-\frac{(\Delta H)}{T}\,dT + (\Delta V)\,dP = 0}}$ or $\overline{\underline{\frac{dP}{dT} = \frac{(\Delta H)}{T(\Delta V)}.}}$

Equations (26) and (27) are alternative forms of *Clapeyron's relation*, which expresses the variation of pressure and temperature for a system in equilibrium at constant composition. In other words, if the temperature of a system in equilibrium at constant composition is varied by an amount dT, equilibrium can only be maintained if the pressure varies by an amount dP such that

$$dP = \frac{(\Delta H)}{T(\Delta V)} \, dT.$$

Suppose for instance that temperature alone can be varied, the pressure remaining constant. Equation (26) then becomes $-(\Delta S) \, dT = 0$, which is possible only when $(\Delta S) = 0$. If $(\Delta S) \neq 0$ (the general case) equilibrium is lost and the system evolves in such a manner that one at least of its constituent phases disappears.

It should be noted that Clapeyron's relation is meaningful only if (ΔS) and (ΔV) are not simultaneously zero. For polymorphic transformations it may be said to express the equilibrium conditions for *first order transformations*, for which the first derivatives of free enthalpy (entropy $S = -(\partial G/\partial T)_P$ and volume $V = (\partial G/\partial P)_T$) exhibit discontinuities ΔS and ΔV.

On the other hand *second order transformations*, for which $\Delta S = \Delta V = 0$, are characterized by discontinuities in the second derivatives of free enthalpy $((\partial^2 G/\partial T^2) = -TC_P; (\partial^2 G/\partial P^2) = -V\chi; (\partial^2 G/\partial P \partial T) = V\alpha)$ and cannot be studied in terms of Clapeyron's relation.

4.2. Some special expressions.

4.2.1.—When one of the phases participating in the reaction is gaseous, it is permissible, as a first approximation, to neglect the volume of the condensed phases relative to that of the gas phase and to put

$$(\Delta V) = V_G.$$

And if the gaseous phase is approximated to a perfect gas, it follows that for one mole

$$V_G = \frac{RT}{P},$$

which on substitution in (26) or (27) yields

$$[28] \qquad \overline{\frac{d(\ln P)}{dT} = \frac{(\Delta S)}{RT}} \quad \text{or} \quad \overline{\frac{d(\ln P)}{dT} = \frac{(\Delta H)}{RT^2}}.$$

These are the alternative forms of the *Clausius-Clapeyron* equation.

4.2.2.—When fluid and solid phases participate simultaneously in the reaction, it has already been shown (*3.2.2*) that at constant temperature

$$d(\Delta G) = (\Delta V_S)\, dP_S + (\Delta V_F)\, dP_F \qquad \text{(equation (13))}.$$

Equation (27) can then be written as

[29] $$-\frac{(\Delta H)}{T}\, dT + (\Delta V_S)\, dP_S + (\Delta V_F)\, dP_F = 0.$$

Equilibrium depends on the three parameters T, P_S, and P_F; and the stability fields of the reactant and product assemblages will be separated by an equilibrium surface in $T - P_S - P_F -$ space.

If P_F is put equal to λP_S equation (29) becomes

$$-\frac{(\Delta H)}{T}\, dT + [(\Delta V_S) + \lambda(\Delta V_F)]\, dP_S = 0$$

or

[30] $$\frac{dP_S}{dT} = \frac{(\Delta S)}{(\Delta V_S) + \lambda(\Delta V_F)} = \frac{(\Delta H)}{T[(\Delta V_S) + \lambda(\Delta V_F)]}.$$

When on the other hand P_S and P_F are independent, $\lambda = 0$ and (30) reduces to

$$\left(\frac{\partial P_S}{\partial T}\right)_{P_F} = \frac{\Delta H}{T(\Delta V_S)}$$

(The Poynting-Clapeyron equation).

The Clapeyron equation thus remains valid in every case on condition that fluid volumes are multiplied by the factor $\lambda = P_F/P_S$.

4.2.3.—By way of illustration, we shall now discuss the form of Clapeyron's relation for solids under stress. In order to simplify the problem we shall, following MacDonald (1957), confine ourselves to isotropic solids subjected to a uniaxial stress system.

Let two solids A and B be in equilibrium in a fluid medium of constant hydrostatic pressure P_1. The composition of the system and of each of the phases is maintained constant. For a uniaxial stress P_3 applied to the solids, it can be shown that

[31] $$\left(\frac{\delta T}{\delta P_3}\right)_{P_1} = \frac{(\delta_A V_A - \delta_B V_B)(P_1 - P_3)}{\Delta S - (\alpha_A V_A - \alpha_B V_B)(P_1 - P_3)}$$

where α is the cubical coefficient of thermal expansion and δ is an elastic coefficient for the isotropic solid.

It is immediately apparent that, all other factors remaining unchanged and in particular the hydrostatic pressure P_1 remaining constant, a uniaxial stress will displace the equilibrium temperature by an increasing amount as the elastic properties of the two solids diverge. This is especially marked for second-order polymorphic transformations, for which $\Delta S = 0$ and $V_A - V_B = \Delta V = 0$, so that

$$\left(\frac{\delta T}{\delta P_3}\right)_{P_1} = \frac{\delta_A - \delta_B}{\alpha_A - \alpha_B}.$$

This equation applies for instance to the order-disorder transformations in feldspars.

It is evident likewise from equation (31) that a diminution in the entropy change ΔS will enhance the influence of stress on equilibrium. In particular for first-order polymorphic transformations the term $(\alpha_A V_A - \alpha_B V_B)(P_1 - P_3)$ is generally negligible compared with ΔS and equation (31) then becomes

$$\left(\frac{\delta T}{\delta P_3}\right)_{P_1} \sim \frac{\delta_A V_A - \delta_B V_B}{\Delta S} (P_1 - P_3).$$

For a constant difference between hydrostatic pressure and stress, $P_1 - P_3 = $ constant, the effect of stress is enhanced when:

the entropy change is very small;

the elastic properties of the two solids are markedly different;

the volume change $V_A - V_B$ is very great.

Thus the andalusite-sillimanite equilibrium is more sensitive to stress than the andalusite-kyanite equilibrium.

In conclusion it must be emphasized that this is still an incompletely understood and slightly studied field. However it is possible to discern, albeit dimly, from what has been said above, the thermodynamic context in which minerals may be classified variously as *stress* or *anti-stress* phases.

VIII

Some Systems
of Constant Composition

1.   Units

Before attempting the solution of the various problems that are the subject of this chapter, it is necessary to establish a coherent system of units. Since enthalpies and entropies are almost always given in *calories* (or in *kilocalories*) and *calories per degree*, it is simplest to express the work done in volume changes in calories also.

It is usual in most scientific work to measure volumes in *cubic centimeters* and pressures in *bars* or in *Kg cm^{-2}*, but the unit of pressure in common use in geology is the *atmosphere*.

1 cal = 4.18 joules = 4.18 × 10^7 ergs = 4.18 × 10^7 barye cm^3 and since 1 bar = 10^6 baryes:

$$1 \text{ cal} = 41.8 \text{ bar cm}^3$$

1 cal = 4.18 joules = 4.18 × 10^7 dynes cm.

Moreover, the unit of weight, the *gram*, is given by

$$1 \text{ g} = 981 \text{ dynes},$$

whence

$$1 \text{ dyne} = \frac{1}{981 \times 10^3} \text{ Kg.}$$

Therefore

$$1 \text{ cal} = \frac{4.18 \times 10^7}{981 \times 10^3} \text{ Kg cm,}$$

that is

$$1 \text{ cal} = 42.6 \text{ Kg cm.}$$

The atmosphere is defined as the pressure exerted by a column of mercury of density 13.59, 1 cm² in cross-section and 76 cm in height. Therefore

$$1 \text{ atm} = 76 \times 1 \times 13.59 \text{ g cm}^{-2} = 1.033 \text{ Kg cm}^{-2}$$

and since 1 cal = 42.6 Kg cm,

$$1 \text{ cal} = \frac{42.6}{1.033} \text{ atm cm}^3,$$

therefore

$$1 \text{ cal} = 41.3 \text{ atm cm}^3.$$

2. The polymorphic transformation graphite-diamond

The objective is the calculation of the respective stability fields of graphite and diamond. Having first discussed the problem in approximate terms, we shall investigate the effect of the temperature-dependence of (ΔC_P) and that of the temperature– and pressure–dependence of (ΔV) on the equilibrium.

2.1. Approximate solution.

The basic data, taken from Rossini et al. (1952), are:

	ΔH^0_{298} cal mole⁻¹	S^0_{298} cal deg⁻¹ mole⁻¹	Density
Graphite	0	1.36	2.25
Diamond	450	0.58	3.51

The molar mass of carbon, M = 12 g mole⁻¹. It will be assumed that $(\Delta C_P) = 0$ and that the stated densities are unaffected by temperature or pressure.

The free-enthalpy change for the transformation graphite → diamond is given by:

$$(\Delta H)^0_T = (\Delta H)^0_{298} = 450 \text{ cal mole}^{-1}$$

$$(\Delta S)^0_T = (\Delta S)^0_{298} = 0.58 - 1.36 = -0.78 \text{ cal deg}^{-1} \text{ mole}^{-1}$$

$$(\Delta V)^0_T = (\Delta V)^0_{298} = 12 \left(\frac{1}{3.51} - \frac{1}{2.25} \right) = -1.91 \text{ cm}^3 \text{ mole}^{-1}.$$

The free enthalpy change is then given by

$$(\Delta G)^P_T = (\Delta H)^0_{298} - T(\Delta S)^0_{298} + P(\Delta V)^0_{298}$$

which yields, when volumes are expressed in cm³ and pressures in atmospheres,

$$(\Delta G)^P_T = 450 + 0.78T - \frac{1.91}{41.3} P,$$

that is

$$(\Delta G)^P_T = 450 + 0.78T - 0.046P.$$

It is immediately apparent that, at atmospheric pressure (P = 1 atm), $(\Delta G)^P_T$ remains positive whatever the temperature T. The system cannot therefore under these conditions ever enter the stability field of diamond. This is the reason why the transformation graphite → diamond is often described as *monotropic*. However, at constant temperature, any increase in pressure decreases the free enthalpy of reaction and therefore favors the reaction in the direction graphite → diamond; in other words the stability field of diamond lies in the high pressure region.

The equilibrium pressure at any temperature can be calculated from the equilibrium condition $(\Delta G)^P_T = 0$, that is:

$$450 + 0.78T - 0.046P = 0$$

or
$$P \sim 9730 + 16.86T,$$

where P is in atmospheres and T in degrees Kelvin. To take two temperatures for example:

$$T = 0°K, \qquad P \sim 9,700 \text{ atm};$$
$$T = 1000°K, \qquad P \sim 26,600 \text{ atm}.$$

2.2. The effect of the temperature dependence of ΔC_P.

The table below gives the specific heats of graphite and diamond in cal deg⁻¹ mole⁻¹ at various temperatures:

T°K	C_P Graph.	C_P Diam.	T°K	C_P Graph.	C_P Diam.	T°K	C_P Graph.	C_P Diam.
25	0.025 0	10^{-4}	250	1.625	1.000	500	3.500	3.325
50	0.120 0	0.002 5	300	2.085	1.500	550	3.717	3.657
100	0.400	0.060	350	2.520	2.012	600	3.90	3.90
150	0.780	0.240	400	2.960	2.500	900	4.95	4.95
200	1.200	0.600	450	3.262	2.970	1 200	5.52	5.52

The heat of reaction for graphite → diamond is known at 25°C and 1 atmosphere pressure: $(\Delta H)^0_{298} = 450$ cal mole^{-1} (Rossini *et al.*, 1952).

The free enthalpy of reaction at 1 atm and T°K is given by

$$(\Delta G)^0_T = (\Delta H)^0_T - T(\Delta S)^0_T$$

where

$$(\Delta H)^0_T = (\Delta H)^0_{298} + \int_{298}^T (\Delta C_P)\, dT$$

and

$$(\Delta S)^0_T = \int_0^T \frac{(\Delta C_P)}{T}\, dT$$

assuming zero entropy of reaction at the absolute zero of temperature. The integrals are evaluated graphically from the curves of figs. 18 and

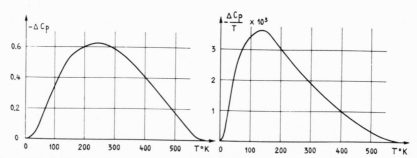

Figs. 18 and 19. Specific heat curves from which the free enthalpy of the graphite-diamond equilibrium can be calculated.

19, $(\Delta C_P) = f(T)$ and $\frac{(\Delta C_P)}{T} = f'(T)$, by measuring for each temperature under consideration the area bounded by the curve, the temperature axis, and the relevant abscissa. A selection of results is given in the table below.

$T°K$		0	100	200	300	400	500	600
$(\Delta H)^0_T - (\Delta H)^0_{298} = \int_{298}^{T} (\Delta C_P)\,dT$		+125	+110	+60	0	−50	−80	−87
$(\Delta S)^0_T = \int_0^T \dfrac{(\Delta C_P)}{T}\,dT$		0	−0.20	−0.54	−0.78	−0.94	−1.00	−1.02

Values of $(\Delta G)^0_T$ can be deduced as:

$T°K$		0	100	200	300	400	500	600
$(\Delta G)^0_T$		575	580	618	684	776	870	975

It should be noticed that above $600°K$ $(\Delta H)^0_T$ and $(\Delta S)^0_T$ remain sensibly constant, *i.e.*, $(\Delta C_P) = 0$; then

$$(\Delta H)^0_T = (\Delta H)^0_{600} = 363 \text{ cal mole}^{-1}$$
$$(\Delta S)^0_T = (\Delta S)^0_{600} = -1.02 \text{ cal deg}^{-1} \text{mole}^{-1}$$
$$(\Delta G)^0_T = (\Delta H)^0_{600} - T(\Delta S)^0_{600} = 363 + 1.02T \text{ cal mole}^{-1}.$$

If ΔV is now assumed to be independent of pressure and temperature, the resulting equilibrium curve is given by

$$(\Delta G)^P_T = (\Delta G)^0_T + P\Delta V = 0$$

whence

$$P = \frac{41.3(\Delta G)^0_T}{1.91} \text{ for P in atm,} \qquad (\Delta G) \text{ in cal.};$$

and for $T \geqslant 600°K$,

$$P = 22.1T + 7870.$$

So that at $T = 1000°K$, $P \sim 30{,}000$ atm. And at $T = 0°K$, $(\Delta G)^0_T = 575$ cal mole^{-1} and $P = \dfrac{41.3 + 575}{1.91}$, or

$$P \sim 12{,}500 \text{ atm.}$$

The resulting curve of equilibrium pressure as a function of temperature is shown in figure 20. Comparison with the $P - T$ curve obtained in paragraph *2.1* shows that there is a perceptible modification, but the curve obtained by assuming that $\Delta C_P = 0$ remains essentially correct, at least in so far as the general aspect of the diagram is concerned. It will now be shown that changes of volume with pressure and temperature likewise have little effect on the equilibrium curve.

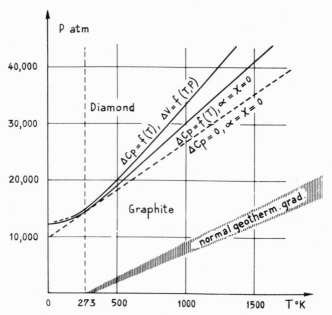

Fig. 20. Equilibrium diagram for graphite ⇌ diamond.

2.3. The effect of the temperature- and pressure-dependence of ΔV.

The molar volumes of graphite and of diamond in their standard states (T ∼ 300°K, P = 1 atm) together with their coefficients of thermal expansion (α) and their isothermal compressibilities (χ), both assumed to be constant, are given below (data from *Handbook of Physical Constants*, 1942, and *Handbook of Chemistry and Physics*, 1962).

	V^0_{300}	α	χ
Graphite	5.33	25×10^{-6}	30×10^{-7}
Diamond	3.42	4×10^{-6}	2×10^{-7}

V in cm^3, α in deg^{-1}, χ in atm^{-1}.

Molar volumes at any pressure and temperature can be calculated from:

$$V^P_T = V^0_T(1 - \chi P)$$

and

$$V^0_T = V^0_{300}[1 + \alpha(T - 300)]$$

so that
$$V_T^P = V_{300}^0(1 - \chi P)[1 + \alpha(T - 300)].$$

If t is such that $t = T - 300$, the equation becomes:
$$V_T^P = V_{300}^0(1 - \chi P)(1 + \alpha t)$$

so that,
$$(\Delta V)_T^P = \Delta V_{300}^0 + (V_D \alpha_D - V_G \alpha_G)t$$
$$- (V_D \chi_D - V_G \chi_G)P - (V_D \alpha_D \chi_D - V_G \alpha_G \chi_G)Pt,$$

where V_G and V_D are the molar volumes of graphite and of diamond at 300°K and 1 atm. Substitution of the data given above leads to:
$$(\Delta V)_T^P = -1.91 - 11 \times 10^{-5}t + 154 \times 10^{-7}P + 3750 \times 10^{-13}tP.$$

Turning now to the calculation of the free enthalpy of reaction $(\Delta G)_T^P$:
$$(\Delta G)_T^P = (\Delta G)_T^0 + \int_1^P (\Delta V)_T^P \, dP$$

therefore
$$(\Delta G)_T^P = (\Delta G)_T^0 - (1.91 + 11 \times 10^{-5}t)P + (77 \times 10^{-7} + 1875 \times 10^{-13}t)P^2,$$

and so, if P is expressed in atmospheres and volume in cm³:
$$(\Delta G)_T^P = (\Delta G)_T^0 - \frac{1.91 + 11 \times 10^{-5}t}{41.3} P + \frac{77 \times 10^{-7} + 1875 \times 10^{-13}t}{41.3} P^2.$$

The equilibrium pressure at any temperature can be calculated by putting $(\Delta G)_T^P = 0$, so that
$$(77 \times 10^{-7} + 1875 \times 10^{-13}t)P^2 - (1.91 + 11 \times 10^{-5}t)P + 41.3(\Delta G)_T^0 = 0.$$

The solution of this quadratic equation leads to the values of P shown below for selected temperatures:

T°K	300	700	1300
P atm	15,600	25,300	41,600

The resulting equilibrium curve is shown in figure 20 together with the curves obtained in earlier paragraphs.

2.4. Conclusions.

At room temperature diamond can only be formed at pressures in excess of 15,000 atm. Graphite and diamond have very different crystal structures and the passage from one to the other is difficult, each of the polymorphs being able to exist *metastably*, that is in disequilibrium, within the stability field of the other. It can be shown by crystal-chemical kinetic considerations that in a general way the transformation from a polymorph I into a polymorph II is facilitated by:

(1) increased depth of penetration (amount of overstepping) into the stability field of II;

(2) increased temperature. Now in the system under consideration, experiments at a sufficiently high constant pressure, yield diamond from graphite only when the temperature is lowered. These two propositions cannot be satisfied simultaneously and at a given pressure there exists an optimum temperature at which the rate of the transformation graphite → diamond passes through a maximum; it falls sharply to very small values on either side of the maximum (fig. 21) and the syn-

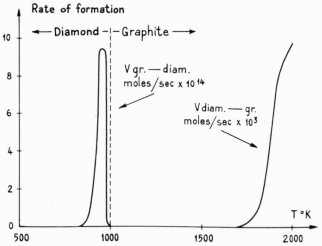

Fig. 21. Kinetics of the transformations graphite → diamond and diamond → graphite according to Hocart and Kern (1959).

thesis of diamond can then be performed only with difficulty (Hocart and Kern, 1959).

For understanding of the natural occurrence of diamond it suffices to compare the equilibrium curve graphite ⇌ diamond with the curve representing the mean geothermal gradient in order to appreciate that diamond cannot form under ordinary conditions; its presence in a rock implies extremely high pressure, a conclusion that is confirmed by petrographic and tectonic studies of its paragenesis in South Africa, Siberia, and elsewhere.

3.   Stability of the silica polymorphs

3.1.   The transformation α-quartz ⇌ β-quartz.

Data: at atmospheric pressure α-quartz changes to β-quartz at 846°K with a heat of reaction $(\Delta H)^0_{846} = 150$ cal mole^{-1}.

It is practically impossible to measure the volume change directly with any accuracy. It can however be calculated from measurements of the thermal expansion of quartz at various temperatures. The curve of $y = \dfrac{V_T - V_0}{V_0}$ exhibits a discontinuity, being composed of two portions, one on either side of 846°K; it suffices to extrapolate the two portions to that temperature and to measure:

$$\Delta y = y_2 - y_1, \quad \text{whence} \quad (\Delta V)_{846} = V_0 \Delta y \quad \text{(fig. 22)}.$$

It emerges that $\Delta V \sim 0.2$ cm^3 mole^{-1} and $V_0 = 22.65$ cm^3 mole^{-1} (*Handbook of Physical Constants*, 1942).

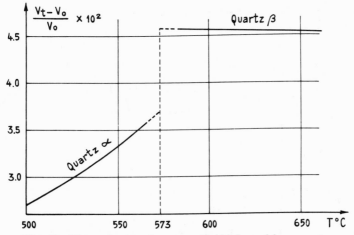

Fig. 22. Thermal expansion curves for high- and low-quartz.

The slope of the equilibrium curve $Q_\alpha \to Q_\beta$ at $P = 1$ atm, $T = 846°K$, is given by Clapeyron's relation,

$$\frac{dP}{dT} = \frac{(\Delta H)}{T(\Delta V)}$$

which here becomes, when pressure is expressed in atm,

$$\frac{dP}{dT} = \frac{150 \times 41.3}{846 \times 0.2} \sim 36.6 \text{ atm deg}^{-1}.$$

If it is assumed that (ΔC_P) is negligible above $850°K$, the equation of the equilibrium curve is immediately obtained as:

$$P = 36.6(T - 846).$$

It remains to determine the stability fields of the two polymorphs. The free enthalpy of reaction may be expressed as:

$$(\Delta G)_T^P = (\Delta H)_{846}^0 - T(\Delta S)_{846}^0 + P\Delta V$$

and, since $(\Delta S)_{846}^0 = \dfrac{(\Delta H)_{846}^0}{846}$, it follows that,

$$(\Delta G)_T^P = (\Delta H)_{846}^0 - T\frac{(\Delta H)_{846}^0}{846} + P(\Delta V) = 150\left(1 - \frac{T}{846}\right) + \frac{0.2}{41.3}P.$$

At constant pressure an increase in temperature produces a decrease in the free enthalpy of reaction and consequently favors reaction in the direction α-quartz $\to \beta$-quartz. It is therefore the latter polymorph that is stable at higher temperatures.

An equilibrium curve, constructed in this manner, is shown in figure 23. Shown for comparison is a curve which Yoder (1950) derived from direct measurement of equilibrium temperature at various pressures.

3.2. The transformations quartz → tridymite → cristobalite.

Data (from Mosesman and Pitzer, 1941):

(1) Molar volumes for the three phases:

$V_{quartz} = 22.65$, $V_{trid} = 26.40$, $V_{crist} = 26.30 \text{ cm}^3 \text{ mole}^{-1}$.

(2) Standard entropies deduced from low temperature specific heat measurements (*i.e.*, 0° to 298°K):

$(S_{298}^0)_{quartz} = 10.00$, $(S_{298}^0)_{trid} = 10.36$, $(S_{298}^0)_{crist} = 10.19 \text{ cal deg}^{-1} \text{ mole}^{-1}$.

(3) Transformation temperatures at 1 atm:

Quartz → tridymite 1140°K, tridymite → cristobalite 1743°K.

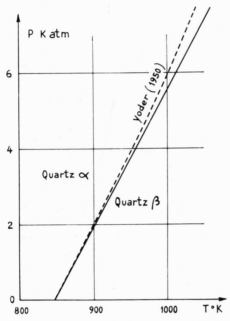

Fig. 23. Equilibrium diagram for low-quartz ⇌ high-quartz.

(4) Heat capacities,

$$H_T - H_{298} = \int_{298}^{T} C_P \, dT$$

for temperatures between 298° and 2000°K:

T°K	$H_T - H_{298}$ (Kcal mole^{-1})			T°K	$H_T - H_{298}$ (Kcal mole^{-1})		
	Quartz	*Tridym.*	*Cristob.*		*Quartz*	*Tridym.*	*Cristob.*
298	0	0	0	850	8.490	8.130	8.270
350	0.581	0.584	0.584	900	9.300	8.950	9.090
400	1.994	1.268	1.208	1 000	10.920	10.590	10.730
450	1.858	1.964	1.845	1 140	13.24	12.92	13.06
500	2.561	2.711	2.560	1 200	14.25	13.94	14.08
550	3.289	3.422	3.567	1 400	17.64	17.37	17.51
600	4.038	4.171	4.311	1 600	21.10	20.85	20.99
650	4.823	4.927	5.069	1 743	23.62	23.38	23.52
700	5.630	5.710	5.850	1 800	24.63	24.39	24.53
750	6.460	6.510	6.650	2 000	28.22	21.98	28.12
800	7.320	7.320	7.460				

For any transformation the change in free enthalpy at constant pressure can be expressed in the form:

$$(\Delta G)^0_T = (\Delta H)^0_{298} - T(\Delta S)^0_{298} - T \int_{298}^{T} \frac{dT}{T^2} \int_{298}^{T} (\Delta C_P) \, dT$$

and since

$$\int_{298}^{T} (\Delta C_P) \, dT = \Delta(H^0_T - H^0_{298})$$

it follows that

$$(\Delta G)^0_T = (\Delta H)^0_{298} - T(\Delta S)^0_{298} - T \int_{298}^{T} \frac{\Delta(H^0_T - H^0_{298})}{T^2} \, dT.$$

The integration may be performed graphically from the plot of $\dfrac{\Delta(H^0_T - H^0_{298})}{T^2}$ as a function of T for the appropriate reaction. The curves shown in fig. 24 represent this function for the transformations quartz → tridymite and tridymite → cristobalite.

The many discontinuities (fig. 24) that are apparent in the enthalpy curves correspond to $\alpha \rightarrow \beta$ transformations within the field of each of the three principal forms:

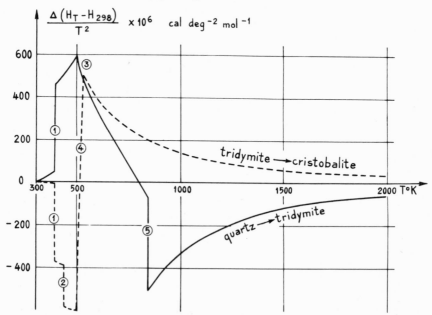

Fig. 24. Enthalpy diagram for the transformations between quartz, tridymite, and cristobalite.

1. α-tridymite $\rightarrow \beta_1$-tridymite 390°K;
2. β_1-tridymite $\rightarrow \beta_2$-tridymite 436°K;
3. β_2-tridymite $\rightarrow \beta_3$-tridymite 498°K;
4. α-cristobalite $\rightarrow \beta$-cristobalite 500–535°K;
5. α-quartz $\rightarrow \beta$-quartz 846°K.

Now, if T_E is the equilibrium temperature at one atmosphere, $(\Delta G)^0_{T_E} = 0$ and

$$(\Delta H)^0_{298} = T_E (\Delta S)^0_{298} + T_E \int_{298}^{T_E} \frac{\Delta (H_T - H_{298})}{T^2} \, dT.$$

Measurement of T_E and of $(\Delta S)^0_{298}$ and graphical evaluation of the integral therefore enable heats of reaction in the standard state to be calculated as

quartz $\rightarrow$ tridymite: $(\Delta H)^0_{298} = +446$ cal mole^{-1},
tridymite $\rightarrow$ cristobalite: $(\Delta H)^0_{298} = -92$ cal mole^{-1},

whence it follows directly that for

quartz $\rightarrow$ cristobalite: $(\Delta H)^0_{298} = 446 - 92 = 354$ cal mole^{-1}.

All the information necessary for the calculation of $(\Delta G)^0_T$ for the three reactions is now available.

The results shown in figure 25 enable the following conclusions

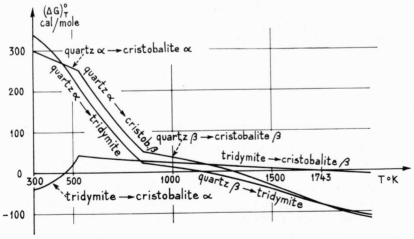

Fig. 25. Free enthalpy diagram for the transformations between low- and high-quartz, tridymite, and low- and high-cristobalite.

to be reached about the transformations at atmospheric pressure:*

(1) The transformations α-quartz $\rightarrow$ β-quartz and α-cristobalite $\rightarrow$ β-cristobalite appear clearly as discontinuities in the slopes of the curves.

(2) Above 1743°K tridymite changes spontaneously to β-cristobalite since (ΔG) for the transformation tridymite $\rightarrow$ β-cristobalite is negative.

(3) Between 1140° and 1743°K tridymite is the stable form of silica since (ΔG) for the transformation tridymite $\rightarrow$ cristobalite is positive and (ΔG) for quartz $\rightarrow$ tridymite is negative.

(4) Below 1140°K quartz is the stable form.

(5) The direction of the transformation quartz $\rightarrow$ β-cristobalite at about 1300°K cannot be predicted theoretically since it occurs within the stability field of tridymite. However kinetic (reaction rate) considerations are capable of explaining the observation that cristobalite maintained metastably below 1743°K will transform directly into quartz at temperatures below 1300°K. †

The transformation quartz $\rightarrow$ β-cristobalite is said to be metastable at normal atmospheric pressure.

Likewise the transformation tridymite $\rightarrow$ α-cristobalite at about 450°K is metastable since it occurs within the stability field of quartz.

Finally, if the dependence of molar volumes on pressure and temperature is neglected, knowledge of $(\Delta G)_T^0$ enables the equilibrium pressure to be calculated for any temperature from the relation:

$$(\Delta G)_T^P = (\Delta G)_T^0 + P(\Delta V) = 0$$

that is

$$P = -\frac{(\Delta G)_T^0}{\Delta V}.$$

For the transformation tridymite $\rightarrow$ cristobalite the calculation can be effected very simply by noticing that the curve giving

* It is sufficient to calculate $(\Delta G_1)_T^0$ for the transformation quartz $\rightarrow$ tridymite and $(\Delta G_2)_T^0$ for the transformation tridymite $\rightarrow$ cristobalite. The change in free enthalpy $(\Delta G_3)_T^0$ for the transformation quartz $\rightarrow$ cristobalite is given directly by $(\Delta G_3)_T^0 = (\Delta G_1)_T^0 + (\Delta G_2)_T^0$.

† Quartz can in these circumstances be formed at temperatures between 1140° and 1300°K, outside its stability field; this is an example of metastable synthesis.

$(\Delta G)_T^0$ as a function of T approximates to a straight line above $800°K$. Therefore, taking the equilibrium temperature $T_E = 1743°K$ as reference temperature:

$$(\Delta G)_T^0 = (\Delta H)_{1743}^0 - T(\Delta S)_{1743}^0.$$

But

$$(\Delta S)_{1743}^0 = \frac{(\Delta H)_{1743}^0}{1743}$$

and

$$(\Delta H)_{1743}^0 = (\Delta H)_{298}^0 + \Delta(H_{1743}^0 - H_{298}^0)$$

whence

$$(\Delta G)_T^0 = [(\Delta H)_{298}^0 + \Delta(H_{1743}^0 - H_{298}^0)] \left(1 - \frac{T}{1743}\right).$$

Therefore

$$(\Delta G)_T^0 = 50 \left(1 - \frac{T}{1743}\right) \sim -0.03(T - 1743).$$

It follows that

$$(\Delta G)_T^P = -0.03(T - 1743) - \frac{0.1}{41.3} P,$$

since $\Delta V = -0.1 \text{ cm}^3$, P is in atm, and ΔG in cal mole^{-1}. The equation of the equilibrium curve is then

$$P = -\frac{0.03(T - 1743) \times 41.3}{0.1} \sim -12(T - 1743).$$

The results of such calculations for each of the transformations are shown in figure 26, where the quartz-tridymite equilibrium curve derived from the direct experimental measurements of Tuttle and Bowen (1958) is also displayed. The significant discrepancy between the experimental and theoretical curves is undoubtedly due to errors in the measurement of heat capacity, and especially to the fact that Tuttle and Bowen worked in the presence of water which is able to enter into partial solid solution with silica and so modify the equilibrium.

3.3. The quartz-coesite transformation.

The only data available for this transformation are direct experimental measurements of equilibrium temperature at various pres-

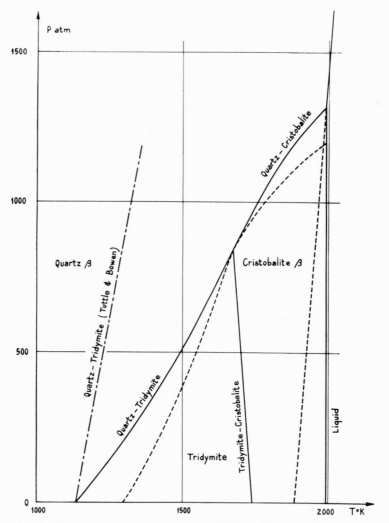

Fig. 26. Stability fields of quartz, tridymite, and cristobalite in the system SiO_2.

sures (MacDonald, 1956; Boyd and England, 1960). The equilibrium curve determined by the latter authors is shown in figure 27. Its equation is

$$P \sim 14.8T + 13{,}000 \text{ (P in atm, T in } °K).$$

It is immediately evident that, as in the case of diamond (see 2.3), coesite cannot form at ordinary pressure.

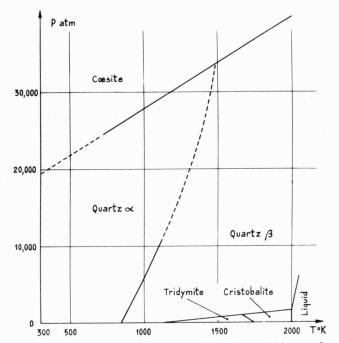

Fig. 27. High pressure diagram for the system SiO_2. Figure 26 is an enlargement of the low pressure part of the diagram.

If 19.9 cm³ is taken as the molar volume of coesite, the enthalpy change and the entropy change for the reaction quartz $\rightarrow$ coesite can be evaluated:

$$V = 19.9 - 22.6 = -2.7 \text{ cm}^3 \text{ mole}^{-1}$$

$$\frac{dP}{dT} \sim 14.8 \text{ atm deg}^{-1}.$$

From Clapeyron's relation $\dfrac{dP}{dT} = \dfrac{(\Delta S)}{(\Delta V)}$, it follows that

$$(\Delta S) = \frac{-2.7 \times 14.8}{41.3} \sim -0.96 \text{ cal deg}^{-1} \text{ mole}^{-1}.$$

And at the point, $T = 1000°K$, $P = 27,800$ atm, on the equilibrium curve

$$(\Delta G) = (\Delta H) - T(\Delta S) + P(\Delta V) = 0,$$

$$(\Delta H) = -0.96 \times 1000 + \frac{27,800 \times 2.7}{41.3} \sim 857 \text{ cal mole}^{-1}.$$

Figure 27, which displays the stability fields of the several polymorphs of silica, is produced by calculations such as that described above. Tridymite and cristobalite are the polymorphs stable at high temperature and low pressure; they are characteristic, although rare, minerals in certain volcanic rocks such as the trachytes and dacites. Quartz is the commonest polymorph in nature, occurring in sedimentary rocks as well as in igneous and metamorphic rocks. Coesite appears to be restricted in Nature to rocks that have been subjected to the impact of large meteorites (Meteor Crater, Arizona; Rieskessel, Bavaria); its stability field being approximately coincident with that of diamond, it has been supposed that it might also occur in diamondiferous rocks and especially in eclogites, but such rocks are mostly silica-deficient and free SiO_2 in any form is absent from them.

4.   The stability of jadeite

4.1. Introduction.

In order to simplify the problem posed by the stability of jadeite and even, to some extent, to facilitate its solution it is necessary to make certain assumptions and reservations:

(1) The system is perfectly dry; or if water is present its influence is neglected and no account is taken of such minerals as analcime, $NaAlSi_2O_6 \cdot 2H_2O$.

(2) No account is taken of elements other than Si, Al, Na, and of course O. In particular, K, Ca, and Fe^{3+}, which can in part substitute for Na and Al in natural jadeite, are neglected.

(3) Finally it is assumed that the composition of each phase remains constant and that the minerals involved cannot enter into solid solution with one another.

In these circumstances the only minerals that can occur in the system are:

nepheline	(Ne)	$NaAlSiO_4$
jadeite	(Jd)	$NaAlSi_2O_6$
albite	(Ab)	$NaAlSi_3O_8$
quartz	(Q)	SiO_2

These minerals can, in theory at least, react with one another according to one of the four following schemes:

A: 1 Jd + 1 Q → 1 Ab
B: 1 Ab + 1 Ne → 2 Jd
C: 1 Ne + 2 Q → 1 Ab
D: 1 Ne + 1 Q → 1 Jd.

These four reactions are not thermochemically independent since C can be considered as A + D, and D as A + B. If (ΔJ_A), (ΔJ_B), (ΔJ_C), and (ΔJ_D) are respectively the changes of a thermodynamic function (enthalpy, entropy, or free enthalpy) in the reactions A, B, C, and D, then

$$(\Delta J_A) + (\Delta J_B) = (\Delta J_D)$$

and

$$2(\Delta J_A) + (\Delta J_B) = (\Delta J_C).$$

It is therefore sufficient for the solution of the problem to calculate the change (ΔJ) for any two of the reactions.

4.2. Data.

(1) Molar volumes of the four phases (in cm^3 $mole^{-1}$) are: quartz 22.6, nepheline 54.2, albite 100.8, jadeite 60.7 (Robertson, Birch, and MacDonald, 1957).

(2) Enthalpy of reaction (in Kcal) in the standard state for each of the four reactions (deduced from the heats of solution of each of the four phases in HF, Kracek, Neuvonen and Burley, 1951):

$(\Delta H_A)^0_{298} = +0.6$, $(\Delta H_B)^0_{298} = -6.2$, $(\Delta H_C)^0_{298} = -5.0$, $(\Delta H_D)^0_{298} = -5.6$.

(3) Entropy of quartz in the standard state: $S^0_{298} = 10.0$ cal deg^{-1} $mole^{-1}$.

(4) Specific heats of nepheline, albite, and jadeite, between 50° and 298°K in cal deg^{-1} $mole^{-1}$ (Kelley, in Adams, 1953):

T°K	Ne	Ab	Jd	T°K	Ne	Ab	Jd
50	4.56	7.80	2.55	200	21.98	37.26	27.93
75	8.35	13.74	6.55	225	23.88	40.26	31.05
100	11.74	19.31	11.34	250	25.60	43.74	33.81
125	14.80	24.52	16.20	275	27.14	46.52	36.27
150	17.46	29.22	20.64	298	28.38	48.96	38.34
175	19.86	33.46	24.51				

Graphical integration of $S^0_{298} = \int_0^{298} \dfrac{C_P}{T}\, dT$ by the procedure that has already been described yields standard state entropies (in cal deg^{-1} mole^{-1}): nepheline = 29.1, albite = 49.2, jadeite = 31.8 (Kelley in Kracek, Neuvonen, and Burley, 1951).

(5) Empirical formulae of the form

$$C_P = a + (b \times 10^{-3})T + (d \times 10^5)T^{-2}$$

describe the temperature dependence of C_P (in cal deg^{-1} mole^{-1} where T is in °K). The parameters a, b, and d are given in the *Handbook of Physical Constants*, 1942, as:

	a	b	d	Range of validity
Quartz ...	10.87	8.7	− 2.4	0 − 500°C
Albite ...	63.80	11.7	−16.8	0 − 1000°C

4.3. Calculation of free enthalpies of reaction and construction of the equilibrium diagram.

From the data given above, the enthalpy, entropy, and volume changes in the standard conditions can be calculated immediately for each of the four reactions:

Reaction	$(\Delta H)^0_{298}$	$(\Delta S)^0_{298}$	$(\Delta V)^0_{298}$
A	+0.6 Kcal	+ 7.4 cal/deg	+17.5 cm^3
B	−6.2	−14.7	−33.6
C	−5.0	+ 0.1	+ 1.4
D	−5.6	− 7.3	−16.1

The variation of (ΔC_P) with temperature must also be known; for this the experimentally determined specific heat curves for the four minerals shown in figure 28 are employed.

For nepheline and jadeite the curves have been plotted to 300°K and extrapolated to higher temperatures. For albite the curve has been plotted to 300°K from the data of Kelley (in Adams, 1953); above that temperature the empirical formula

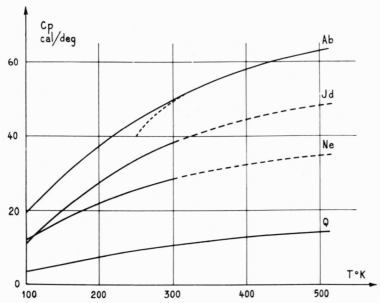

Fig. 28. Temperature-dependence of the specific heats of nepheline, jadeite, albite, and quartz.

$C_P = 63.8 + (11.7 \times 10^{-3})T - (16.8 \times 10^5)T^{-2}$ yields a curve that must fit the lower temperature section precisely at 300°K. The curve for quartz is obtained from the empirical formula

$$C_P = 10.87 + (8.7 \times 10^{-3})T - (2.4 \times 10^5)T^{-2}$$

supplemented below 273°K by some direct measurements of the specific heat at low temperatures.

It can be verified from these curves that above 300°K (ΔC_P) for each of the four reactions is effectively zero. By way of example and to make the matter completely clear, the curve of (ΔC_P) for reaction B $(Ab + Ne \rightarrow 2\,Jd)$ is displayed in figure 29. Therefore a good approximation to the equilibrium relationship is provided by

$$(\Delta G)_T^0 = (\Delta H)_{298}^0 - T(\Delta S)_{298}^0.$$

And for the four reactions which concern us it follows that:

$$\begin{aligned}
\text{A:} \quad & (\Delta G)^0_T = 600 - 7.4T, \\
\text{B:} \quad & (\Delta G)^0_T = -6200 + 14.7T, \\
\text{C:} \quad & (\Delta G)^0_T = -5000 - 0.1T, \\
\text{D:} \quad & (\Delta G)^0_T = -5600 + 7.3T.
\end{aligned}$$

Equilibrium temperatures at one atmosphere are therefore:

$$\text{A} \sim 81°\text{K, B} \sim 422°\text{K, D} \sim 767°\text{K.}$$

Reaction C occurs with decrease of free enthalpy at all tempera-

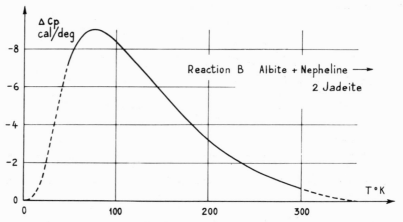

Fig. 29. Temperature-dependence of the specific heat of reaction for Ab + Ne → 2 Jd. Above 300°K, (ΔC_P) is quite small.

tures: the assemblage quartz + nepheline is therefore always unstable at atmospheric pressure.

If variation of volume with temperature and pressure is neglected, it is a simple matter to calculate free enthalpies of reaction under any conditions from

$$(\Delta G)^P_T = (\Delta G)^0_T + P\Delta V.$$

The assumption that volumes are effectively independent of temperature and pressure is acceptable for this system; for reaction B, for instance, Yoder and Weir (1951) calculated from measurements of isothermal compressibility and thermal expansion the value of ΔV at various temperatures and pressures:*

* Yoder and Weir used values slightly different from those given on p. 125 for the molar volumes of albite, nepheline, and jadeite in the standard state: albite = 100.633,

$$V = -33.6 + (22.7 \times 10^{-4})T - (6.16 \times 10^{-6})T^2$$
$$+ (23.15 \times 10^{-10})T^3 + (2.40 \times 10^{-4})P - (2.71 \times 10^{-9})P^2,$$

where V is in cm^3, P in atm, T in °K.

P	T	ΔV
1	293	−33.48
1	973	−35.26
10^4	293	−31.41
10^4	973	−33.19

The variation of ΔV is clearly small; it is effectively negligible since at temperatures of about 1000°K the equilibrium pressure is of the order of 10,000 atm, as will be shown below.

The free enthalpies of reaction can therefore be expressed as:

A: $(\Delta G)_T^P = \quad 600 - \quad 7.4T + \dfrac{17.5}{41.3} P = \quad 600 - 7.4T + 0.424P,$

B: $(\Delta G)_T^P = -6200 + 14.7T - \dfrac{33.6}{41.3} P = -6200 + 14.7T - 0.814P,$

C: $(\Delta G)_T^P = -5000 - \quad 0.1T + \dfrac{1.4}{41.3} P = -5000 - 0.1T + 0.034P,$

D: $(\Delta G)_T^P = -5600 + \quad 7.3T - \dfrac{16.1}{41.3} P = -5600 + 7.3T - 0.390P.$

The equations of the equilibrium curves are readily obtained by putting $(\Delta G)_T^P = 0$:

$$\begin{aligned}
A: &\quad P = 17.46T - 1416, \\
B: &\quad P = 18.07T - 7620, \\
C: &\quad P = \quad 2.95T + 147{,}500, \\
D: &\quad P = 18.72T - 14{,}371.
\end{aligned}$$

The curves are shown in figure 30, with the exception of that for reaction C, the display of which would require enlargement of the diagram since the equilibrium pressure for the reaction Ne + 2 Q → Ab increases with temperature starting from a value as high as 147,500 atm at 0°K.

nepheline = 54.293, jadeite = 60.724 cm^3 mole^{-1}; the discrepancy does not significantly affect the conclusions.

4.4. Discussion of results.

It is worth mentioning at the outset that the composition of the system can be described in terms of the end-members quartz and nepheline mixed in suitable proportions.

It is clear from figure 30 that the three equilibrium lines, for

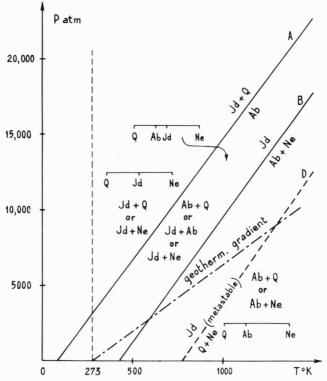

Fig. 30. Equilibrium diagram for assemblages involving only nepheline, jadeite, albite, and quartz.

A, B, and D, divide the P-T area into four fields. It is now necessary to determine what the stable mineral association in each of these fields is. In order to do that the temperature-dependence at constant pressure (say, 10,000 atm) of ΔG must be examined for each of the four reactions, A, B, C, and D.

Starting with a mixture of quartz and nepheline, reaction may occur according to either of the equations:

$$C: \quad 1 \, Ne + 2 \, Q \rightarrow 1 \, Ab$$
$$D: \quad 1 \, Ne + 1 \, Q \rightarrow 1 \, Jd.$$

In conditions where both reactions are simultaneously possible, $(\Delta G_C) < 0$ and $(\Delta G_D) < 0$, it suffices to consider only that which results in the greater diminution of free enthalpy. Suppose for instance that

$$(\Delta G_D) < (\Delta G_C) < 0.$$

There exists a reaction A consequent on C and D such that

$$1 \, Jd + 1 \, Q \rightarrow 1 \, Ab \qquad \text{with} \qquad (\Delta G_A) = (\Delta G_C) - (\Delta G_D) > 0.$$

If it is imagined that the reaction that results in the smaller diminution of free enthalpy, in this case C, has taken place initially, then the

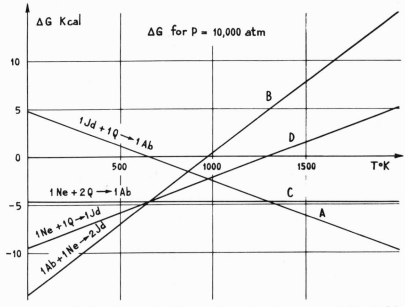

Fig. 31. Free enthalpy diagram for the several reactions between nepheline, jadeite, albite, and quartz.

albite formed by that reaction will be decomposed into quartz + jadeite by the reverse of reaction A, since $(\Delta G_A) > 0$; and the net result will be the same as if reaction D alone had taken place.

Between 0°K and 660°K $(\Delta G_D) < (\Delta G_C) < 0$; reaction D therefore proceeds in the direction $Q + Ne \rightarrow Jd$ until one at least of the initial phases has been eliminated. Depending on whether there is an excess of quartz or of nepheline, one of the two parageneses

jadeite + quartz
jadeite + nepheline

will therefore be produced.* Jadeite and quartz cannot react to form albite by reaction A since $(\Delta G_A) > 0$.

Between 660°K and 980°K $(\Delta G_C) < (\Delta G_D) < 0$; reaction C runs in the direction $Q + Ne \rightarrow Ab$ until one at least of the two initial phases has been eliminated. Depending on whether there is excess of quartz or of nepheline one of the parageneses

albite + quartz
albite + nepheline

results. But the second of these is not stable since $(\Delta G_B) < 0$, and the products will react to give jadeite by reaction B until either albite or nepheline has been eliminated. The stable associations in this temperature interval are therefore

albite + quartz
jadeite + albite
jadeite + nepheline.

Between 980°K and 1300°K $(\Delta G_C) < (\Delta G_D) < 0$; as in the previous case one of the parageneses

albite + quartz
albite + nepheline

is produced. But here both associations are stable since $(\Delta G_B) > 0$.

Above 1300°K $(\Delta G_C) < 0 < (\Delta G_D)$; that (ΔG_D) is now positive is not important since quartz and nepheline react under all conditions according to C to give albite. In other words the equilibrium $Q + Ne \rightleftharpoons Jd$ is metastable.

It remains to explore the region of very high pressures. (ΔG) can readily be calculated, say at 1000°K where the following inequalities are obtained.

Between 16,000 and 150,450 atm, $(\Delta G_B) < (\Delta G_D) < (\Delta G_C) < 0 <$

---

* In figure 30 the parageneses are shown with the aid of an auxiliary diagram which is analyzed more closely on p. 258.

(ΔG_A); reaction D runs in the direction $Q + Ne \rightarrow Jd$ and the two possible associations are

quartz   + jadeite

nepheline + jadeite.

Above 150,450 atm, $(\Delta G_B) < (\Delta G_D) < 0 < (\Delta G_C) < (\Delta G_A)$; that (ΔG_C) is positive produces no change in the assemblages listed for the previous range. Here too the equilibrium $Ne + 2Q \rightleftharpoons Ab$ is metastable.

The results obtained in the preceding paragraphs make it possible to label the stability fields shown on figure 30. The conclusions set out below, which are in good accord with observation of natural parageneses, can be drawn directly from figure 30.

The association quartz + nepheline cannot exist stably under any conditions.

The $P - T$ curve for a normal geothermal gradient has been superimposed on figure 30. The associations $Ab + Q$ and $Ab + Ne$ clearly cover almost the whole of the geological field, while the associations $Jd + Ab$ and $Jd + Ne$ occupy a very restricted field: jadeite is thus a rare mineral. However, it is possible for jadeite to be found under a normal gradient within silica-deficient rocks at temperatures below about 600°K. Conversely, the assemblage $Jd + Q$ in rocks with a silica excess can only be explained in terms of the operation of a special type of metamorphism, *high pressure metamorphism* characterized by a particularly high geothermal gradient (see fig. 17, p. 96).

The problem of the stability of jadeite is of considerable geophysical interest. It is known that at a certain depth in the crust, seismic waves exhibit a discontinuity in their velocity of propagation, which is interpreted as a sharp change in elastic properties and called the Mohorovicic discontinuity. Two hypotheses have been proposed to explain this discontinuity: the first calls for a sudden change of chemical composition, feldspathic above the discontinuity and ultrabasic below; the second requires only the appearance of new dense minerals, such as spinels, garnets, jadeite, etc., without any marked change in bulk composition. It would seem that, as far as jadeite is concerned, what has been said in the preceding pages leads to a refutation of the second hypothesis: it is albite, not jadeite, that is stable at great depth. But it is necessary to be quite sure that the assumptions that have been made are valid; in particular the geothermal gradient that has been chosen is quite hypothetical and a slight change in slope of the curve would modify the conclusion, as would the presence of elements such as K, Ca, Fe, etc. (a point that was made at the start of this section).

Finally, jadeite is theoretically stable in the absence of quartz at ordinary temperatures and pressures. Nevertheless, its synthesis from a nepheline-albite glass has only been achieved at pressures in excess of 10,000 atm. Even if it is admitted that the data used are not very accurate the discrepancy cannot thereby be explained away. Indeed the experimental evidence can only be interpreted in terms of kinetic considerations: the rate of formation of jadeite is extremely slow under the standard conditions, becoming appreciable only far within its stability field.

5. The instability of the quartz-olivine association

Olivine, $(Mg, Fe)_2SiO_4$, can react with quartz according to the equation

$$(Mg, Fe)_2SiO_4 + SiO_2 \rightarrow 2(Mg, Fe)SiO_3.$$

olivine   quartz   pyroxene

The pyroxene so formed may be orthorhombic (enstatite-ferrosilite) or monoclinic (clinoenstatite-clinoferrosilite). It will be assumed that the changes in the thermodynamic functions on transition from orthorhombic to monoclinic pyroxene are negligible relative to the changes involved in the reaction with which we are concerned.*

5.1. Data.

5.1.1.—Molar volumes in cm^3 $mole^{-1}$ (Deer, Howie, and Zussmann, 1962):

Quartz	22.65	Enstatite	31.06
Forsterite	44.30	Ferrosilite	33.33
Fayalite	46.79		

---

* This is an important assumption since some of the data used below relate to orthorhombic pyroxenes and some to monoclinic pyroxenes.

It follows immediately that:

for reaction A:

quartz + forsterite → 2 enstatite, $\Delta V_A = -4.83$ cm³,

for reaction B:

quartz + fayalite → 2 ferrosilite, $\Delta V_B = -2.78$ cm³.

5.1.2.—Heats of reaction (determined from heats of solution of the various compounds in hydrofluoric acid by Sahama and Torgeson, 1949—see p. 48):

reaction A: $(\Delta H_A)^0_{347} = -2620$ cal,

reaction B: $(\Delta H_B)^0_{347} = -310$ cal.

5.1.3.—Standard entropies (Kelley and King, 1961) in cal deg⁻¹ mole⁻¹:

Quartz	10.00,	Clinoenstatite	16.22,
Forsterite	22.75,	Fayalite	34.70,

whence, for reaction A: $(\Delta S_A)^0_{298} = -0.31$ cal deg⁻¹ mole⁻¹.

5.1.4.—High temperature specific heats (Kelley, 1960 and *Handbook of Physical Constants*, 1942):

Quartz: $C_P = 11.22 + 8.20 \times 10^{-3}T - 2.70 \times 10^5 T^{-2}$,
Forsterite: $C_P = 34.73 + 6.48 \times 10^{-3}T - 7.76 \times 10^5 T^{-2}$,
Enstatite: $C_P = 23.28 + 8.04 \times 10^{-3}T - 5.57 \times 10^5 T^{-2}$,

whence, for reaction A: $(\Delta C_P) = 0.61 + 1.4 \times 10^{-3}T - 0.68 \times 10^5 T^{-2}$.

5.1.5.—Coefficient of compressibility, $\chi = -\dfrac{1}{P}\dfrac{V_P - V_0}{V_0}$, where P is in atm. (*Handbook of Physical Constants*, 1942):

Quartz:	27×10^{-7}	Enstatite:	10×10^{-7}
Forsterite:	8×10^{-7}		

5.1.6.—Thermal expansion, *i.e.*, increase in volume between 20°C and t°C expressed as a percentage of the volume at 20°C (*Handbook of Physical Constants*, 1942):

t°C	100	200	400	500	600	800	1000
Quartz	0.4	0.8	1.9	2.7	4.5	4.4	4.3
Pyroxenes..	0.1–0.2	0.3–0.4	0.8–1.0		1.3–1.5	1.9–2.2	2.6–2.9
Olivine ...	0.2	0.5	1.1		1.8	2.5	3.3

5.2. The reaction quartz + forsterite → 2 enstatite.

The temperature dependence of the free enthalpy of reaction at 1 atm is given by

$$(\Delta G)^0_T = (\Delta H)^0_{298} - T(\Delta S)^0_{298} + \int_{298}^{T} (\Delta C_P)\, dT - T \int_{298}^{T} \frac{(\Delta C_P)}{T}\, dT.$$

Now (ΔC_P) is given by a function of the form $(\Delta C_P) = a + bT - dT^{-2}$, whence

$$\int_{298}^{T} (\Delta C_P)\, dT = a(T - 298) + \frac{b}{2}(T^2 - 298^2) + d\left(\frac{1}{T} - \frac{1}{298}\right).$$

Putting $B = 298a + \dfrac{b \times 298^2}{2} + \dfrac{d}{298}$, the expression becomes,

$$\int_{298}^{T} (\Delta C_P)\, dT = aT + \frac{b}{2}T^2 + dT^{-1} - B$$

which can be evaluated, from the data of *5.1.4*, as

$$\int_{298}^{T} (\Delta C_P)\, dT = 0.61T + 0.7 \times 10^{-3}T^2 + 0.68 \times 10^5 T^{-1} - 472.$$

At this point it is convenient to derive $(\Delta H)^0_{298}$ from the value of $(\Delta H)^0_{347}$ given in *5.1.2*, by evaluation of the integral,

$$\int_{298}^{347} (\Delta C_P)\, dT = (\Delta H)^0_{347} - (\Delta H)^0_{298} = 19 \text{ cal}$$

whence $(\Delta H)^0_{298} = -2620 - 19 = -2639$ cal. Since

$$\frac{(\Delta C_P)}{T} = aT^{-1} + b - dT^{-3}$$

it follows that

$$\int_{298}^{T} \frac{(\Delta C_P)}{T}\, dT = a \ln \frac{T}{298} + b(T - 298) + \frac{d}{2}\left(\frac{1}{T^2} - \frac{1}{298^2}\right)$$

and by substitution of $A = a \ln 298 + 298b + \dfrac{d}{2 \times 298^2}$ the expression becomes

$$\int_{298}^{T} \frac{(\Delta C_P)}{T} \, dT = a \ln T + bT + \frac{d}{2} T^{-2} - A$$

where

$$a = 1.405, \quad b = 1.4, \quad \frac{d}{2} = 0.34, \quad \text{and} \quad A = -4.28.$$

The expression for $(\Delta G)_T^0$ thus becomes

$$(\Delta G)_T^0 = (\Delta H)_{298}^0 - T(\Delta S)_{298}^0 - aT \ln T \\ - b/2 \, T^2 + d/2 \, T^{-1} + (a + A)T - B$$

which can for this reaction be evaluated as

$$(\Delta G)_T^0 = -3111 - 1.405T \ln T + 5.197T \\ - 0.7 \times 10^{-3}T^2 + 0.34 \times 10^5 T^{-1}.$$

It is immediately evident that $(\Delta G)_T^0$ remains negative at all values of T: the quartz-forsterite assemblage is therefore always unstable at atmospheric pressure.

The pressure dependence of the free enthalpy of reaction is given by

$$(\Delta G)_T^P = (\Delta G)_T^0 + \int_1^P (\Delta V)_T^P \, dP.$$

If ΔV is assumed to be independent of P and T, the expression becomes

$$(\Delta G)_T^P = (\Delta G)_T^0 + P\Delta V,$$

for $P \gg 1$ atm. In the present case $\Delta V = -4.83$ cm^3 and therefore since $(\Delta G)_T^0$ is always negative, so is $(\Delta G)_T^P$. In other words the association quartz-forsterite is unstable at all temperatures and pressures.

It remains now to show that this result remains valid when the coefficients of compressibility and of thermal expansion are taken into account. By definition,

$$V^P = V^0(1 - \chi P)$$

therefore

$$\Delta V^P = \Delta V^0 - P(2\chi_{En}V_{En}^0 - \chi_Q V_Q^0 - \chi_{F_0}V_{F_0}^0)$$

and, inserting the data of 5.1.5,

$$\Delta V^P = -4.83 + 1.54 \times 10^{-7}P.$$

Thus as long as P is not extremely large, its influence is negligible;

indeed ΔV remains negative at all pressures less than 300 kb. It is therefore legitimate to write

$$(\Delta G)_T^P = (\Delta G)_T^0 + P(\Delta V)_T^0.$$

The value of $V_T - V_0 = \dfrac{\alpha V_0}{100}$ is known for various temperatures for each of the phases involved. Therefore,

$$(\Delta V)_T^0 = (\Delta V)_0^0 + T(2V_{0En}\alpha_{En} - V_{0Q}\alpha_Q - V_{0F_0}\alpha_{F_0}) \times 10^{-2}$$

can be evaluated in cm³ at various temperatures as:

$T°K$	300	500	800
$(\Delta V)_T^0$	−4.83	−5.06	−5.45

$(\Delta V)_T^0$ thus remains negative and the previously established result stands without modification.

Before considering the iron-bearing olivines, one further point remains to be dealt with. $(\Delta G)_T^0$ can be calculated by assuming successively that:

(1) $(\Delta C_P) = 0$ to give $(\Delta G_1)_T^0$,
(2) $(\Delta C_P) = $ constant $= (\Delta C_P)_{298}^0 \sim 0.4\ \text{cal deg}^{-1}$ to give $(\Delta G_2)_T^0$.

In the first case,

$$(\Delta G_1)_T^0 = (\Delta H)_{298}^0 - T(\Delta S)_{298}^0 = -2620 + 0.31T$$

and in the second,

$$(\Delta G_2)_T^0 = (\Delta H)_{298}^0 - T(\Delta S)_{298}^0 + T(\Delta C_P)(1 + \ln 298)$$
$$- (\Delta C_P)T \ln T - 298(\Delta C_P)$$

whence

$$(\Delta G_2)_T^0 = -2739 + 2.99T - 0.92T \log T.$$

It can readily be shown that $(\Delta G_2)_T^0$ remains negative for all P and that $(\Delta G_1)_T^0$ is negative for $T < 8450°K$. Thus the second approximation leads to the same result as the complete calculation. And so in practice does the first since temperatures in excess of 2000°K are not envisaged in geology.

5.3. The reaction quartz + fayalite → 2 ferrosilite.

The solution of the problem posed by the equilibrium conditions of this reaction runs into a major difficulty at the outset: the standard

entropy of ferrosilite is not known. However knowledge of the specific
heat of ferrosilite at 60°C (25.2 cal deg^{-1} mole^{-1}, *Handbook of Physical
Constants*, 1942) considered in the light of the general character of the
variation of ΔC_P with temperature for various natural compounds
of iron and magnesium has enabled Weisbrod (1963) to calculate the
standard entropy very approximately as:

$$S^0_{298} \text{ (ferrosilite)} \sim 26 \pm 2 \text{ cal deg}^{-1} \text{ mole}^{-1}.$$

It follows then that the standard entropy of reaction is given by

$$(\Delta S)^0_{298} = 52 \pm 6 - (10 + 34.7) \sim 7 \pm 4 \text{ cal deg}^{-1}.$$

The semi-empirical formula of Meissner (1948) leads to a
similar value of $(\Delta S)^0_{298}$. Meissner's formula is:

$$(\Delta S)^0_{298} = 3\Delta_1 + \tfrac{8.0}{3}\Delta_2 + \tfrac{10.0}{3}\Delta_3 - \tfrac{2.0}{3}\Delta_4 - 4\Delta_5 + 20L + 10P_1 + 5P_2,$$

where

Δ_1 = the algebraic sum of the gaseous molecules involved in
    reaction, with the exception of H_2, CO_2, SO_2, CS_2, CO,
    NO, CNH, C_2H_2, C_2H_4, $HCHO$,

Δ_2 = the same for H_2, CO_2, SO_2, CS_2,

Δ_3 = the same for CO, NO, CNH, C_2H_2, C_2H_4, $HCHO$,

Δ_4 = the algebraic sum of the number of atoms involved in the
    solid or liquid reaction products, except for H, B, C, Si,
    and the halogens,

Δ_5 = the same for B, C, Si, and the halogens,

L = the algebraic sum of the liquid molecules,

P_1 = the algebraic sum of molecules of organic solids,

P_2 = the algebraic sum of molecules of inorganic solids containing
    Ag^+, Cu^+, Fe^{2+}, Cr^{2+}, Mn^{2+} (other solid inorganic com-
    pounds count as zero).

When all the compounds involved in the reaction are in the
condensed state,

$$\Delta_1 = \Delta_2 = \Delta_3 = \Delta_4 = \Delta_5 = 0$$

whence

$$(\Delta S)^0_{298} = 20L + 10P_1 + 5P_2.$$

For the reaction under consideration $L = P_1 = 0$ and $P_2 = 1$, therefore $(\Delta S)^0_{298} = 5$ cal deg^{-1}.

It will become evident from the study of the reaction under consideration here that, although $(\Delta S)^0_{298}$ may only be known very imprecisely, it is sufficient to know that $(\Delta S)^0_{298} > 0$.

It was shown in the case of the reaction quartz + forsterite → 2 enstatite that the approximation (ΔC_P) = constant is permissible; so it will be assumed that for the reaction at present under consideration $(\Delta C_P) \sim 5.5$ cal deg^{-1}. Therefore

$$(\Delta G)^0_T = (\Delta H)^0_{298} - T(\Delta S)^0_{298} + f(T)$$

where

$$f(T) = T(\Delta C_P)(1 + \ln 298) - (\Delta C_P)T \ln T - 298(\Delta C_P)$$
$$= -1640 - 12.67T \log T + 36.84T.$$

It can readily be seen that $f(T) < 0$ for $T > 300°K$ and, since $(\Delta H)^0_{298} = -310$ cal and $-T(\Delta S)^0_{298} < 0$, it follows that $(\Delta G)^0_T$ is likewise negative. Moreover since $\Delta V = -2.78$ cm^3, $(\Delta G)^P_T$ is negative at all temperatures and pressures: quartz and fayalite, like quartz and forsterite, cannot therefore coexist in the same rock.

5.4. Conclusions.

The instability of the quartz-olivine association has been demonstrated for all temperatures, pressures, and compositions of olivine; and indeed it is true to say that the quartz-olivine association is not observed in the rocks, except for a few occurrences where the olivine is always very iron-rich, nearly pure fayalite. Some fayalite granites in Nigeria, some quartz-gabbros from Skaergaard, Greenland, and some volcanics with an acid glass from Arran, Scotland, may be mentioned. Thermodynamics cannot explain the exceptions and it is necessary to postulate that the reactions leading toward equilibrium must be very slow so that a metastable assemblage can persist.

Bowen and Schairer (1935) recorded the crystallization of a tridymite-fayalite assemblage from a FeO-SiO$_2$ melt. This also would appear to be an instance of metastable synthesis. On the other hand the observation by these authors of the thermal decomposition of a pyroxene into olivine and tridymite would appear to require the existence of a real stability field for the assemblage tridymite-fayalite. It may be that the value used above for the specific heat of ferrosilite is in error. A value of 21–22 cal deg^{-1} mole^{-1} would lead to $(\Delta G)_T^0 > 0$, consistent with Bowen and Schairer's experimental results.

6.   The equilibrium quartz + calcite → wollastonite + CO$_2$

6.1. Nernst's approximation.

This method, used by Goldschmidt (1912), is today of scarcely more than historical interest and furthermore its exposition requires a rather long preliminary calculation. It has, however, seemed worth describing here, for some writers still apply it to equilibria involving a gas phase and, moreover, its argument is not immediately obvious.

6.1.1.—It is convenient first to consider the sublimation of a pure crystalline substance. If it is assumed that the vapor obeys the Perfect Gas Equation, the pressure p of the vapor at a temperature T can be evaluated from the Clausius-Clapeyron equation:

$$\frac{d \ln p}{dT} = \frac{(\Delta H)_T}{RT^2}.$$

Nernst proposed an entirely empirical equation to describe the dependence of the heat of sublimation $(\Delta H)_T$ on temperature:*

$$(\Delta H)_T = (\Delta H)_0 + 1.75RT - \epsilon T^2.$$

Therefore

$$\frac{d \ln p}{dT} = \frac{(\Delta H)_0}{RT^2} + \frac{1.75}{T} - \frac{\epsilon}{R}$$

and, integrating,

$$\ln p = -\frac{(\Delta H)_0}{RT} + 1.75 \ln T - \frac{\epsilon T}{R} + C'$$

* The expression $(\Delta H)_T = (\Delta H)_0 + \int_0^T (\Delta C_P)\, dT$ is rigorously true and Nernst's equation amounts to the arbitrary assumption that $(\Delta C_P) = 1.75\, R - 2\epsilon T$.

where C' is a constant of integration. In logarithms to the base 10 this becomes,

$$\log p = -\frac{(\Delta H)_0}{2.303RT} + 1.75 \log T - \frac{\epsilon T}{2.303R} + C.$$

The constant $C = \dfrac{C'}{2.303}$ is known as the *chemical constant*. Except for hydrogen, the value of the chemical constants of the common gases, determined by experimental measurements of p, approximates to 3.1 (oxygen 2.8; chlorine 3.1; ammonia 3.3; carbon dioxide 3.3).

It is appropriate at this stage to explore the physical significance of the chemical constant. And this may be done by considering the matter in a highly classical manner. Making the same assumptions as before (perfect gas, molar volume of the crystalline phase $\ll$ the molar volume v of the gas),

$$(\Delta G)_T^p = (\Delta G)_T^0 + \int_0^p v\, dp$$

and since

$$pv = RT,$$
$$(\Delta G)_T^p = (\Delta G)_T^0 + RT \ln p.$$

The equilibrium condition is $(\Delta G)_T^p = 0$, therefore

$$\ln p = -\frac{(\Delta G)_T^0}{RT} = -\frac{(\Delta H)_T^0}{RT} + \frac{(\Delta S_v)_T^0}{R}.$$

But

$$(\Delta H)_T^0 = (\Delta H)_0^0 + \int_0^T (\Delta C_P)\, dT$$

and

$$(\Delta S_v)_T^0 = (\Delta S_v)_0^0 + \int_0^T \frac{(\Delta C_P)}{T}\, dT.$$

The kinetic theory of gases indicates that the specific heat of a gas can be broken down into two terms, one independent of temperature (C_0) and the other temperature dependent (C_T):

$$\Delta C_P = C_0 + C_T - C_S$$

where C_S is the specific heat of the crystalline phase. Therefore

$$(\Delta H)_T^0 = (\Delta H)_0^0 + C_0 T + \int_0^T (C_T - C_S)\, dT,$$

and

$$(\Delta S_v)_T^0 = (\Delta S_v)_0^0 + C_0 \ln T + \int_0^T \frac{C_T - C_S}{T}\, dT.$$

Substitution into the expression for $\ln p$ yields

$$\ln p = -\frac{(\Delta H)_0^0}{RT} + \frac{C_0}{R} \ln T - \frac{1}{RT} \int_0^T (C_T - C_S)\, dT$$
$$+ \frac{1}{R} \int_0^T \frac{C_T - C_S}{T}\, dT + \frac{(\Delta S_v)_0^0 - C_0}{R}.$$

Comparison with the expression obtained from Nernst's approximation shows that the term $\dfrac{(\Delta S_v)_0^0 - C_0}{R}$ corresponds to the chemical constant.

6.1.2.—It remains now to see how the chemical constant can be used to solve equilibrium problems that involve a gas-phase. We shall restrict ourselves here to the reaction quartz + calcite $\rightarrow$ wollastonite + CO_2, the general case being postponed to a later chapter.

Let p be the equilibrium pressure of CO_2 at temperature T, and assume that CO_2 approximates to a perfect gas and that the volume of the solids is negligible in relation to that of the gas. Once again

$$\ln p = -\frac{(\Delta G)_T^0}{RT} = -\frac{(\Delta H)_T^0}{RT} + \frac{(\Delta S)_T^0}{R}$$

therefore

$$\ln p = -\frac{(\Delta H)_0^0}{RT} + \frac{(\Delta S)_0^0}{R} - \frac{1}{RT} \int_0^T (\Delta C_P)\, dT + \frac{1}{R} \int_0^T \frac{(\Delta C_P)}{T}\, dT$$

where

$$(\Delta C_P) = C_{CO_2} + C_{Wo} - C_{cal} - C_{quartz}.$$

Put

$$C_{cal} + C_{quartz} - C_{Wo} = C_S$$

and

$$C_{CO_2} = C_0 + C_T,$$

C_0 being independent of temperature. Therefore

$$(\Delta C_P) = C_0 + C_T - C_S$$

and

$$\ln p = -\frac{(\Delta H)_0^0}{RT} + \frac{C_0}{R} \ln T - \frac{1}{RT} \int_0^T (C_T - C_S) \, dT$$

$$+ \frac{1}{R} \int_0^T \frac{C_T - C_S}{T} \, dT + \frac{(\Delta S)_0^0 - C_0}{R}.$$

But $(\Delta S)_0^0$ can be expanded as

$$(\Delta S)_0^0 = S_{0\,CO_2}^0 + S_{0\,Wo}^0 - S_{0\,cal}^0 - S_{0\,quartz}^0$$

where $S_{0\,CO_2}^0$ is the entropy of CO_2 in the gaseous state at absolute zero. If $S_{0\,CO_2}^{0'}$ represents the entropy of crystalline CO_2 at absolute zero and $(\Delta S_v)_0^0$ the entropy of vaporization of CO_2 at absolute zero

$$S_{0\,CO_2}^0 = S_{0\,CO_2}^{0'} + (\Delta S_v)_0^0$$

thence

$$(\Delta S)_0^0 = S_{0\,CO_2}^{0'} + S_{0\,Wo}^0 - S_{0\,cal}^0 - S_{0\,quartz}^0 + (\Delta S_v)_0^0$$

and putting

$$(\Delta S_c)_0^0 = S_{0\,CO_2}^{0'} + S_{0\,Wo}^0 - S_{0\,cal}^0 - S_{0\,quartz}^0$$

it follows that

$$(\Delta S)_0^0 = (\Delta S_c)_0^0 + (\Delta S_v)_0^0.$$

$(\Delta S_c)_0^0$ represents the entropy of reaction at absolute zero with all the reactants and products in the crystalline state. According to Nernst's Theorem (the so-called Third Law) $(\Delta S_c)_0^0$ is zero and so

$$(\Delta S)_0^0 = (\Delta S_v)_0^0.$$

It is evident then that the term

$$\frac{(\Delta S)_0^0 - C_0}{R} = \frac{(\Delta S_v)_0^0 - C_0}{R}$$

is none other than the conventional chemical constant C' for CO_2 and so the expression for $\ln p$ can be rewritten as

$$\ln p = -\frac{(\Delta H)_0^0}{RT} + \frac{C_0}{R} \ln T - \frac{1}{RT} \int_0^T (C_T - C_S) \, dT$$

$$+ \frac{1}{R} \int_0^T \frac{C_T - C_S}{T} \, dT + C'.$$

Since the coefficients necessary for the evaluation of the integrals are often undetermined, it is convenient to put $C_T - C_S = 0$ as a first approximation. Then

$$\ln p = -\frac{(\Delta H)_0^0}{RT} + \frac{C_0}{R} \ln T + C'$$

or in logarithms to the base 10,

$$\log p = -\frac{(\Delta H)_0^0}{2.303RT} + \frac{C_0}{R} \log T + C.$$

It is immediately obvious that Nernst's approximation amounts in this case to putting $\dfrac{C_0}{R} = 1.75$, so that

$$\log p = -\frac{(\Delta H)_0^0}{4.57T} + 1.75 \log T + C.$$

This is the approximate equation used by Goldschmidt for the equilibrium quartz + calcite → wollastonite + CO_2, with the constants taken as:

$$(\Delta H)_0^0 = 25{,}300 \text{ cal}; \qquad C = 3.2.$$

6.2. The use of standard data (after Danielsson, 1950).

The high temperature specific heats of the phases involved are given by Kelley (1960) as:

wollastonite . $C_P = 26.64 + 3.60 \times 10^{-3}T - 6.52 \times 10^5 T^{-2}$; $(273 - 1450°K)$
CO_2. . . . . $C_P = 10.55 + 2.16 \times 10^{-3}T - 2.04 \times 10^5 T^{-2}$; $(273 - 2500°K)$
calcite. . . . . . $C_P = 24.98 + 5.24 \times 10^{-3}T - 6.20 \times 10^5 T^{-2}$; $(273 - 1200°K)$
quartz. . . . . . $C_P = 11.22 + 8.20 \times 10^{-3}T - 2.70 \times 10^5 T^{-2}$; $(273 - \ 846°K)$

Therefore

$$(\Delta C_P) = 0.99 - 7.68 \times 10^{-3}T + 0.34 \times 10^5 T^{-2}$$

and so

$$(\Delta H)_T - (\Delta H)_{298} = \int_{298}^{T} (\Delta C_P) \, dT$$

$$= 0.99T - 3.84 \times 10^{-3}T^2 - 0.34 \times 10^5 T^{-1} + 156.$$

$(\Delta H)_{298}$ can be calculated from the known heats of reaction:

$$CaCO_3 \rightarrow CaO + CO_2; \qquad (\Delta H)_{298} = 42{,}310 \text{ cal}$$
$$\text{(Roth, Berendt, and Wirths, 1941),}$$

$$CaO + SiO_2 \rightarrow CaSiO_3; \qquad (\Delta H)_{298} = -21{,}250 \text{ cal}$$
$$\text{(Torgeson and Sahama, 1948).}$$

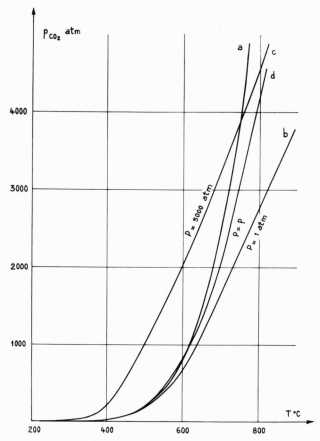

Fig. 32. Partial pressure of CO_2 as a function of temperature for the reaction quartz + calcite → wollastonite + CO_2.

(a) CO_2 treated as a perfect gas at a total pressure (P) of 1 atm.
(b) CO_2 treated as a real gas at a total pressure (P) of 1 atm.
(c) CO_2 treated as a real gas with a lithostatic pressure (P) of 5000 atm.
(d) CO_2 treated as a real gas with a lithostatic pressure (P) equal to the partial pressure (p) of CO_2.

Therefore for the reaction

$CaCO_3 + SiO_2 \rightarrow CaSiO_3 + CO_2$, $(\Delta H)_{298} = 42,310 - 21,250 = 21,060$ cal,

and consequently

$$(\Delta H)_T = 21,216 + 0.99T - 3.84 \times 10^{-3}T^2 - 0.34 \times 10^5 T^{-1}.$$

In order to provide some variety in the mode of calculation the Gibbs-Helmholtz equation will be applied in the form

$$\frac{\partial(\Delta G/T)}{\partial T} = -\frac{(\Delta H)_T}{T^2}$$

whence

$$\frac{\partial(\Delta G/T)}{\partial T} = -\frac{21{,}216}{T^2} - \frac{0.99}{T} + 3.84 \times 10^{-3} + \frac{0.34 \times 10^5}{T^3},$$

which becomes on integration between 298 and $T°K$

$$\frac{(\Delta G)_T^0}{T} - \frac{(\Delta G)_{298}^0}{298} = \int_{298}^{T} \frac{(\Delta H)_T}{T^2}\, dT$$

$$= 21{,}216T^{-1} - 0.99 \ln T + 3.84 \times 10^{-3}T$$
$$- 0.17 \times 10^5 T^{-2} - 66.49.$$

Now $(\Delta G)_{298}^0 = (\Delta H)_{298}^0 - 298(\Delta S)_{298}^0$ and $(\Delta S)_{298}^0$ can be evaluated from the standard entropies of the phases involved (Kelley, 1941):

Wollastonite	19.6 cal deg^{-1} mole^{-1}	
CO$_2$	51.1	—
Calcite	22.2	—
Quartz	10.1	—

whence

$$(\Delta S)_{298}^0 = 38.4 \text{ cal deg}^{-1}$$

and

$$\frac{(\Delta G)_{298}^0}{298} = \frac{21{,}060}{298} - 38.4 = 32.25 \text{ cal deg}^{-1};$$

therefore

$$(\Delta G)_T^0 = 21{,}216 - 34.24T - 0.99T \ln T + 3.84 \times 10^{-3}T^2 - 0.17 \times 10^5 T^{-1}.$$

The free enthalpy of reaction can now be calculated at all pressures and temperatures from

$$(\Delta G)_T^{P,p} = (\Delta G)_T^0 + \int_0^P \Delta V\, dP + \int_0^p v\, dp$$

where

P = pressure applied to the solid phases (total pressure),
p = partial pressure of CO$_2$,
ΔV = volume change on reaction for the solid phases,
v = molar volume of CO$_2$.

The first integral will be neglected at this stage, so that

$$(\Delta G)_T^p = (\Delta G)_T^0 + \int_0^p v \, dp.$$

This equation is rigorously true when P = 1 atm and becomes increasingly approximate as P increases in magnitude. If it is further assumed that CO_2 obeys the Perfect Gas Equation, $pv = RT$ and

$$(\Delta G)_T^p = (\Delta G)_T^0 + RT \ln p.$$

It suffices to insert the equilibrium condition $(\Delta G)_T^p = 0$ to determine the equilibrium pressure of CO_2 at any temperature:

$$\ln p = -\frac{(\Delta G)_T^0}{RT} \qquad \text{or} \qquad \log p = -\frac{(\Delta G)_T^0}{2.303RT}.$$

Substitution of the expression for $(\Delta G)_T^0$ and evaluation of R yields:

$$\log p = 7.48 + 0.498 \log T - 0.84 \times 10^{-3}T - 4636T^{-1} + 0.037 \times 10^5 T^{-2}.$$

This equation is strictly valid only below 846°K; at that temperature α-quartz changes to β-quartz with a heat of transformation represented by ΔH_{transf}. With the values used by Danielsson, $\Delta H_{transf} = 290$ cal mole^{-1} and C_P (β-quartz) = 14.41 + 1.94 × $10^{-3}T$, the expression for $\log p$ between 846 and 1030°K is

$$\log p = 11.61 - 1.107 \log T - 0.155 \times 10^{-3}T - 4603T^{-1} - 0.258 \times 10^5 T^{-2}.$$

The curve of equilibrium pressure of CO_2 as a function of temperature (fig. 32, curve (a)) can thus be drawn. At $p = 1$ atm it lies at T = 280°C.

6.3. Correction for the non-ideality of CO_2 gas.

Experiment shows that as p_{CO_2} increases, carbon dioxide ceases to approximate to a perfect gas. The departure from ideality is commonly represented by one or the other of the coefficients

$$Z = \frac{pv}{RT} \qquad \text{or} \qquad \alpha = \frac{RT}{p} - v;$$

Z tends to 1 and α to zero as p becomes very small (fig. 33). It follows that

$$v = Z\frac{RT}{p} = \frac{RT}{p} + RT\frac{Z-1}{p} \qquad \text{or} \qquad v = \frac{RT}{p} - \alpha$$

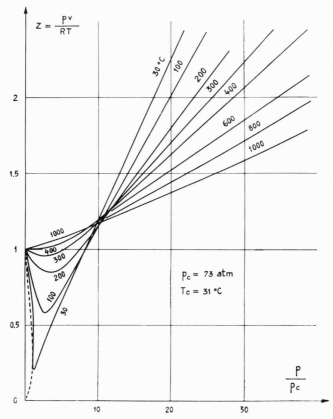

Fig. 33. Departure of CO_2 from the perfect gas equation.

and therefore

$$\int_0^p v\,dp = RT \ln p + RT \int_0^p \frac{Z-1}{p}\,dp \quad \text{or} \quad \int_0^p v\,dp = RT \ln p - \int_0^p \alpha\,dp$$

since

$$(\Delta G)_T^p = (\Delta G)_T^0 + \int_0^p v\,dp,$$

$$\ln p = -\frac{(\Delta G)_T^0}{RT} - \int_0^p \frac{Z-1}{p}\,dp \quad \text{or} \quad \ln p = -\frac{(\Delta G)_T^0}{RT} + \frac{1}{RT}\int_0^p \alpha\,dp.$$

It should be noticed that this last equation can be obtained directly. For a perfect gas, as has already been shown,

$$\ln p = -\frac{(\Delta G)_T^0}{RT}.$$

For a real gas this expression becomes

$$\ln f = -\frac{(\Delta G)_T^0}{RT}$$

where f is the fugacity of the gas. Therefore putting $f = \gamma p$, where γ is the coefficient of fugacity,

$$\ln p = -\frac{(\Delta G)_T^0}{RT} - \ln \gamma.$$

But it has already been seen (p. 83) that

$$RT \ln \gamma = -\int_0^p \alpha \, dp$$

and therefore

$$\ln p = -\frac{(\Delta G)_T^0}{RT} + \frac{1}{RT} \int_0^p \alpha \, dp.$$

The solution of either of these equations poses a minor practical problem: the integrations can only be performed graphically from the curve of $\dfrac{Z-1}{p}$ or α as a function of p at any given temperature (fig. 34). The integrals are themselves functions of pressure and so the equations cannot be solved formally.

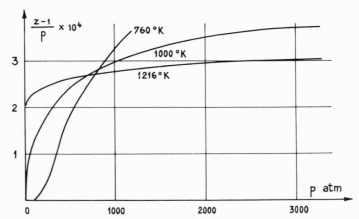

Fig. 34. Curve for the calculation of corrections for the non-ideality of CO_2.

Graphical solution: putting the value of the integral equal to $f(p)$,

$$\ln p = -\frac{(\Delta G)_T^0}{RT} + f(p) \qquad \text{or} \qquad \log p = -\frac{(\Delta G)_T^0}{2.303 RT} + \frac{f(p)}{2.303}.$$

If now the curves of $\log p$ and $\dfrac{1}{2.303}\left(f(p) - \dfrac{(\Delta G)_T^0}{RT}\right)$ are plotted on the same graph as functions of p at a given temperature T, the abscissa of their point of intersection is the equilibrium pressure at that temperature.

Solution by successive approximation: put $-\dfrac{(\Delta G)_T^0}{RT} = \ln p_1$, where p_1 is the equilibrium pressure at temperature T when the gas is assumed to be perfect (curve (a) of fig. 32) and let p_0 be the solution of the equation

$$\ln p = -\frac{(\Delta G)_T^0}{RT} + f(p) = \ln p_1 + f(p).$$

It should be borne in mind that p_1 will not differ much from p_0. Begin by calculating $f(p_1)$ and

$$\ln p_2 = \ln p_1 + f(p_1)$$
$$\ln p_3 = \ln p_1 + f(p_2)$$
$$\dotfill$$
$$\ln p_n = \ln p_1 + f(p_{n-1}).$$

It can be shown that p_n tends toward p_0 as n tends to infinity. It is sufficient therefore to carry the calculation for each temperature only as far as is necessary to obtain a value of the desired accuracy. It is thus possible by correcting curve (a) point by point to trace out the corresponding curve (b), which takes the non-ideality of CO_2 into account.

6.4. *Effect of lithostatic pressure.*

Returning to the general equation

$$(\Delta G)_T^P = (\Delta G)_T^0 + \int_0^p v \, dp + \int_0^P \Delta V \, dP$$

with

$$\Delta V = V_{W_0} - V_{Ca} - V_Q$$
$$= 39.9 - 37.0 - 22.6 = -19.7 \text{ cm}^3,$$

and neglecting the variation of ΔV with P and T, substitute the expression obtained above for $\int_0^p v\,dp$ to give

$$(\Delta G)_T^{P,p} = (\Delta G)_T^0 + RT \ln p + RT \int_0^p \frac{Z-1}{p}\,dp + P\Delta V.$$

Therefore at equilibrium

$$\ln p = -\frac{(\Delta G)_T^0}{RT} - \int_0^p \frac{Z-1}{p}\,dp - \frac{P\Delta V}{RT}.$$

Thus it is possible to calculate the equilibrium pressure of CO_2 for various values of P and T. In figure 32 curve (c) represents $p = f(T)$ for P = 5000 atm and curve (d) represents $p = f(T)$ for P = p.

It may be of interest also to consider the case in which lithostatic pressure is an independent variable, p_{CO2} being known *a priori*. Then

$$P = -\frac{(\Delta G)_T^0}{\Delta V} - \frac{RT}{\Delta V} \int_0^p \frac{Z-1}{p}\,dp - \frac{RT \ln p}{\Delta V}.$$

And in the special case where $p = \lambda P$ this expression becomes

$$P = -\frac{(\Delta G)_T^0}{\Delta V} - \frac{RT}{\Delta V} \int_0^{p=P} \frac{Z-1}{p}\,dp - \frac{RT \ln P}{\Delta V} - \frac{RT \ln \lambda}{\Delta V},$$

λ being a constant.

Figure 35 displays curves representing the dependence of the lithostatic pressure P on equilibrium temperature in various circumstances: curve (a) corresponds to partial pressure of CO_2, $p_{CO2} = 1$ atm, curve (b) to $p_{CO2} = 100$ atm, curve (c) to $p_{CO2} = P$, and curve (d) to $p_{CO2} = 0.3P$.

6.5. *The metamorphism of siliceous limestones.*

The reaction quartz + calcite → wollastonite + CO_2 has for long interested petrologists. The data used in the calculations made above are known with some precision and it has been supposed that the equilibrium might serve as an indicator of temperature in metamorphism. The comparative commonness of wollastonite in metamorphosed calcareous rocks would make such an indicator of widespread application.

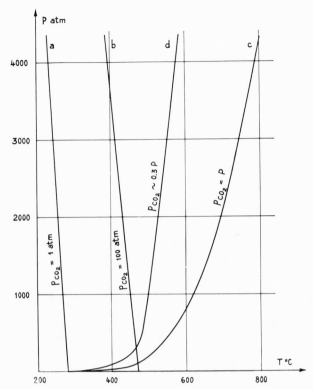

Fig. 35. Effect of lithostatic pressure and temperature on the reaction quartz + calcite → wollastonite + CO_2. Curves a and b relate to CO_2 at a constant partial pressure (p_{CO_2}) independent of the lithostatic pressure. Curves c and d relate to partial pressures of CO_2 (p_{CO_2}) proportional to the lithostatic pressure (P).

In order to simplify the discussion it is useful to distinguish two sets of conditions which lead to quite different equations.

6.5.1.—Case I: a porous rock whose pores do not intercommunicate. The critical factor here is that any CO_2 liberated in the reaction cannot escape. Consider the reaction in the form:

$$m\,Q + n\,Ca \rightarrow (m - \nu)Q + (n - \nu)\,Ca + \nu\,Wo + \nu\,CO_2$$

and let V be the initial volume of the system, $\dfrac{rV}{100}$ the volume of the pores initially, and ΔV the change in the volume of the solid phases in reaction per mole of wollastonite formed.

On completion of the reaction the volume of the system will be $V - \dfrac{rV}{100} + \nu \Delta V$, and the volume v of the pores, that is the volume available for accommodation of liberated CO_2, will be given by

$$v = \frac{rV}{100} - \nu \Delta V.$$

If CO_2 approximates to a perfect gas, $pv = \nu RT$ and substitution into the preceding equation then yields

$$\nu = \frac{rVp}{100(RT + p\,\Delta V)}.$$

For a given lithostatic pressure P, the pressure of CO_2 is completely determined at a given temperature; and so consequently is ν. In other words in this case, in contrast to the examples that have been worked out in earlier paragraphs, the reaction does not continue until the initial phases have been completely dissipated. It proceeds only until the pressure of CO_2 reaches the value fixed by the temperature and available volume; it is therefore possible for the assemblage quartz-calcite-wollastonite-CO_2 to occur at equilibrium.

It is interesting to calculate the proportion x of wollastonite present at equilibrium in the rock. If V_{Wo} is the molar volume of wollastonite,

$$x = 100\ \frac{\nu V_{Wo}}{V - \dfrac{rV}{100} + \nu\Delta V}$$

which becomes if $\dfrac{rV}{100} - \nu\,\Delta V$ is neglected, $x = 100\,\dfrac{\nu V_{Wo}}{V}$. Replacement of ν by the value found for it above yields

$$x = \frac{rp V_{Wo}}{RT + p\,\Delta V}.$$

Now $V_{Wo} \sim 40$ cm³ mole⁻¹, $\Delta V \sim -20$ cm³, and R ~ 82 atm cm³ deg⁻¹, therefore, for p in atm,

$$x \sim \frac{40rp}{82T - 20p}.$$

The table below gives a selection of values of x for $P = 1$ atm.

r	$T°C$	x
0.1	280	8.8×10^{-5}
—	360	7.7×10^{-4}
—	465	6.6×10^{-3}
1	280	8.8×10^{-4}
—	360	7.7×10^{-3}
—	465	6.6×10^{-2}
10	280	8.8×10^{-3}
—	360	7.7×10^{-2}
—	465	6.6×10^{-1}

Under these conditions the volume percentage of wollastonite formed remains quite small. The probability of meeting the mineral in a suite of thin sections is correspondingly small and microscopic examination would usually indicate its absence. In other words, even if the slow rate of reaction, the effect of retrograde metamorphism, or any other cause that might inhibit the formation of wollastonite is excluded, its apparent absence from a rock provides no strong indication that that rock has not been raised to a temperature in excess of the equilibrium temperature.

6.5.2.—Case II. Suppose now that *circulation of the fluid phase is possible* in such a way as to liberate CO_2 as it forms in the course of the reaction. Equilibrium is evidently unattainable and the reaction proceeds until one at least of the reactant phases has been completely consumed. The only assemblages possible are therefore quartz + calcite, or quartz + wollastonite, or calcite + wollastonite.

It is clear from figure 32 that at a given lithostatic pressure P, the equilibrium temperature will be strongly dependent on p_{CO_2}. Now this partial pressure of CO_2 may be difficult to evaluate for the geological environment of the reaction and in these circumstances the equilibrium calcite + quartz $\rightarrow$ wollastonite + CO_2 can only be used as a *geological thermometer* with the greatest circumspection.[*][†]

[*] Writers who have discussed this question have generally concluded, from various considerations, petrographic and otherwise, that the partial pressure of CO_2 must be raised to about the same value as the lithostatic pressure.

[†] See also Harker and Tuttle (1956).

IX

Systems and Phases
of Variable Composition

1.   The nature of the problem

It has been assumed in the preceding chapters that the systems under investigation and their constituent phases are of constant composition. That restriction was imposed simply because the mathematical apparatus necessary for the discussion of systems of variable composition had not yet been developed; that will be done in the following paragraphs.

For the generalized reaction

$$\sum_i n_i M_i \rightarrow \sum_j n'_j M'_j$$

the free enthalpy of reaction is given by

$$(\Delta G) = \sum_j n'_j G'_j - \sum_i n_i G_i.$$

This equation is rigorously valid only if each component is restricted to a single phase $\alpha, \beta \ldots$, but an analogous equation can be written in terms of the phases involved in reaction so as to be generally true

$$(\Delta G) = \sum_\beta n'^\beta G'^\beta - \sum_\alpha n^\alpha G^\alpha.$$

Any increment in the free enthalpy of a system can (p. 73) be expressed as*

$$dG = \left(\frac{\partial G}{\partial T}\right)_{P,n_i} dT + \left(\frac{\partial G}{\partial P}\right)_{T,n_i} dP + \sum_i \left(\frac{\partial G}{\partial n_i}\right)_{T,P} dn_i$$

---

* Neglecting all variables other than T, P, n, such as surface tension, magnetic field, and so on.

156

and for any one of the constituent phases of the system

$$dG^\alpha = \left(\frac{\partial G^\alpha}{\partial T}\right)_{P,n_i} dT + \left(\frac{\partial G^\alpha}{\partial P}\right)_{T,n_i} dP + \sum_i \left(\frac{\partial G^\alpha}{\partial n_i}\right)_{P,T} dn_i.$$

The variation of G with temperature and pressure has already been thoroughly examined, but nothing has yet been said about the manner in which free enthalpy varies with composition. Without such knowledge, the equilibrium conditions for a reaction in which the composition of the system—or that of any of the phases involved—may vary, cannot be established.

Consider, for instance, a reaction in the course of which two gaseous substances are liberated. Together they constitute a single gas phase α of free enthalpy G^α. In order to establish the conditions of equilibrium, it will clearly be necessary to express G^α as a function of (1) the molar free enthalpy of each gas, and (2) the relative proportion of each gas in the gas phase, that is the composition of the gas phase.

In order to make the significance of what follows quite clear, *the examples of the previous chapter* will be taken one by one and for each it will be shown how knowledge of the variation of G with composition leads, at least formally, to the resolution of some difficulties that have hitherto been neglected.

Quartz $\rightleftharpoons$ tridymite. The experimental curve of Tuttle and Bowen (1958) for the quartz $\rightleftharpoons$ tridymite equilibrium is significantly different from that obtained by calculation (see fig. 26) and it has been pointed out that the discrepancy might be due to the presence of water in solid solution in silica. The equilibrium condition is $(\Delta G) = G_{Tr} - G_Q = 0$, where the symbols Tr and Q refer to tridymite and quartz considered as *phases* rather than as chemical compounds. If the dependence of G_{Tr} and G_Q on water content are known, the effect on the equilibrium conditions of the presence of water in the system can be determined.

The stability of jadeite. The problem is just the same as in the previous example: if the dependence of the free enthalpy of jadeite on the concentrations of Fe^{3+}, Ca, etc., is known and, similarly, that of albite on the concentrations of K, Ca, etc., then it is possible to deal with the presence of these elements in the system. Consider for instance the reaction

albite + nepheline $\rightarrow$ 2 jadeite.

In the presence of lime, the reaction must be written as

plagioclase + nepheline → 2 omphacite*.

The compositions of plagioclase and pyroxene are variable; thus the equilibrium conditions can only be calculated if it is known how the free enthalpy of these minerals depends on composition.

The assemblage quartz—olivine. It was shown above that neither the assemblage quartz—forsterite, nor quartz—fayalite, is stable; and the conclusion was crudely extended to the whole composition range of olivine. However, such an extension can be valid only when the dependence of the free enthalpies of olivine and of pyroxene on composition are known: it cannot be known *a priori* whether there is a composition in the olivine range at which the free enthalpy change (ΔG) for the reaction quartz + olivine → pyroxene is positive.

The reaction calcite + quartz → wollastonite + CO_2. If an additional fluid substance, and the most likely one is water, is present in the system, the free enthalpy of reaction has to be written as

$$(\Delta G) = G_F + (G_{Wo} - G_Q - G_{Cal})$$

where G_F represents the free enthalpy of the single fluid phase. The magnitude of G_F depends on the relative proportions of the two constituents, CO_2 and H_2O, in the fluid phase. This is then a system in which the composition of *one* phase may be variable.

Now it has been supposed that quartz was effectively present in the system initially, but it may be that calcite reacts with introduced silica, perhaps derived from the surrounding rocks, and then it is necessary to express the reaction as

calcite + SiO_2 → wollastonite + CO_2.

The introduced silica may be fixed as quartz, if the association quartz—calcite is stable; or it may react immediately with calcite, in which case the free enthalpy change will depend on the concentration of SiO_2 in the rock, silica not being present as a distinct solid phase.

It is evident then that the study of systems of variable composition is geologically important: it enables the problems posed by *reactions between minerals of variable composition* to be solved and it is necessary for the

---

* Omphacite is a pyroxene intermediate in composition between jadeite and diopside.

thermodynamic interpretation of *metasomatism*, a process of some importance in both petrology and ore genesis. It is, however, not necessary always to regard the assumption of the constancy of composition of a system or of its individual phases as an inadmissible approximation. Experience shows that in many cases the approximate results so obtained can lead to valid and consequently interesting conclusions.

2.   Partial molar quantities

2.1. Definition.

In general the variation of any thermodynamic function J as a function of temperature, pressure, and composition of the system can be expressed by the equation

$$dJ = \left(\frac{\partial J}{\partial T}\right)_{P,n_i,n_j} dT + \left(\frac{\partial J}{\partial P}\right)_{T,n_i,n_j} dP + \sum_i \left(\frac{\partial J}{\partial n_i}\right)_{T,P,n_j} dn_i.$$

Partial derivatives such as $\left(\dfrac{\partial J}{\partial n_i}\right)_{T,P,n_j}$ *are described as partial molar quantities and are represented by the symbol* J_i. Thus

[1] $$dJ = \left(\frac{\partial J}{\partial T}\right)_{P,n_i,n_j} dT + \left(\frac{\partial J}{\partial P}\right)_{T,n_i,n_j} dP + \sum_i J_i \, dn_i.$$

For free enthalpy the expression becomes

$$dG = -S \, dT + V \, dP + \sum_i \bar{G}_i \, dn_i$$

and for volume

$$dV = \alpha V \, dT - \chi V \, dP + \sum_i \bar{V}_i \, dn_i;$$

the expression for the total volume change thus includes a term for thermal expansion, a term for isothermal compressibility, and lastly terms relating to changes in composition.

Therefore partial molar quantities take account, other things being equal, of changes in the thermodynamic functions due to an increase dn_i or a decrease $-dn_i$ of each component i, that is:

[2] $$dT = 0, \qquad dP = 0, \qquad dJ = \sum_i J_i \, dn_i.$$

Integration at constant composition, that is, at constant J_i, yields

[3] $T = \text{Constant}, \qquad P = \text{Constant}, \qquad J = \sum_i n_i \bar{J}_i.$

It should be noticed that for phases that contain only a single component i, $J = n_i \bar{J}_i$, therefore

[4] $\bar{J}_i = J_i$

J_i being the corresponding molar quantity of the component in question under the same conditions of temperature and pressure.

In practice it is always difficult to determine a partial derivative of the type $\left(\dfrac{\partial G}{\partial n_1}\right)_{T,P,n_2,n_3\ldots}$ and consequently not easy to study the variation in free enthalpy of a mixture of components 1, 2, 3, ... at mole contents n_1, n_2, n_3, ... as the concentration of component 1 alone varies. However, in the special case of a perfect gas or an ideal solution partial molar quantities can be expressed very simply.

2.2. Application to perfect gases and ideal solutions.

The ideal solution will be rigorously defined in a subsequent paragraph. It suffices for the present purpose to state that ideal liquid or solid solutions obey the same rules as perfect gases; in particular, all the equations that will now be established for perfect gases are also valid for ideal solutions. For that reason ideal solutions have been introduced at this stage, before it is convenient to give their complete definition.

Perfect gases and ideal solutions are of much greater interest in geology than might be supposed *a priori*. Extension to real gases is a simple matter; fugacity (see p. 81) has merely to be substituted for pressure in the equations derived below. The solid solutions that are the common rock-forming mineral groups can in many cases be regarded as ideal: this is so, for instance, for the olivines and the orthopyroxenes. The plagioclase feldspars are in this respect most instructive: at relatively low temperatures albite and anorthite do not form (p. 49) an ideal solid solution, but the departure from ideality is nevertheless very slight and can be neglected to yield quite a good approximation.

2.2.1. Volume.—Consider a mixture of perfect gases at temperature T and pressure P. The partial molar volume of component i is given by

$$\bar{V}_i = \left(\frac{\partial V}{\partial n_i}\right)_{P,T,n_j}.$$

Since all perfect gases have the same equation of state,

$$V = \frac{RT}{P} \sum_i n_i \quad \text{and therefore} \quad \bar{V}_i = \frac{RT}{P}.$$

But $\dfrac{RT}{P} = V_i$, where V_i is the molar volume of component i under the same conditions of temperature and pressure. Therefore

[5] $$\bar{V}_i = V_i$$

and

[6] $$V = \sum_i n_i \bar{V}_i = \sum_i n_i V_i.$$

Thus *for perfect gases volume is an additive property*, a conclusion that was reached experimentally by Dalton in 1801.

The same is true for ideal solutions; for instance, the volume of an olivine composed of n_1 moles of fayalite and n_2 moles of forsterite is given by

$$V = n_1 V_{Fa} + n_2 V_{Fo}$$

and the molar volume by

$$V_{Ol} = \frac{V}{n_1 + n_2} = \frac{n_1}{n_1 + n_2} V_{Fa} + \frac{n_2}{n_1 + n_2} V_{Fo},$$

which, on writing the molar concentration of fayalite, $n_1/(n_1 + n_2)$, as x becomes

$$V_{Ol} = x V_{Fa} + (1 - x) V_{Fo}.$$

On the other hand a non-ideal solution does not obey the additive rule and then

$$\bar{V}_i \neq V_i \quad \text{and} \quad V \neq \sum_i n_i V_i.$$

Figure 36 shows the dependence of the unit-cell dimensions of melilite on composition. In so far as volume is concerned melilite can evidently be regarded as an ideal solid solution.

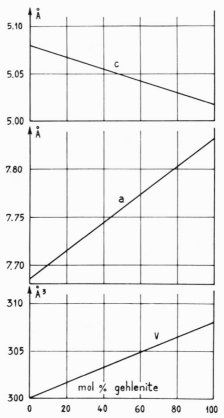

Fig. 36. Dimensions, a and c, and volume, $V = a^2c$, of the tetragonal unit-cell of melilite as a function of the molar percentage of the gehlenite end-member. After
Neuvonen, 1952.

2.2.2. Partial pressure.—Consider a mixture of perfect gases occupying
a volume V at temperature T and let n_i be the number of moles of
constituent i. The *partial pressure* p_i of constituent i is defined as the
pressure that it would have if it alone occupied the volume V at the
temperature T, that is

[7] $$p_i V = n_i\, RT.$$

Since all perfect gases have the same equation of state

[8] $$PV = nRT \qquad \text{with} \qquad n = \sum_i n_i,$$

P being the total pressure of the gas mixture. Comparison of (7) with (8) leads to the two equations:

[9] $$P = \sum_i p_i$$

[10] $$p_i = P\frac{n_i}{n} = P\frac{n_i}{\sum\limits_i n_i}.$$

It is convenient to express the content of constituent i in the mixture in terms of the *mol fraction* x_i of that constituent:

[11] $$x_i = \frac{n_i}{\sum\limits_i n_i}; \qquad (0 \leqslant x_i \leqslant 1).$$

Equation (10) can then be rewritten as

[12] $$p_i = Px_i.$$

2.2.3. Internal energy and enthalpy.—Classical thermodynamics provides no means of evaluating the internal energy of a gaseous constituent of a mixture. But it will be assumed that for a perfect gas the partial molar internal energy of constituent i is equal to the molar internal energy that constituent i would have if it existed alone under the same conditions of temperature and pressure, that is

[13] $$\overline{U}_i = U_i$$

and consequently

[14] $$U = \sum_i n_i U_i.$$

This postulate of classical thermodynamics can be proved quite simply by statistical thermodynamics. It follows immediately that *enthalpy* is an *additive property:*

$$H = U + PV$$

and taking (6) and (14) into account

$$H = \sum_i n_i U_i + P \sum_i n_i V_i = \sum_i n_i(U_i + PV_i)$$

since

$$H_i = U_i + PV_i$$

it follows that

[15] $$H = \sum_i n_i H_i$$

therefore

[16] $$\overline{H}_i = H_i.$$

Equations (13), (14), (15), and (16) are likewise valid for ideal solutions. Consider for instance the heat of solution of olivine in hydrofluoric acid at given temperature and pressure

$$(\Delta H)_{Ol} = H'_{Ol} - H_{Ol}$$

where H_{Ol} and H'_{Ol} are respectively the absolute molar enthalpies of olivine and of the solution at the experimental T and P. If the solution is very dilute, and assuming that forsterite and fayalite form an ideal solid solution, it follows that

$$H_{Ol} = x H_{Fa} + (1 - x) H_{Fo}$$

and

$$H'_{Ol} = x H'_{Fa} + (1 - x) H'_{Fo}$$

where

H_{Fa} = molar enthalpy of pure fayalite,
H_{Fo} = molar enthalpy of pure forsterite,
H'_{Fa} = molar enthalpy of the fayalite solution,
H'_{Fo} = molar enthalpy of the forsterite solution,

$$x = \frac{Fa}{Fa + Fo} = \text{mol fraction of fayalite in the olivine.}$$

Therefore

$$(\Delta H_{Ol}) = x(H'_{Fa} - H_{Fa}) + (1 - x)(H'_{Fo} - H_{Fo})$$

and putting

$$H'_{Fa} - H_{Fa} = (\Delta H_{Fa}),$$
$$H'_{Fo} - H_{Fo} = (\Delta H_{Fo}),$$

it follows that

$$(\Delta H)_{Ol} = x(\Delta H)_{Fa} + (1 - x)(\Delta H)_{Fo}$$

where $(\Delta H)_{Fa}$ and $(\Delta H)_{Fo}$ are respectively the molar heats of solution of pure fayalite and pure forsterite at the given T and P. The measurements of Sahama and Torgeson (1949) show that the heat of solution of olivine in HF is effectively a linear function of the fayalite content x of the olivine, demonstrating that olivine can be regarded as an ideal solid solution (see p. 49).

It should be noticed that *the heat of formation of an ideal solid solution from its end-member components is zero.* For instance for olivine:

$$\underset{\text{fayalite}}{x\text{Fe}_2\text{SiO}_4} + \underset{\text{forsterite}}{(1 - x)\text{Mg}_2\text{SiO}_4} \rightarrow \underset{\text{olivine}}{(\text{Fe}_x\text{Mg}_{1-x})_2\text{SiO}_4}$$

$$(\Delta \text{H}) = \text{H}_{\text{Ol}} - x\text{H}_{\text{Fa}} - (1 - x)\text{H}_{\text{Fo}}$$

but

$$\text{H}_{\text{Ol}} = x\text{H}_{\text{Fa}} + (1 - x)\text{H}_{\text{Fo}}$$

therefore

$$(\Delta \text{H}) = 0.$$

This is not true for non-ideal solutions: for instance in the classical case of a water—sulphuric acid mixture, which is produced with great evolution of heat, the enthalpy change is given by:

$$(\Delta \text{H}) = \text{H}_{\text{Sol}} - x\text{H}_{\text{H}_2\text{SO}_4} - (1 - x)\text{H}_{\text{H}_2\text{O}}$$

with

$$\text{H}_{\text{Sol}} = x\overline{\text{H}}_{\text{H}_2\text{SO}_4} + (1 - x)\overline{\text{H}}_{\text{H}_2\text{O}}$$

whence

$$(\Delta \text{H}) = x(\overline{\text{H}}_{\text{H}_2\text{SO}_4} - \text{H}_{\text{H}_2\text{SO}_4}) + (1 - x)(\overline{\text{H}}_{\text{H}_2\text{O}} - \text{H}_{\text{H}_2\text{O}}).$$

The solution is non-ideal, therefore

$$\overline{\text{H}}_{\text{H}_2\text{SO}_4} \neq \text{H}_{\text{H}_2\text{SO}_4}, \qquad \overline{\text{H}}_{\text{H}_2\text{O}} \neq \text{H}_{\text{H}_2\text{O}}$$

and in this case $(\Delta \text{H}) < 0$.

2.2.4. Entropy.—The entropy of a perfect gas can be expressed (see p. 80) as a function of pressure at any given temperature:

$$d\text{S} = -\text{R}d \ln \text{P} \qquad \text{or} \qquad \text{S} = \text{S}^0 - \text{R} \ln \text{P}$$

where S^0 is the entropy of the gas at the reference pressure at the temperature under consideration.

It will be assumed again that these equations also remain valid for a mixture of ideal gases:

[17] $$\overline{d\text{S}}_i = -\text{R}d \ln p_i$$

and

[18] $$\overline{\text{S}}_i = \text{S}_i^0 - \text{R} \ln p_i$$

where p_i is the partial pressure of the gaseous component i and S_i^0 its molar entropy at unit pressure at the given temperature.

Substitution of equations (10) and (12),

$$p_i = \frac{n_i}{\sum_i n_i} P = x_i P$$

leads to

[19] $$\overline{dS}_i = -R d \ln P - R d \ln x_i$$

and

$$\overline{S}_i = S_i^0 - R \ln P - R \ln x_i$$

which on putting

$$S_i^0 - R \ln P = S_i^P$$

becomes

[20] $$\overline{S}_i = S_i^P - R \ln x_i.$$

S_i^P is defined as the molar entropy of pure component i at pressure P at the given temperature and x_i is the mol fraction of component i in the mixture.

Equation (20) is clearly applicable also to ideal solutions. The standard entropy of an olivine $Fa_x Fo_{(1-x)}$ can thus be calculated:

$$\overline{S}_{Fa} = S_{Fa} - R \ln x$$
$$\overline{S}_{Fo} = S_{Fo} - R \ln (1 - x)$$

then

$$S_{Ol} = x \overline{S}_{Fa} + (1 - x) \overline{S}_{Fo}$$

and therefore

$$S_{Ol} = x S_{Fa} + (1 - x) S_{Fo} - R[x \ln x + (1 - x) \ln (1 - x)].$$

Unlike volume, internal energy, and enthalpy, *the entropy of an ideal mixture is not an additive property.*

2.2.5. Free enthalpy.—Partial molar free enthalpy is defined by the equation

[21] $$\overline{G}_i = \left(\frac{\partial G}{\partial n_i} \right)_{T,P,n_j},$$

and is *of considerable practical significance; so much so that it has been separately named as the chemical potential, classically represented by the symbol μ_i and is the subject of section 3 of this chapter.*

2.3. *Experimental determination of partial molar quantities.*

With the exception of the special cases that have been mentioned above, it is not in general possible to derive simple expressions for the partial molar quantities relative to a component in a mixture. The problem can, however, always be tackled graphically by the so-called *tangent method* when the magnitude of the corresponding molar function of the mixture has been determined experimentally at several compositions. Consider for instance a mixture of two components A and B, whose mol fractions are x_A and x_B. Let J be the magnitude of a molar quantity for the mixture $A_{x_A}B_{x_B}$, $\bar{J}_A$ and $\bar{J}_B$ being the corresponding partial molar quantities. Then:

$$(n_A + n_B)J = n_A\bar{J}_A + n_B\bar{J}_B,$$

that is

$$J = x_A\bar{J}_A + x_B\bar{J}_B.$$

Putting $x_A = x$, it follows that $x_B = (1 - x)$ and

$$J_x = x(\bar{J}_A - \bar{J}_B) + \bar{J}_B.$$

The tangent to the curve $J = f(x)$ has slope $\dfrac{dJ}{dx} = \bar{J}_A - \bar{J}_B$ and passes through the point J_x, x; its equation is therefore

$$y = (\bar{J}_A - \bar{J}_B)x + \bar{J}_B;$$

and for $x = 0, y = \bar{J}_B$, while for $x = 1, y = \bar{J}_A$. The tangent thus makes intercepts on the lines $x = 0$, $x = 1$ equal respectively to the partial molal quantities $\bar{J}_B$ and $\bar{J}_A$.

In particular the tangent to the curve at $x = 0$ cuts the axis $x = 1$ at $\bar{J}_A^0$, which represents the partial molal quantity of A in an infinitely dilute solution of A in B.

The molar quantity for a mixture of xA and $(1 - x)$B is given by

$$\Delta J = J_{mixture} - \{x J_A + (1 - x)J_B\},$$

that is,

$$\Delta J = x\bar{J}_A + (1 - x)\bar{J}_B - \{x J_A + (1 - x)J_B\}$$

or

$$\Delta J = x(\bar{J}_A - J_A) + (1 - x)(\bar{J}_B - J_B).$$

As $x \to 0$, $\bar{J}_B \to J_B$ and $\bar{J}_A \to J_A^0$; therefore $\Delta J \to x(J_A^0 - J_A)$, which is known as the initial quantity (volume, heat, etc.) of solution A in B.

Figure 37 thus represents the variation of the molar volume

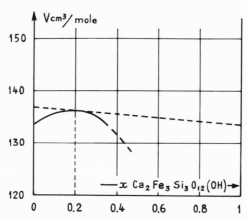

Fig. 37. Molar volume of epidote as a function of the content, x, of the ferrian end-member. The dashed line illustrates how the partial molal volumes for $x = 0.20$ can be evaluated by the tangent method.

of epidotes between $Ca_2Al_3Si_3O_{12}(OH)$ and $Ca_2Fe_3Si_3O_{12}(OH)$. The partial molar volumes of the aluminian and the ferrian end-members can thus be calculated for example for a mineral containing 20 molar percent $Ca_2Fe_3Si_3O_{12}(OH)$ as:

$$\bar{V}_{Fe} = 133.6 \text{ cm}^3$$
$$\bar{V}_{Al} = 136.8 \text{ cm}^3.$$

---

3.   Chemical potential

3.1. Definition.

The chemical potential μ_i of a component i was defined by Gibbs by means of the equation

[22] $\mu_i = \left(\dfrac{\partial U}{\partial n_i}\right)_{S,V,n_j}$

The quantity μ_i therefore represents a coefficient of proportionality between variation in the internal energy of the system (or phase) and variation in the number of moles of component i:

$$dS = 0, \quad dV = 0, \quad dn_j = 0; \quad dU = \mu_i \, dn_i.$$

It is a simple matter to show that the chemical potential so defined is the partial molar free enthalpy $\overline{G}_i$ of component i:

$$U = G - PV + TS,$$

therefore

$$dU = dG - P\,dV - V\,dP + T\,dS + S\,dT,$$

but

$$dG = \left(\frac{\partial G}{\partial T}\right)_{P,n_i,n_j} dT + \left(\frac{\partial G}{\partial P}\right)_{T,n_i,n_j} dP + \sum_i \left(\frac{\partial G}{\partial n_i}\right)_{T,P,n_j} dn_i$$

and

$$\left(\frac{\partial G}{\partial T}\right)_{P,n_i,n_j} = -S \quad \text{and} \quad \left(\frac{\partial G}{\partial P}\right)_{T,n_i,n_j} = V$$

therefore substitution in the expression for dU yields

$$dU = -P\,dV + T\,dS + \sum_i \left(\frac{\partial G}{\partial n_i}\right)_{T,P,n_j} dn_i.$$

Comparison with

$$dU = \left(\frac{\partial U}{\partial V}\right)_{S,n_i,n_j} dV + \left(\frac{\partial U}{\partial S}\right)_{V,n_i,n_j} dS + \sum_i \left(\frac{\partial U}{\partial n_i}\right)_{S,V,n_j} dn_i$$

yields

$$\left(\frac{\partial G}{\partial n_i}\right)_{T,P,n_j} = \left(\frac{\partial U}{\partial n_i}\right)_{S,V,n_j}$$

and therefore

[23]
$$\mu_i = \overline{G}_i = \left(\frac{\partial G}{\partial n_i}\right)_{T,P,n_j}$$

The expression for variation of free enthalpy can therefore be written quite generally in the form:

[24]
$$dG = -S\,dT + V\,dP + \sum_i \mu_i \, dn_i$$

neglecting, as usual, parameters other than temperature (or entropy), pressure (or volume), and composition. At constant temperature and pressure, equation (24) becomes

[25] $\qquad dT = 0, \qquad dP = 0; \qquad dG = \sum_i \mu_i \, dn_i.$

Integration of equation (25) at constant composition, and therefore at constant μ_i, yields:

[26] $\qquad T = \text{Constant}, \qquad P = \text{Constant}; \qquad G = \sum_i \mu_i n_i.$

For phases or systems that contain only a single component i,

$$G = n_i G_i$$

and therefore

[27] $\qquad\qquad\qquad\qquad \mu_i = G_i.$

3.2. Some properties of chemical potential.

3.2.1.—Its intensive nature. Chemical potential is an intensive property: it is the same for every portion of a phase and consequently it depends only on the composition and not on the mass of the phase.

Let two portions of the same phase of masses m_1 and $m_2 = \lambda m_1$ contain respectively n_i and λn_i moles of component i. And let μ_i^1 and μ_i^2 be the chemical potentials of component i in the two samples and G_1 and $G_2 = \lambda G_1$ be their free enthalpies; then

$$\mu_i^1 = \left[\frac{\partial G_1}{\partial n_i}\right]_{T,P,n_j} \qquad \text{and} \qquad \mu_i^2 = \left[\frac{\partial(\lambda G_1)}{\partial(\lambda n_i)}\right]_{T,P,n_j}.$$

Therefore

$$\mu_i^1 = \mu_i^2.$$

3.2.2.—Condition for equilibrium. When several phases are in equilibrium in so far as a particular component i is concerned, the chemical potential of that component is the same in every phase at the given temperature and pressure.

Consider the system composed of phases $\alpha, \beta, \ldots$. For each phase,

[28] $\qquad\qquad dG^\alpha = -S^\alpha \, dT + V^\alpha \, dP + \sum_i \mu_i^\alpha \, dn_i^\alpha$

and for the whole system,

[29] $$dG = \sum_\alpha dG^\alpha.$$

Equations (28) and (29) become at constant temperature and pressure,

[30] $$dT = 0, dP = 0; \quad dG^\alpha = \sum_i \mu_i^\alpha \, dn_i^\alpha,$$

[31] $$dT = 0, dP = 0; \quad dG = \sum_\alpha \sum_i \mu_i^\alpha \, dn_i^\alpha.$$

Now suppose that a quantity dn_i of component i passes from phase α into phase β at constant temperature and pressure; then

$$dn_i^\beta = -dn_i^\alpha = dn_i.$$

If the system undergoes no other change in composition, equation (31) becomes

$$dT = 0, dP = 0; \quad dG = \mu_i^\alpha \, dn_i^\alpha + \mu_i^\beta \, dn_i^\beta,$$

and

$$dG = (\mu_i^\beta - \mu_i^\alpha) \, dn_i.$$

The condition for equilibrium, and therefore for reversibility, is

$$dT = 0, dP = 0; \quad dG = 0,$$

therefore at equilibrium

[32] $$\overline{dT = 0, dP = 0, \mu_i^\beta = \mu_i^\alpha.}$$

When a heterogeneous system is in physicochemical equilibrium, equation (32) must be true for every component and every phase.

3.2.3. Direction of change.—In order that a component should be able to pass spontaneously from a phase α to a phase β, it is a necessary condition that its chemical potential should be greater in phase α than in phase β. In a system undergoing a natural process the free enthalpy of the system satisfies,

$$dT = 0, dP = 0; \quad dG < 0,$$

therefore, with the same conventions as in paragraph *3.2.2*,

$$dT = 0, dP = 0, (\mu_i^\beta - \mu_i^\alpha) \, dn_i < 0,$$

and, since dn_i has been chosen positive,

[33] $$dT = 0, dP = 0; \quad \mu_i^\alpha > \mu_i^\beta.$$

This equation expresses the conditions for the natural evolution of a

system at constant temperature and pressure, while the comple-
mentary equation (32) expresses the conditions of equilibrium.

3.2.4. The Gibbs-Duhem Equation.—Consider equation (26),

$$T = \text{Constant}, \qquad P = \text{Constant}, \qquad G = \sum_i \mu_i n_i.$$

The chemical potential μ_i is a function of temperature, pressure,
and concentration; and if these parameters are made to vary
simultaneously, the increment in free enthalpy will be

$$dG = \sum_i \mu_i \, dn_i + \sum_i n_i \, d\mu_i.$$

Comparison with

$$dG = -S \, dT + V \, dP + \sum_i \mu_i \, dn_i$$

yields

[34] $$-S \, dT + V \, dP - \sum_i n_i \, d\mu_i = 0$$

and therefore at constant temperature and pressure:

[35] $$dT = 0, \qquad dP = 0; \qquad \sum_i n_i \, d\mu_i = 0.$$

This is known as the Gibbs-Duhem Equation; it is a necessary
restrictive condition between variations in chemical potential of
the various components of a mixture at constant temperature and
pressure. Thus in a phase with two components only

$$n_1 \, d\mu_1 + n_2 \, d\mu_2 = 0$$

that is to say, if the chemical potential of one component is
increased, that of the other is of necessity decreased at constant
temperature and pressure.

3.3. Dependence of chemical potential on temperature and pressure.

3.3.1. Constant pressure.

[36] $$dG = \left(\frac{\partial G}{\partial T}\right)_{P,n_i,n_j} dT + \sum_i \left(\frac{\partial G}{\partial n_i}\right)_{P,T,n_j} dn_i.$$

Since dG is a perfect differential its second derivatives with respect to temperature and composition are related (see p. 38) by

$$\left[\frac{\partial}{\partial T}\left(\frac{\partial G}{\partial n_i}\right)_{T,}\right]_{n_i} = \left[\frac{\partial}{\partial n_i}\left(\frac{\partial G}{\partial T}\right)_{n_i}\right]_T$$

and therefore

[37]
$$\left(\frac{\partial \mu_i}{\partial T}\right)_{P,n_i,n_j} = -\left(\frac{\partial S}{\partial n_i}\right)_{T,P,n_j} = -\bar{S}_i.$$

Similarly it can easily be shown that

[38]
$$\left[\frac{\partial(\mu_i/T)}{\partial T}\right]_{P,n_i,n_j} = -\frac{\bar{H}_i}{T^2}.$$

3.3.2. Constant temperature.—An analogous derivation leads also to the equation:

[39]
$$\left(\frac{\partial \mu_i}{\partial P}\right)_{T,n_i,n_j} = \left(\frac{\partial V}{\partial n_i}\right)_{P,T,n_j} = \bar{V}_i.$$

It is apparent then that all the equations derived in Chapter VI for variation of free enthalpy remain valid for chemical potential on condition that the explicit values of the partial derivatives are replaced by the corresponding partial molar quantities (compare especially (37), (38), (39) with (11'), (22), (12') on pages 77 and 78).

3.4. Dependence of chemical potential on composition—the explicit expression for chemical potential.

It must be said at the outset that classical thermodynamics in general can give no account of the dependence of chemical potential on composition. As for the other partial molar quantities, recourse must be had to statistical thermodynamics. The discussion that follows will be restricted in this paragraph to perfect gases and in the next to solutions.

At a given temperature the free enthalpy of a perfect gas can be expressed as a function of its pressure (see p. 80)

$$dG = RT\, d \ln P \quad \text{or} \quad G = G^0 + RT \ln P.$$

It will be assumed that these equations remain valid when the gas enters into a mixture with the proviso that the total pressure P is replaced by the partial pressure p_i, whence

[40] $\overline{dG}_i = RT \, d \ln p_i$

[41] $\overline{G}_i = G_i^0 + RT \ln p_i.$

And since partial molar free enthalpy $\overline{G}_i$ is identical with chemical potential μ_i, these equations become at constant temperature,

[42] [43] $d\mu_i = RT \, d \ln p_i$ $\qquad$ $\mu_i = \mu_i^0 + RT \ln p_i.$

$\mu_i^0 = G_i^0$ is the chemical potential, and therefore the molar free enthalpy, of component i taken alone at unit pressure at the given temperature.

It should be noticed that if the reference pressure differs from unity, equation (43) must be rewritten as

[44] $\mu_i = \mu_i^{P_0} + RT \ln \dfrac{p_i}{P_0}.$

If now in equation (43) the partial pressure p_i is replaced by the corresponding mol fraction x_i of component i at total pressure P, the equation becomes

[45] $\mu_i = \mu_i^0 + RT \ln P + RT \ln x_i$

and therefore if μ_i^P is defined by

$$\mu_i^0 + RT \ln P = \mu_i^P$$

equation (43) becomes

[46] $\mu_i = \mu_i^P + RT \ln x_i$

and it follows that

[47] $d\mathrm{T} = 0, \; dP = 0; \quad d\mu_i = RT \, d \ln x_i.$

These two equations are fundamental. They are valid, as will be shown, for all perfect mixtures, whether of gases, or liquid or solid solutions. μ_i^P is then the chemical potential or molar free enthalpy of pure component i at the pressure P at the given temperature.

3.5. Application to solutions.

3.5.1.—Ideal solutions are defined as those in which the chemical potential of each and every component obeys equations (46) and (47):

$$\mu_i = \mu_i^P + RT \ln x_i,$$
$$d\mathrm{T} = 0, \quad dP = 0; \qquad d\mu_i = RT \, d \ln x_i.$$

On this basis ideal solutions can be divided into two types, which differ from one another in the meaning to be given to the quantity μ_i^P.

(1) *Perfect solutions.* Equation (46) remains valid for all values of x_i between 0 and 1. Such solutions, which behave ideally over the whole composition range, are exactly analogous to perfect gas mixtures. μ_i^P is identical with the chemical potential (or molar free enthalpy) of component i taken alone at the pressure P at the given temperature.

Many solid solutions are known that can be considered to be perfect in so far as isomorphous substitution is concerned. Thus the chemical potential of the component enstatite in a pyroxene can be expressed as:

$$\mu_{En}^{Pyr} = \mu_{En}^{P} + RT \ln x \qquad \text{where} \qquad x = \frac{En}{En + Fs} = \frac{Mg}{Mg + Fe}$$

$$\text{and} \qquad \mu_{En}^{P} = G_{En}^{P}.$$

(2) *Very dilute solutions.* All solutions tend toward ideality at very low concentration. Equation (46) then again becomes valid, but μ_i^P no longer has the significance that it had previously for *all* the components involved in the solution.

Consider for instance the solute components 1, 2, ... i in very dilute solution in a solvent that will be represented by the subscript "0". Then,

[48] $$\mu_0 = \mu_0^P + RT \ln x_0$$

[49] $$\mu_i = \mu_i^P + RT \ln x_i.$$

As the concentration of the solvent is increased the solution becomes increasingly dilute and therefore approximates more and more closely to ideality. The equations above remain valid and in the limit the solution approaches pure solvent. In these conditions, it is evident that μ_0^P is the chemical potential of the pure solvent at pressure P at the given temperature.

If, on the other hand, the concentration of the solute i, for example, is increased, the solution soon ceases to be ideal. Equation (49) in particular ceases to be applicable long before the component i can be considered to approach purity: μ_i^P is therefore not the chemical potential of pure component i.

3.5.2. Real solutions.—Just as in the case of real gases it was convenient to introduce the concept of fugacity (p. 81), so for non-ideal solutions

G. N. Lewis introduced *activity*, the activity a_i of component i being a function such that at constant temperature and pressure

[50] $$\overline{d\mu_i = RT \, d \ln a_i}$$

and

[51] $$\overline{\mu_i = \mu_i^P + RT \ln a_i.}$$

The activity a_i can often conveniently be expressed as a function of the mol fraction x_i of component i and an *activity coefficient* γ_i such that

$$a_i = \gamma_i x_i.$$

Equation (51) then becomes

[52] $$\mu_i = \mu_i^P + RT \ln \gamma_i + RT \ln x_i.$$

The term $RT \ln \gamma_i$ is a measure of the departure of the solution from ideality since for ideal solutions $\gamma_i = 1$.

Now it is not always possible to put $\gamma_i = 1$ for every component of an ideal* solution without being confronted with the following dilemma:

(1) If γ_i is put equal to unity for every component, equations (48) and (49) become applicable; but in those equations μ_i^P cannot represent the chemical potential of the pure component. (2) If on the other hand μ_i^P is taken to be the chemical potential of the pure component, it can be argued from equation (52) in the same way as it was argued from equations (48) and (49) previously that if γ_0 for the solvent is put equal to unity, then γ_i for the solutes cannot be unity.

3.5.3.—It remains to say a word about a type of solution that is of particular importance in the field of solid solutions. This is the class of *regular solutions*, of which perfect solutions constitute a special case.†
As for perfect solutions the entropy of regular solutions is given by

[53] $$S = \sum_i x_i \bar{S}_i,$$

---

* Perfect solutions are quite clearly an exception.
† Here too statistical thermodynamics provides a simple model of intracrystalline interactions that serves as a basis for the definition of strictly regular solutions.

where

[54] $$\bar{S}_i = S_i^0 - R \ln x_i,$$

S and S_i^0 being respectively the molar entropies of the solution and of the pure component i. On the other hand, the formation of regular solutions from their pure components involves a *heat of mixing* (ΔH) such that for one mole of solution

[55] $$(\Delta H) = \sum_i x_i(\bar{H}_i - H_i^0) = \sum_i x_i(\overline{\Delta H}_i),$$

where H_i is the partial molar entropy of component i and H_i^0 the molar enthalpy of pure i. Since

$$\mu_i = \bar{G}_i = \bar{H}_i - T\bar{S}_i,$$

[56] $$\mu_i = H_i^0 - TS_i^0 + RT \ln x_i + \overline{\Delta H}_i.$$

In the case of a regular solution containing only components A and B, the quantity $\overline{\Delta H}_i$ can simply be written as

[57] $$\overline{\Delta H}_A = N\omega x_P^2 \qquad \text{and} \qquad \overline{\Delta H}_B = N\omega x_A^2.$$

Since

$$H_i^0 - TS_i^0 = G_i^0 = \mu_i^0,$$

it follows that

[58] $$\mu_A = \mu_A^0 + RT \ln x_A + N\omega x_B^2$$
$$\mu_B = \mu_B^0 + RT \ln x_B + N\omega x_A^2$$

where

μ_A^0, μ_B^0 = chemical potentials of pure A and B,

x_A, x_B = mol fractions of A and B

N = Avogadro's number

ω = the energy necessary to interchange a molecule of A with one of B in the mixture.

If equation (58) is compared with the equation for the chemical potential of a component in a real solution

$$\mu_i = \mu_i^0 + RT \ln x_i + RT \ln \gamma_i,$$

it is evident that the activity coefficients of the components in a regular solution have precisely defined values for a given composition:

[59] $$\ln \gamma_A = \frac{N\omega}{RT} x_B^2; \qquad \ln \gamma_B = \frac{N\omega}{RT} x_A^2.$$

4.   Displacement of equilibrium

In studying systems at constant composition we discussed the manner in which, for instance, the pressure of a system initially in equilibrium at given P and T, would have to change in order to maintain equilibrium when the temperature was varied (Clapeyron's relation). Similarly MacDonald's equation indicates the manner in which the temperature of a system must vary for the system to remain in equilibrium when it is under stress.

Consider a system, or a phase, in equilibrium with the exterior, at given P, T, etc. The mol fraction of component i is as usual denoted by x_i. How must this quantity vary so that equilibrium will be maintained when pressure, temperature, shearing stress, etc., are allowed to vary? That is the question that the succeeding paragraphs attempt to answer.

4.1. Dependence of composition on temperature.

Consider for instance two phases α and β containing a common component i and let a_i^α, a_i^β be the activities of the component common to the two phases. If at given pressure, the system is in equilibrium at a temperature T,

$$\mu_i^\alpha = \mu_i^\beta$$
$$\mu_i^\alpha = \mu_i^{0\alpha} + RT \ln a_i^\alpha,$$
$$\text{and} \quad \mu_i^\beta = \mu_i^{0\beta} + RT \ln a_i^\beta.$$

where $\mu_i^{0\alpha}$ and μ_i^0 are constants for the given temperature and pressure Therefore

$$\ln \frac{a_i^\beta}{a_i^\alpha} = \frac{\mu_i^{0\alpha} - \mu_i^{0\beta}}{RT}.$$

Differentiating with respect to T,

$$R \frac{\partial \ln (a_i^\beta/a_i^\alpha)}{\partial T} = \frac{\partial(\mu_i^{0\alpha}/T)}{\partial T} - \frac{\partial(\mu_i^{0\beta}/T)}{\partial T}$$

and recalling that $\dfrac{\partial(\mu_i^0/T)}{\partial T} = -\dfrac{H_i^0}{T^2}$ (p. 173), it follows that

$$R \frac{\partial \ln (a_i^\beta/a_i^\alpha)}{\partial T} = \frac{H_i^{0\beta} - H_i^{0\alpha}}{T^2}$$

and putting $H_i^{0\beta} - H_i^{0\alpha} = \Delta H_i^0$, the heat of the phase change $\alpha \to \beta$ for the pure component i,

[60]
$$\frac{\partial \ln (a_i^\beta / a_i^\alpha)}{\partial T} = \frac{\Delta H_i^0}{RT^2}.$$

If the variation of ΔH_i^0 with temperature can be neglected, then $\Delta C_{Pi}^0 = 0$ and equation (60) can be integrated to give

[61]
$$\ln \frac{a_i^\beta}{a_i^\alpha} = \frac{\Delta H_i^0}{R} \left(\frac{1}{T_i^0} - \frac{1}{T} \right)$$

where T_i^0 is the temperature at which the two phases are in equilibrium when only component i is present.

When the two phases approximate to perfect mixtures equations (60) and (61) become

[60']
$$\frac{\partial \ln (x_i^\beta / x_i^\alpha)}{\partial T} = \frac{\Delta H_i^0}{RT^2}$$

[61']
$$\ln \frac{x_i^\beta}{x_i^\alpha} = \frac{\Delta H_i^0}{R} \left(\frac{1}{T_i^0} - \frac{1}{T} \right).$$

Equations (60), (61), (60'), and (61') are simplified in the case of a pure crystalline substance (component i, phase α) in equilibrium with a solution, or melt (phase β), containing several components of which i is one. Then $a_i^\alpha = 1$ and a_i^β can be written simply as a_i, whence

[62]
$$\frac{\partial \ln a_i}{\partial T} = \frac{\Delta H_i^0}{RT^2}$$

and if ΔH_i^0 is independent of temperature,

[63]
$$\ln a_i = \frac{\Delta H_i^0}{R} \left(\frac{1}{T_i^0} - \frac{1}{T} \right)$$

moreover if the solution is perfect,

[62']
$$\frac{\partial \ln x_i}{\partial T} = \frac{\Delta H_i^0}{RT^2}$$

[63']
$$\ln x_i = \frac{\Delta H_i^0}{R} \left(\frac{1}{T_i^0} - \frac{1}{T} \right)$$

where T_i^0 is the temperature of fusion of the pure crystalline substance i at the given pressure and ΔH_i^0 its heat of fusion at that pressure.

It should be noticed that if the solution is ideal, but not perfect, ΔH_i^0 is as defined above only for the solvent.

It has been implicitly assumed that a_i tends to x_i for very dilute solutions as x_i tends to zero. In these conditions μ_i^0 represents (p. 168) the chemical potential of pure component i when i is the solvent, but not when i is the solute. If i is a solute component ΔH_i^0 represents what may be called the *heat of primary solution*, that is the heat of solution of one mole of solute in a very large amount of solvent.

Since ΔH_i^0 is very commonly positive, equation (63') indicates that the solubility of component i increases with rising temperature; this is sometimes called the *Schröder-Le Chatelier Law*.

The importance of this phenomenon in geology is self-evident. To select from many possible applications, one way of explaining so-called *hydrothermal* mineralization is to invoke a fluid, more particularly an aqueous fluid that circulates in fractures and is capable of dissolving in *hot zones* significant amounts of the elements present in the surrounding rocks; in the course of its ascent its temperature will fall, solubilities will decrease, and various elements must be precipitated from solution. The solubility of titanium in minerals such as biotite and the amphiboles can be explained in a similar manner: it is well known to the petrologist that volcanic biotites and hornblendes are richer in titanium than are those of metamorphic rocks formed at a much lower temperature.

Equation (63') moreover provides a basis for the discussion of crystallization from molten mixtures. Consider a liquid mixture of two components A and B, whose mol fractions are x_A and x_B, and assume that the mixture is perfect (if it is not, the same equations will hold when activity is substituted for mol fraction). The temperatures at which the liquid is in equilibrium at a given pressure either with pure crystalline A or with pure crystalline B are given respectively by equations (64) and (64'):

[64]
$$\ln x_{\mathrm{A}} = \frac{\Delta H_{\mathrm{A}}^0}{R} \left(\frac{1}{T_{\mathrm{A}}^0} - \frac{1}{T} \right)$$

[64′]
$$\ln x_{\mathrm{B}} = \frac{\Delta H_{\mathrm{B}}^0}{R} \left(\frac{1}{T_{\mathrm{B}}^0} - \frac{1}{T} \right).$$

The temperature so calculated evidently represents the temperature at which A in the one case, or B in the other, begins to crystallize from the liquid mixture. The two curves $T = f(x_{\mathrm{A}})$ and $T = f(x_{\mathrm{B}})$ drawn on the same diagram (fig. 38) intersect at the *eutectic* point.

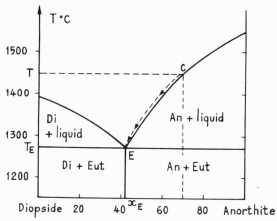

Fig. 38. Crystallization diagram for the system diopside-anorthite.

At the corresponding temperature T_{E} and composition x_{E} the liquid mixture is in equilibrium with both crystalline phases A and B. T_{E} and x_{E} can be evaluated from the equations:

[65]
$$\begin{cases} \ln x_{\mathrm{E}} = \dfrac{\Delta H_{\mathrm{A}}^0}{R} \left(\dfrac{1}{T_{\mathrm{A}}^0} - \dfrac{1}{T_{\mathrm{E}}} \right) \\ \ln (1 - x_{\mathrm{E}}) = \dfrac{\Delta H_{\mathrm{B}}^0}{R} \left(\dfrac{1}{T_{\mathrm{B}}^0} - \dfrac{1}{T_{\mathrm{E}}} \right). \end{cases}$$

If therefore a bath of liquid of composition x_{A}, x_{B} is cooled from T_0 to T_1, the crystalline component A will crystallize first if $x_{\mathrm{A}} > x_{\mathrm{E}}$. The liquid phase will be impoverished to a corresponding extent in A and if the temperature continues to be lowered, its composition will be displaced along the curve CE until the eutectic point E is reached. When $T = T_{\mathrm{E}}$ an eutectic mixture of A and B will crystallize. An identical argument would apply to B if the initial composition of the liquid phase were such that $x_B > x_E$.

The course of crystallization will evidently be affected by the formation of a solid solution between A and B. This is so, for instance, in the crystallization of liquids of olivine composition, which will be discussed in the next chapter (p. 195).

4.2. Dependence of composition on pressure.

Consider, as in 4.1, two phases α and β with a common component i in equilibrium at a given temperature and pressure; then

$$\mu_i^\alpha = \mu_i^\beta$$

where

$$\mu_i = \mu_i^0 + RT \ln a_i$$

so that

$$\ln \frac{a_i^\beta}{a_i^\alpha} = \frac{\mu_i^{0\alpha} - \mu_i^{0\beta}}{RT}.$$

Differentiation with respect to P yields

$$RT \frac{\partial \ln (a_i^\beta/a_i^\alpha)}{\partial P} = \frac{\partial \mu_i^{0\alpha}}{\partial P} - \frac{\partial \mu_i^{0\beta}}{\partial P}$$

and since

$$\frac{\partial \mu_i^0}{\partial P} = V_i^0$$

it follows that

$$\frac{\partial \ln (a_i^\beta/a_i^\alpha)}{\partial P} = -\frac{V_i^{0\beta} - V_i^{0\alpha}}{RT}.$$

Putting $V_i^{0\beta} - V_i^{0\alpha} = \Delta V_i^0$ for the volume change accompanying the passage of one mole of i from phase α to phase β, this becomes

[66]
$$\frac{\partial \ln (a_i^\beta/a_i^\alpha)}{\partial P} = -\frac{\Delta V_i^0}{RT}.$$

If variation of ΔV_i^0 with pressure and temperature can be neglected, equation (66) can be integrated immediately to

[67]
$$\ln \frac{a_i^\beta}{a_i^\alpha} = \frac{\Delta V_i^0}{RT} (P_i^0 - P)$$

where P_i^0 is the pressure at which the two phases would be in equilibrium at the given temperature if the only component present were i.

If the two phases are perfect solutions, the activities in equations (66) and (67) can be replaced by mol fractions.

In the case of equilibrium between a pure crystalline component i and a solution, equations (66) and (67) become

[68] $$\frac{\partial \ln a_i}{\partial P} = -\frac{\Delta V_i^0}{RT}$$

[69] $$\ln a_i = \frac{\Delta V_i^0}{RT} (P_i^0 - P),$$

where P_i^0 is the pressure at melting of pure crystalline i at the given temperature and ΔV_i^0 is the volume change on melting of pure i.*

4.3. The idea of force of crystallization.

Consider a crystal composed essentially of component i in equilibrium at given P and T with the surrounding medium (solution, melt, or other crystals). The activity of i in the surrounding medium will be given by equation (69) as

$$\ln a_i = \frac{\Delta V_i^0}{RT} (P_i^0 - P).$$

If now the pressure is increased by an amount dP at constant temperature, disequilibrium will result. Since ΔV_i^0 is generally positive, equilibrium can only be re-established by decrease of a_i, that is, the crystal will grow. Now the change in pressure will affect simultaneously the crystal and the surrounding medium. When the increase in pressure is applied *only* to the crystal, it will have the effect of increasing the chemical potential of the crystal since $d\mu_i = V_i\,dP$, and the chemical potential of component i in the surrounding medium must increase for equilibrium to be maintained; since the pressure on the medium is taken to be constant, it becomes necessary for a_i to increase and therefore for the crystal to dissolve. The new equilibrium condition is therefore

$$d\mu_i^{\text{crystal}} = d\mu_i^{\text{medium}},$$

whence

[70] $$V_i^{0c}\,dP = RT\,d \ln a_i$$

where V_i^{0c} is the molar volume of the crystalline component. Let a_{i1}

* The comments relating to ΔH_i^0 in the previous paragraph apply also to ΔV_i^0.

be the activity of i at equilibrium when crystal and medium are subjected to the same pressure P, and a_{i2} the activity of i when the crystal is subjected to an over-pressure ΔP. Integration of equation (70) is immediate, if it is assumed that V_i^{0c} is independent of P:

[71] $$\ln \frac{a_{i2}}{a_{i1}} = \frac{V_i^{0c}}{RT} \Delta P.$$

It is apparent that equation (70) is closely related to the equation that was established on p. 105 under the name of Poynting's equation; this is made clearer when equation (70) is written in the form

$$\left(\frac{\partial \ln a_i}{\partial P_S} \right)_{P_F} = \frac{V_i^{0c}}{RT}$$

where P_S is the pressure applied to the solid and P_F the pressure applied to the surrounding medium.

Equation (71) is also of interest in that it gives precise thermodynamic expression to the idea of *force of crystallization*, a concept familiar to petrologists and metallurgists from the works of Seng (1937) and Ramberg (1947, 1952), but often ill defined and poorly understood.

Let a crystal of pure component i be in equilibrium with the surrounding medium at a given temperature T and pressure P. The activity (or mol fraction if the medium approximates to a perfect solution) of component i in the medium is then a_{i1}, the saturation activity, and

$$\ln a_{i1} = \frac{\Delta V_i^0}{RT} (P_i^0 - P).$$

If for any reason the activity of i changes to a new value $a_{i2} > a_{i1}$, the medium becomes supersaturated in i and disequilibrium results. *The force of crystallization of pure crystalline i can be defined as the notional over-pressure ΔP that must be applied to the solid to maintain equilibrium with the medium supersaturated in i at the given temperature and pressure, ΔP being given by:*

[72] $$\Delta P = \frac{RT}{V_i^{0c}} \ln \frac{a_{i2}}{a_{i1}}.$$

If the degree of supersaturation β is defined by $\dfrac{a_{i2}}{a_{i1}} = \beta$, equation (72) becomes

[73]
$$\Delta P = \frac{RT \ln \beta}{V_i^{0c}}.$$

This definition corresponds to that of Ramberg, who defined force of crystallization in terms of $1/V_i^{0c}$, since at given T, P and β, ΔP and $1/V_i^{0c}$ are proportional.

The idea of a force of crystallization has been investigated experimentally by Correns and Steinborn (1939), the principle of whose apparatus is illustrated in figure 39. Initially a crystal of pure com-

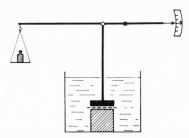

Fig. 39. The concept of force of crystallization as illustrated by Correns and Steinborn (1939).

ponent i is placed in a tank in equilibrium with a solution saturated in component i (activity a_{i1}). A piston resting on the top surface of the crystal is connected to a balance beam at one extremity of which is a scale pan containing weights and at the other a pointer reading against a scale initially at zero. A filter paper is intercalated between piston and crystal in order that the top surface of the crystal can remain in contact—and so exchange matter—with the solution. Component i is then added to the solution, whose activity changes from a_{i1} to $a_{i2} > a_{i1}$. The crystal will grow and the pointer will tend to move across the scale. It can be returned to zero and the crystal be maintained in equilibrium with the supersaturated solution by applying to the crystal an over-pressure ΔP through the piston by adding the appropriate weight to the scale pan.

The value of ΔP necessary to maintain equilibrium at various values of $\ln \beta = \ln \dfrac{a_{i2}}{a_{i1}}$ is then plotted on a graph (fig. 40). According to equation (73), the graph will be linear:

$$\Delta P = \frac{RT}{V_i^{0c}} \ln \beta.$$

In fact, Correns and Steinborn plotted ΔP against $\ln \beta' = \ln \dfrac{x_{i2}}{x_{i1}}$. At low concentrations, they found a linear relationship between ΔP and $\ln \beta'$, as would be expected since the solution can then be

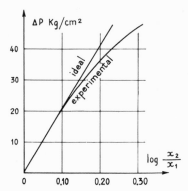

Fig. 40. Graph of applied pressure against degree of supersaturation, $\beta = \dfrac{x_2}{x_1} > 1$, of an aqueous solution in equilibrium with a crystal of alum. Relaxation of pressure on the crystal will lead to disequilibrium resulting in further growth of the crystal.

considered as ideal with $\ln \beta' \sim \ln \beta$. For higher values of x_{i2}/x_{i1} there was increasing departure from linearity as x_{i2}/x_{i1} increased, since for more concentrated solutions

$$\Delta P = \frac{RT}{V_i^{0c}} \ln \frac{x_{i2}}{x_{i1}}$$

must be replaced by the rigorous relationship

$$\Delta P = \frac{RT}{V_i^{0c}} \left(\ln \frac{x_{i2}}{x_{i1}} + \ln \frac{\gamma_{i2}}{\gamma_{i1}} \right).$$

4.4. Riecke's Principle.

Throughout the preceding paragraph it was implicitly assumed that the over-pressure applied to the crystal was an isotropic pressure exerted similarly on every face of the crystal. In the experiments of

Correns and Steinborn that was not so, for obvious practical reasons.

Consider a crystal in equilibrium with the surrounding medium at given temperature and hydrostatic pressure. If an over-pressure ΔP is applied to it, the crystal will dissolve and the medium will consequently become more concentrated. But what will be the result of applying a uniaxial stress P_1 to the crystal (fig. 41)?

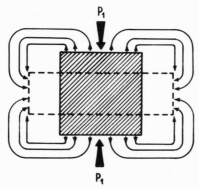

Fig. 41. Transport of matter when a crystal in contact with solution is subjected to stress: the crystal will develop a lamellar or prismatic habit.

The faces normal to the direction of stress are no longer in equilibrium with the saturated solution: the crystal will therefore dissolve from these faces and the solution will become supersaturated. But the stress is not applied similarly to those faces that are inclined or parallel to the direction of stress; these latter are not in equilibrium with the supersaturated solution and will grow in order to lower the concentration of i in the surrounding medium. The resultant effect is a migration of component i from the faces under maximum stress to the other faces and the crystal tends to spread in the plane perpendicular to the direction of stress.

An explanation is thus provided of the observation that some minerals that are usually more or less equidimensional in habit may in certain circumstances commonly have prismatic or tabular habit.

4.5. Dependence of composition on gravitational field-strength.

4.5.1.—The effect of taking into account a gravitational field will be examined first for the function *free enthalpy* (see also p. 86, and

Ramberg, 1952). It will be recalled that the most general expression for the internal energy of a system is

[74] $$dU = T\,dS - P\,dV + \sum_i \mu_i\,dn_i + dw$$

where w represents work other than that due to the effect of pressure. If dm is the change in mass of the system,

$$dw = \Phi\,dm$$

and if

$$m = \sum_i n_i M_i$$

then

$$dw = \sum_i M_i \Phi\,dn_i$$

and substitution in (74) leads to

[75] $$dU = T\,dS - P\,dV + \sum_i (\mu_i + M_i\Phi)\,dn_i.$$

The change in free enthalpy follows immediately as

[76] $$dG = -S\,dT + V\,dP + \sum_i (\mu_i + M_i\Phi)\,dn_i.$$

4.5.2. Phase equilibrium.—Consider now two phases α and β which have a common component i but differ in composition and in their position in the gravitational field. The change in free enthalpy when dn_i moles of i pass from α to β at constant temperature and pressure is given by:

$$dG^\alpha = -(\mu_i^\alpha + M_i\Phi^\alpha)\,dn_i$$
$$dG^\beta = \quad (\mu_i^\beta + M_i\Phi^\beta)\,dn_i.$$

At equilibrium $dG = dG^\alpha + dG^\beta = 0$ and since $dn_i \neq 0$,

[77] $$\mu_i^\alpha + M_i\Phi^\alpha = \mu_i^\beta + M_i\Phi^\beta$$

and in general

[78] $$\mu_i + M_i\Phi = \text{Constant.}$$

Equation (78) is more useful in practice in its differential form:

[79] $$\underline{d\mu_i + M_i\,d\Phi = 0.}$$

In a gravitational field that allows the exchange of a component i, the variation in gravitational potential is compensated by an opposite variation in the chemical potential of component i and consequently there will be variation in the distribution of component i.

Equation (79) finds immediate application to the establishment of the general law of hydrostatic equilibrium. For a pure component i at constant temperature

$$d\mu_i = d\mu_i^0 = dG_i$$

and since

$$dG_i = V_i\, dP$$

it follows that

$$V_i\, dP + M_i\, d\Phi = 0$$

but

$$\frac{M_i}{V_i} = \rho_i$$

where ρ_i represents density, and therefore

$$dP = -\rho_i\, d\Phi.$$

Now within the Earth (see p. 86),

$$d\Phi = -g\, dh$$

and therefore

[80] $$\overline{dP = +\, g\rho_i\, dh.}$$

For a mixture of density ρ_M, where

$$\rho_M = M_{M/V_M} = \sum_i x_i M_i / \sum x_i \overline{V}_i$$

clearly

[81] $$dP = -\rho_M\, d\Phi$$

and therefore

$$dP = g\rho_M\, dh.$$

4.5.3. *Solutions.*—When i is a component in a solid- or liquid-solution, the change $d\mu_i$ in chemical potential at constant temperature is given by

$$d\mu_i = \left(\frac{\partial \mu_i}{\partial P}\right)_{a_i} dP + \left(\frac{\partial \mu_i}{\partial a_i}\right)_P da_i.$$

But

$$\left(\frac{\partial \mu_i}{\partial P}\right)_{a_i} = \overline{V}_i \qquad \text{and} \qquad \left(\frac{\partial \mu_i}{\partial a_i}\right)_P = \frac{RT}{a_i};$$

therefore

$$d\mu_i = \overline{V}_i\, dP + RT\, d\ln a_i.$$

Substitution of the expression for $d\mathrm{P}$ given by (81) leads to

$$d\mu_i = -\rho_\mathrm{M}\overline{V}_i \, d\Phi + \mathrm{RT} \, d\ln a_i$$

and then from equation (79):

[82]
$$\overline{\mathrm{RT} \, d\ln a_i = (\overline{V}_i\rho_\mathrm{M} - \mathrm{M}_i) \, d\Phi.}$$

In this form the relationship is of more theoretical than practical interest. It can however easily be integrated for a perfect binary mixture $A_{x_\mathrm{A}}B_{x_\mathrm{B}}$. Then,

$$a_\mathrm{A} = x_\mathrm{A}$$
$$\overline{V}_\mathrm{A} = V_\mathrm{A}$$
$$\rho_\mathrm{M} = \frac{x_\mathrm{A}\mathrm{M}_\mathrm{A} + x_\mathrm{B}\mathrm{M}_\mathrm{B}}{x_\mathrm{A}V_\mathrm{A} + x_\mathrm{B}V_\mathrm{B}}$$

and putting

$$x_\mathrm{A} = x \quad \text{and} \quad x_\mathrm{B} = 1 - x$$

equation (82) becomes

[83]
$$\mathrm{RT} \, d\ln x = \left(V_\mathrm{A}\frac{x\mathrm{M}_\mathrm{A} + (1-x)\mathrm{M}_\mathrm{B}}{xV_\mathrm{A} + (1-x)V_\mathrm{B}} - \mathrm{M}_\mathrm{A}\right) d\Phi.$$

Integration between two positions of gravitational field strength Φ_1 and Φ_2 yields

[84]
$$V_\mathrm{B}\ln\frac{x_2}{x_1} - V_\mathrm{A}\ln\frac{1-x_2}{1-x_1} = \frac{V_\mathrm{A}\mathrm{M}_\mathrm{B} - V_\mathrm{B}\mathrm{M}_\mathrm{A}}{\mathrm{RT}}(\Phi_2 - \Phi_1)$$

which on substitution of $\rho_\mathrm{A} = \dfrac{\mathrm{M}_\mathrm{A}}{V_\mathrm{A}}$ and $\rho_\mathrm{B} = \dfrac{\mathrm{M}_\mathrm{B}}{V_\mathrm{B}}$, where ρ_A and ρ_B are the densities of pure A and pure B respectively, becomes

[85]
$$V_\mathrm{B}\ln\frac{x_2}{x_1} - V_\mathrm{A}\ln\frac{1-x_2}{1-x_1} = \frac{V_\mathrm{A}V_\mathrm{B}(\rho_\mathrm{B} - \rho_\mathrm{A})}{\mathrm{RT}}(\Phi_2 - \Phi_1).$$

Now if h is the depth of the system *below* the surface of the Earth (see p. 86), $d\Phi = -g \, dh$ and equations (83) and (85) become

[83']
$$\mathrm{RT}\frac{\partial \ln x}{\partial h} = g\frac{(1-x)V_\mathrm{A}V_\mathrm{B}}{xV_\mathrm{A} + (1-x)V_\mathrm{B}}(\rho_\mathrm{A} - \rho_\mathrm{B}),$$

[85']
$$V_\mathrm{B}\ln\frac{x_2}{x_1} - V_\mathrm{A}\ln\frac{1-x_2}{1-x_1} = g\frac{V_\mathrm{A}V_\mathrm{B}(\rho_\mathrm{A} - \rho_\mathrm{B})}{\mathrm{RT}}(h_2 - h_1).$$

Consider, for instance, a body of peridotite thick enough for the effect not to be negligible. Equation (83') shows that the mol fraction of the more dense component of the olivine, that is fayalite, is greater the deeper the level in the body. Assume that equation (85') may be simplified at sufficiently small values of x so that the terms in $\ln(1 - x)$ can be neglected, then

[86]
$$\ln \frac{x_2}{x_1} = g \frac{V_A(\rho_A - \rho_B)}{RT} (h_2 - h_1).$$

To provide some indication of the order of magnitude of the effect, data for an iron-poor peridotite may be considered:

$$g = 981 \text{ c.g.s. units}$$
$$R = 8.3136 \times 10^7 \text{ erg deg}^{-1} \text{ mole}^{-1}$$
$$V_{Fa} = 46.7 \text{ cm}^3 \text{ mole}^{-1}$$
$$\rho_{Fa} = 4.36 \text{ g cm}^{-3}$$
$$\rho_{Fo} = 3.22 \text{ g cm}^{-3}.$$

In this case

$$\log \frac{x_2}{x_1} \sim 27 \frac{h_2 - h_1}{T},$$

where T is in °K and h in km. For a temperature of the order of 800°K,

$$h_2 - h_1 \sim 300 \text{ meters}, \qquad \frac{x_2}{x_1} \sim 1.02;$$

$$h_2 - h_1 \sim 3000 \text{ meters}, \qquad \frac{x_2}{x_1} \sim 1.26.$$

These ratios correspond to a relative variation in the mol fraction x of 2% in the former and 26% in the latter case. The effect of gravitational field is thus negligible for small differences in depth, but may become important for very thick formations such as are commonly found in regionally metamorphosed terrain.

X

Some Examples of the Use of Chemical Potential

1.   Vapor pressure of solutions

1.1. The general case.

Consider a solution containing several components in equilibrium with its vapor at given temperature and pressure. Let f_i be the fugacity of component i in the vapor and a_i its activity in the solution. The chemical potential of i in the solution is then given by

[1] $$\mu_i^{L} = \mu_i^{0L} + RT \ln a_i$$

and in the vapor phase by

[2] $$\mu_i^{G} = \mu_i^{0G} + RT \ln f_i.$$

At equilibrium, the component i must have the same chemical potential in both phases

$$\mu_i^{L} = \mu_i^{G}$$

and therefore

[3] $$\ln \frac{f_i}{a_i} = \frac{\mu_i^{0L} - \mu_i^{0G}}{RT}.$$

At any given temperature and pressure the quantity $\dfrac{\mu_i^{0L} - \mu_i^{0G}}{RT}$ is constant and consequently the equilibrium condition can be written as

[4] $$\overline{f_i = k_i a_i.}$$

At constant temperature and pressure the activity of any component

192

in the solution is proportional to the fugacity of that component in the vapor.

1.2. Ideal solutions—Raoult's Law.

It will be assumed that the vapor is, to a first approximation, a perfect gas, so that

$$f_i = p_i$$

and equation (4) becomes

[5] $$p_i = k_i a_i.$$

If the solution is also ideal, equation (5) becomes

[6] $$p_i = k_i x_i$$

where x_i is the mol fraction of component i in the solution.

Now if ideality persists as x_i tends to unity, equation (6) will remain valid and then

[7] $$p_i^0 = k_i$$

where p_i^0 is the partial pressure of pure component i at the given T and P. From equations (6) and (7) it follows that

[8] $$p_i = p_i^0 x_i.$$

This is *Raoult's Law of Vapor Pressure*. When the component concerned is the solvent of a dilute solution, the law takes on another, also useful, form. Using the subscript i for solutes and the subscript 0 for the solvent,

$$p_0 = p_0^0 x_0$$

where

$$x_0 = 1 - \Sigma x_i$$

therefore

$$p_0 = p_0^0 (1 - \Sigma x_i)$$

and, putting $p_0 - p_0^0 = \Delta p_0$, it follows that

[9] $$\frac{\Delta p_0}{p_0^0} = \Sigma x_i.$$

Equation (9) means that the relative lowering of the vapor pressure of the solvent is equal to the sum of the mol fractions of the solutes.

1.3. Non-ideal dilute solutions.

Consider a dilute solution, for example, of sodium chloride in water. Assume that the vapor approximates to a perfect gas, so that fugacity may be equated with partial pressure, and neglect the vapor pressure of NaCl, so that the vapor pressure of the solution may be approximated to that of the solvent, in this case water. Then equation (5) becomes

$$p_{H_2O} = k_{H_2O}\ a_{H_2O}$$

which can be expanded as

[10] $$p_{H_2O} = k_{H_2O}\ \gamma_{H_2O}\ x_{H_2O}$$

where γ_{H_2O} is the activity coefficient of water. Since water is the solvent, $\gamma_{H_2O} \to 1$ as $x_{H_2O} \to 1$, the solution tending to ideality at extreme dilution, and therefore

$$k_{H_2O} = p^0_{H_2O}$$

where $p^0_{H_2O}$ is the vapor pressure of pure water under the specified conditions. Therefore equation (10) becomes

[11] $$p_{H_2O} = p^0_{H_2O}\ \gamma_{H_2O}\ x_{H_2O}$$

which can be rewritten as

[12] $$\frac{p_{H_2O}}{p^0_{H_2O}} = \gamma_{H_2O}\ (1 - x_{NaCl}).$$

This equation is important in that it shows that the value of γ_{H_2O} can be determined experimentally from knowledge of $p^0_{H_2O}$ and x_{NaCl} and measurement of p_{H_2O}.

The mol fraction x_{NaCl} can be expressed in terms of the concentration c_{NaCl} in moles per liter and the molar volume of water V_{H_2O} as

$$x_{NaCl} = \frac{V_{H_2O}\ c_{NaCl}}{1000} = 18 \times 10^{-3}\ c_{NaCl}$$

whence equation (12) becomes

[13] $$\frac{p_{H_2O}}{p^0_{H_2O}} = \gamma_{H_2O}\ (1 - 18 \times 10^{-3}\ c_{NaCl}).$$

Substitution in equation (13) of data from Rossini *et al.* (1952) and from the *Tables annuelles de Constantes et Données numériques* yields the values of γ_{H_2O} shown in the table below, where the activity coefficient of water can be seen clearly to decrease as concentration of NaCl increases but to be almost independent of temperature.

T °C	p_{H_2O} mm Hg	c_{NaCl} moles/liters	p_{H_2O} mm Hg	γ_{H_2O}
25	23.752	0.4	23.444	0.994
		2.0	22.134	0.966
		5.0	19.135	0.885
100	760.0	0.5	747.7	0.993
		2.0	707.9	0.966
		5.0	617.0	0.892

The values of γ_{H_2O} shown in the table will be made use of in a later paragraph (p. 277).

2.   Crystallization of a peridotitic magma

Consider a melt of initial composition $2(Fe_{x_M}Mg_{1-x_M})O \cdot SiO_2$, which can be regarded as a mixture of molten fayalite and forsterite in proportions corresponding to $Fa_{x_M}Fo_{1-x_M}$. When the temperature is lowered, suppose that olivine of composition $Fa_x Fo_{1-x}$ crystallizes. At a given temperature and pressure, the condition for equilibrium between crystals and melt can be expressed as equality of chemical potential in the two phases for forsterite and for fayalite, thus

$$\begin{cases} \mu_{Fo}^C = \mu_{Fo}^L \\ \mu_{Fa}^C = \mu_{Fa}^L. \end{cases}$$

And the chemical potentials can be written in terms of activities, for instance for fayalite,

$$\mu_{Fa}^C = \mu_{Fa}^{0C} + RT \ln a_{Fa}$$
$$\mu_{Fa}^L = \mu_{Fa}^{0L} + RT \ln a'_{Fa}.$$

Therefore at equilibrium,

[14] $$RT \ln \frac{a'_{Fa}}{a_{Fa}} = \mu_{Fa}^{0C} - \mu_{Fa}^{0L}.$$

The quantity $\mu_{Fa}^{OL} - \mu_{Fa}^{OC}$ is none other than the molar free enthalpy of fusion of pure fayalite at the temperature T, which may be written as $(\Delta G_{Fa})_T$, so that equation (14) becomes

[15]
$$\ln \frac{a'_{Fa}}{a_{Fa}} = -\frac{(\Delta G_{Fa})_T}{RT}.$$

But at P = 1 atm,

$$(\Delta G_{Fa})_T = (\Delta H_{Fa}) - T(\Delta S_{Fa})$$

so that at T_0, the melting point of pure fayalite at 1 atm,

$$(\Delta G_{Fa})_{T_0} = 0$$

and

$$(\Delta S_{Fa})_{T_0} = \frac{(\Delta H_{Fa})_{T_0}}{T_0}.$$

Further, if ΔC_P is assumed to be zero between T and T_0,

$$(\Delta S_{Fa})_T = (\Delta S_{Fa})_{T_0}; \qquad (\Delta H_{Fa})_T = (\Delta H_{Fa})_{T_0}$$

and

[16]
$$\frac{(\Delta G_{Fa})_T}{T} = (\Delta H_{Fa}) \left(\frac{1}{T} - \frac{1}{T_0} \right)$$

so that

[17]
$$\ln \frac{a'_{Fa}}{a_{Fa}} = \frac{(\Delta H_{Fa})}{R} \left(\frac{1}{T_0} - \frac{1}{T} \right).$$

Likewise for forsterite,

[17']
$$\ln \frac{a'_{Fo}}{a_{Fo}} = \frac{(\Delta H_{Fo})}{R} \left(\frac{1}{T'_0} - \frac{1}{T} \right).$$

If both crystalline and molten olivine approximate to perfect mixtures,

$$a'_{Fa} = x' \; ; \qquad a_{Fa} = x$$
$$a'_{Fo} = 1 - x'; \qquad a_{Fo} = 1 - x$$

where x' and x are the mol fractions of fayalite in the melt and in crystalline olivine at equilibrium. Then

[18]
$$\left\{ \begin{array}{l} \ln \dfrac{x'}{x} = \dfrac{(\Delta H_{Fa})}{R} \left(\dfrac{1}{T_0} - \dfrac{1}{T} \right) \\[2ex] \ln \dfrac{1 - x'}{1 - x} = \dfrac{(\Delta H_{Fo})}{R} \left(\dfrac{1}{T'_0} - \dfrac{1}{T} \right). \end{array} \right.$$

These two last equations enable x and x' to be calculated as functions of T, the only data required being:

$T_0 = 1478°K$ for the melting point of fayalite,
$T'_0 = 2163°K$ for the melting point of forsterite,
$(\Delta H_{Fa}) \sim (\Delta H_{Fo}) \sim 14$ Kcal mole^{-1} for the enthalpy of fusion,
(Data from Bowen and Schairer, 1935).

Therefore, taking R $\sim$ 2 cal deg^{-1},

[19]
$$\begin{cases} \ln \dfrac{x'}{x} = 7000 \left(\dfrac{1}{1478} - \dfrac{1}{T}\right) \\ \ln \dfrac{1-x'}{1-x} = 7000 \left(\dfrac{1}{2163} - \dfrac{1}{T}\right). \end{cases}$$

Two curves, the solidus $x = f(T)$ and the liquidus $x' = f(T)$, can

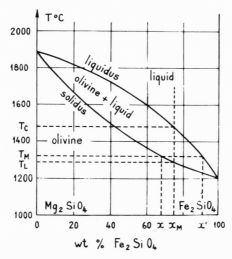

Fig. 42. Melting or crystallization diagram for the olivine solid solution according to the experimental data of Bowen and Schairer (1935). The curves calculated from equations (19) are closely similar.

thus be drawn to give respectively the composition of crystalline olivine and that of the melt at each temperature (fig. 42).* Starting,

* The curves shown here are those determined experimentally by Bowen and Schairer (1935). Agreement with the calculated curves is excellent and may be taken as confirmation of the hypothesis of perfect mixing in both the melt and the crystalline phase.

for instance, from a magma of composition $Fe_{z_M}Mg_{1-z_M}$, olivine begins to crystallize on cooling to the temperature T_c (fig. 42), the temperature of beginning of crystallization. At the temperature T_M a liquid of composition $Fe_{x'}Mg_{1-x'}$ coexists with crystalline olivine of composition Fe_xMg_{1-x}. Finally at the temperature T_L, the temperature of final crystallization (or for the reverse process, the temperature of beginning of melting), the system becomes completely crystalline, olivine crystallizing now with the same composition as the original magma, $Fe_{z_M}Mg_{1-z_M}$. The composition of the phase crystallizing obviously changes composition in the course of cooling from the temperature of its first appearance; the crystals formed however may very easily be non-homogeneous, but under geological conditions it might be supposed that such crystals would, usually, subsequently react internally at equilibrium to homogenize their composition.

In figure 43 a crystallization diagram is given for melilite, which

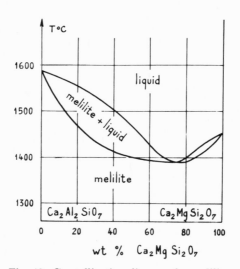

Fig. 43. Crystallization diagram for melilite.

is rather more complicated. It is characterized by a common minimum on the solidus and liquidus; at the minimum temperature crystalline and liquid phases of identical composition are in equilibrium.

3.   Unmixing from solid solutions

The phenomenon of unmixing, or exsolution, from solid solutions is well known to petrologists and mineralogists. In the low-temperature, or intermediate-temperature, alkali feldspars (orthoclase, microcline) it manifests itself by the appearance of lamellae, veinlets, or droplets essentially albitic in composition inset in a dominantly potassic feldspathic matrix; these are exsolution perthites. On the other hand in the high-temperature feldspars (the sanidines) exsolution is non-existent. These observations are interpreted by saying that at high temperature the alkali feldspars constitute a single homogeneous phase, and that with falling temperature, there is separation into two distinct phases, one relatively sodic and the other relatively potassic; in the perthites the latter forms the matrix and the process is spoken of as unmixing of the feldspar phase. Many oxide and sulphide ore-minerals exhibit unmixing as do some meteoritic minerals. An attempt will be made below to show in what circumstances unmixing can occur.

3.1. Perfect solutions.

Consider two phases α and α' at equilibrium. For any component i at equilibrium:

$$\mu_i^\alpha = \mu_i^{\alpha'}.$$

If moreover both phases are perfect solutions

[20] $$\mu_i^0 + RT \ln x_i = \mu_i^0 + RT \ln x_i'$$

where x_i and x_i' are the mol fractions of i in α and α'. Therefore

[21] $$\ln \frac{x_i}{x_i'} = 0, \quad \text{and} \quad x_i = x_i'.$$

In other words two isostructural phases of the same composition will be in equilibrium. Only a single phase will therefore occur and it can be said that perfect solutions cannot unmix.

3.2. Regular solutions.

Consider now a binary mixture with two phases α and α' of different composition coexisting at equilibrium; then

$$A_x B_{1-x} \rightleftharpoons A_{x'} B_{1-x'}.$$

For component A for instance the equilibrium condition will be

$$\mu_A^\alpha = \mu_A^{\alpha'}$$

with

$$\mu_A^\alpha = \mu_A^0 + RT \ln a_A$$
$$\mu_A^{\alpha'} = \mu_A^0 + RT \ln a_A'$$

so that

[22]
$$\ln \frac{a_A}{a_A'} = 0$$

that is

[23]
$$\ln \frac{x}{x'} + \ln \frac{\gamma_A}{\gamma_A'} = 0.$$

In the simple case of regular solutions (p. 177)

[24]
$$\begin{cases} \ln \gamma_A = \dfrac{N\omega}{RT} (1 - x)^2 \\[2mm] \ln \gamma_A' = \dfrac{N\omega}{RT} (1 - x')^2 \end{cases}$$

and the equilibrium condition becomes

$$\ln \frac{x}{x'} = \ln \gamma_A' - \ln \gamma_A$$

that is

[25]
$$\ln \frac{x}{x'} = \frac{N\omega}{RT} [(1 - x')^2 - (1 - x)^2].$$

And for component B

[25']
$$\ln \frac{1 - x}{1 - x'} = \frac{N\omega}{RT} [x'^2 - x^2].$$

The pair of equations (25) and (25') are equivalent to the pair

$$\begin{cases} x' = 1 - x \\[2mm] \ln \dfrac{x}{1 - x} = \dfrac{N\omega}{RT} (2x - 1) \end{cases}$$

if the solution $x = x'$ is disregarded.

This last equation can be solved graphically by plotting $y_1 = \ln \dfrac{x}{1 - x}$ against x as shown in fig. 44. The curve is symmet-

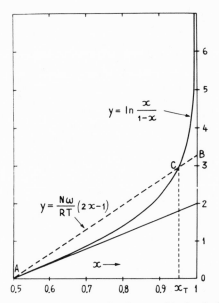

Fig. 44. Auxiliary curve for the graphical solution.

rical about the point $x = 0.5$, $y = 0$ and is therefore shown in the figure only for the range $0.5 \leqslant x \leqslant 1$. At $x = 0.5$, $y = 0$, $\dfrac{dy_1}{dx} = 4$.

The line $y_2 = \dfrac{N\omega}{RT} (2x - 1)$, which passes through the point $x = 0.5$,

$y = 0$ for all values of $\dfrac{\omega}{T}$, and has a slope $\dfrac{dy_2}{dx} = \dfrac{2N\omega}{RT}$ is also shown on

fig. 44. For the two curves to intersect, that is for the equation to

have roots, it is necessary that $\dfrac{dy_2}{dx} > \left(\dfrac{dy_1}{dx}\right)_{x=0.5}$, therefore

[27] $\dfrac{2N\omega}{RT} > 4$,   i.e., $T < \dfrac{N\omega}{2R}$.

The temperature $T_c = \dfrac{N\omega}{2R}$, below which exsolution can occur, is

described as the critical temperature of unmixing. At $T > T_c$ a single phase is stable over the whole composition range of the solid solution $0 \leqslant x \leqslant 1$. At $T < T_c$ separation into two phases of composition $A_x B_{1-x}$ and $A_{1-x} B_x$ can occur. Figure 45 displays the dependence of x on $N\omega/RT$. The curve of x as a function of T might also

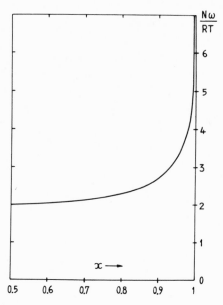

Fig. 45. Unmixing curve for a regular solution as a function of $1/T$.

be drawn, but for that it would be necessary to know ω, which is itself a function of T.

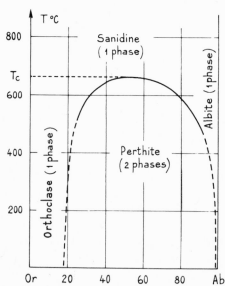

Fig. 46. Unmixing diagram for the alkali feldspars (after Laves, 1952).

Figure 46 shows the unmixing curve, or solvus, for the alkali feldspars. It is significantly asymmetrical about $x = 0.5$ and the alkali feldspars cannot therefore, at least in so far as exsolution is concerned, be considered to be strictly regular solutions.

4.   Effect of pressure on the solubility of FeS in blende

The sulphides of zinc and iron can exist in three structurally quite distinct forms, excluding pyrite:

(1) blende (Zn, Fe)S, with up to 40% FeS,
(2) wurtzite, which has some degree of structural resemblance to blende, with up to 50% FeS,
(3) pyrrhotite FeS, which can contain very little ZnS.

The experimentally determined phase diagram, fig. 47, shows the stability fields of the three polymorphs at atmospheric pressure.

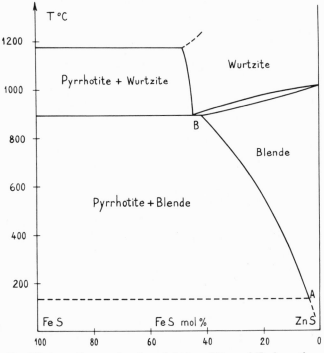

Fig. 47. Equilibrium diagram for the sulphides of Zn and Fe from the experimental data of Kullerud (1953).

Some attempt will now be made to complete the phase diagram by evaluation of the effect of pressure on the solubility of FeS in blende. This problem is important since ferroan blendes may be used as a geological thermometer by measurement of their iron content and reference to the curve AB of fig. 47. It is therefore necessary to know how pressure will modify the equilibrium conditions.

Consider a crystal of pyrrhotite in equilibrium with ferroan blende at given P and T:

$$\mu_{Fe}^{Py} = \mu_{Fe}^{Bl}$$

and

$$\mu_{Fe}^{Bl} = \mu_{Fe}^{0Bl} + RT \ln x$$

therefore

[28]
$$\ln x = \frac{\mu_{Fe}^{Py} - \mu_{Fe}^{0Bl}}{RT}$$

where x is the mol fraction of FeS in blende. The quantity $\mu_{Fe}^{0Bl} - \mu_{Fe}^{Py}$ is the free enthalpy of solution of FeS in blende, that is the free enthalpy necessary for:

(1) Conversion of FeS from the pyrrhotite structure to the blende structure.
(2) Substitution in the blende structure of one Fe ion for a Zn ion.

Putting $\mu_{Fe}^{0Bl} - \mu_{Fe}^{Py} = (\Delta G)_T^P$, it follows that

[29]
$$\ln x = -\frac{(\Delta G)_T^P}{RT}$$

which on differentiation with respect to pressure becomes

[30]
$$\frac{d \ln x}{dP} = -\frac{1}{RT} \frac{d(\Delta G)}{dP} = -\frac{\Delta V}{RT}.$$

Integration between P_1 and P, corresponding to mol fractions x_1 and x, assuming ΔV to be independent of pressure, yields

[31]
$$\ln \frac{x}{x_1} = -\frac{\Delta V}{RT} (P - P_1).$$

Then taking as the reference state $P_1 = 1$ atm ($\ll$ P) and $x_1 = x_0$ (the equilibrium composition at 1 atm at the temperature T),

[32]
$$\ln \frac{x}{x_0} = -\frac{\Delta V}{RT} P.$$

With $(\Delta V) \sim 6.25$ cm^3 mole^{-1}, the following values of $\dfrac{x}{x_0}$ are obtained (Kullerud, 1953):

P$_{atm}$ T °C	1	1000	2000	3000	4000	5000
200	6.17	5.25	4.48	3.79	3.22	2.75
300	9.35	8.17	7.17	6.26	5.47	4.80
400	13.17	11.70	10.49	9.35	8.35	7.45
500	17.48	15.80	14.30	12.95	11.75	10.64
600	22.35	20.49	18.73	17.15	15.73	14.40
700	27.93	25.80	23.82	22.07	20.36	18.84
800	34.25	31.82	29.70	27.66	25.80	23.95

It is evident from the table that pressure inhibits the solution of FeS in blende. The results are summarized in fig. 48.

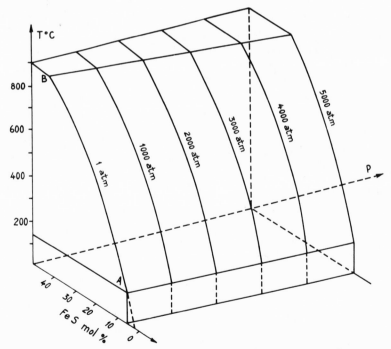

Fig. 48. Mol fraction of FeS in blende as a function of temperature and pressure according to Kullerud (1953).

5.   The equilibrium calcite + silica → wollastonite + CO₂ in an open system (after Miyashiro, 1960)

The equilibrium conditions for the system calcite + quartz → wollastonite + CO₂ as a function of temperature, lithostatic pressure, and pressure of CO₂ were examined on p. 141. The problem that concerns us here, although the same minerals are involved, is rather different. Consider for instance a body of pure calcite, completely quartz-free, but surrounded by quartz-rich rocks. In certain circumstances silica can diffuse from the surroundings toward the marble and as it arrives there react with calcite to form wollastonite and CO₂ according to the equation

$$\underset{\text{calcite}}{\text{CaCO}_3} + \underset{\text{quartz}}{\text{SiO}_2} \rightarrow \underset{\text{wollastonite}}{\text{CaSiO}_3} + \text{CO}_2.$$

Silica does not constitute a distinct and separate phase in the system. It is what Korzhinkii (1957) has called a *mobile* component, whose chemical potential is determined by *external factors*, that is by factors external to the strictly defined system.

At any given temperature and pressure the equilibrium condition is

$$\mu_{\text{Cal}} + \mu_{\text{SiO}_2} = \mu_{\text{Wo}} + \mu_{\text{CO}_2}.$$

The composition of the phases calcite and wollastonite, which may be regarded as pure components, is fixed; their chemical potentials are therefore constant and on differentiation the equilibrium condition becomes

$$d(\mu_{\text{CO}_2})/d(\mu_{\text{SiO}_2}) = 1.$$

The chemical potential of carbon dioxide can be expressed in terms of its fugacity as

$$d\mu_{\text{CO}_2} = \text{RT} \, d \ln f$$

whence

$$\frac{\text{RT} \, d \ln f}{d\mu_{\text{SiO}_2}} = 1 \quad \text{(fig. 49).}$$

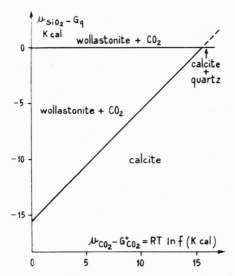

Fig. 49. Graph of chemical potential of silica against fugacity of CO_2 for the reaction calcite + silica → wollastonite + CO_2 at a lithostatic pressure of 800 atm and temperature, T = 1000°K.

It now remains to attach a definite meaning to μ_{SiO_2}. The equilibrium condition $\mu_{Cal} + \mu_{SiO_2} = \mu_{Wo} + \mu_{CO_2}$ can be rewritten as

$$\mu_{SiO_2} - G_q = (G_{Wo} + \mu_{CO_2}) - (G_{Cal} + G_q).$$

But

$$\mu_{CO_2} = G^0_{CO_2} + RT \ln f$$
$$G_{Wo} = G^0_{Wo} + PV_{Wo}$$
$$G_{Cal} = G^0_{Cal} + PV_{Cal}$$
$$G_q = G^0_q + PV_q$$

whence

$$\mu_{SiO_2} - G_q = (\Delta G)^0_T + RT \ln f + P\Delta V$$

where P is the lithostatic pressure applied to the solids, $(\Delta G)^0_T$ and ΔV are the free enthalpy and volume changes of the solids in the reaction

calcite + quartz → wollastonite + CO_2

at 1 atm; ΔV is taken to be independent of P.

Now $(\Delta G)^0_T$ has already been calculated on p. 147. Substitution of approximate numerical values for $(\Delta G)^0_T$ etc., yields

$$\mu_{SiO_2} - G_q = 25{,}600 - 40.8\,T + 4.575\log f - 0.477\,P.$$

Equilibrium is therefore attained when the four independent variables, chemical potential of silica, temperature, lithostatic pressure and fugacity of CO_2, satisfy the equation given above. Suppose that lithostatic pressure and fluid pressure are fixed, for example, so that

$$P = P_{CO_2} = 800 \text{ atm},$$

then $f \sim 1000$ atm for temperatures of the order of 500–1000°C and the equilibrium condition becomes

$$\mu_{SiO_2} - G_q = 25{,}220 - 27.1\,T.$$

On figure 50 the *relative chemical potential* of silica, that is $\mu_{SiO_2} - G_q$, is plotted as a function of equilibrium temperature. When free

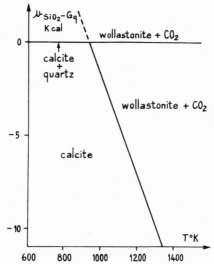

Fig. 50. Equilibrium temperature for the system calcite + silica → wollastonite + CO_2 as a function of the chemical potential of silica at a lithostatic pressure of 800 atm and $P_{CO_2} = 800$ atm.

quartz is present in the marble, $\mu_{SiO_2} - G_q = 0$. The condition $\mu_{SiO_2} - G_q > 0$ cannot persist since silica must then crystallize as quartz until $\mu_{SiO_2} = G_q$. When quartz is absent from the marble,

$\mu_{SiO_2} < G_q$, that is, $\mu_{SiO_2} - G_q < 0$. The equilibrium temperature therefore increases as the chemical potential of silica decreases. At a given pressure it is least when $\mu_{SiO_2} = G_q$, that is, when free quartz is present in the marble. Thus at a sufficiently high temperature, a pure limestone can be progressively transformed into a wollastonite-marble by influx of silica and without the appearance of quartz in the assemblage at any stage.

XI

The Law of Mass Action: Equilibrium Constants

The Law of Mass Action, which follows straightforwardly from the Second Law of Thermodynamics, provides a means of establishing precise conditions for equilibrium in the most general case.

1. Theoretical argument

1.1. General conditions for heterogeneous equilibrium.

Consider a heterogeneous system of components $A_1, A_2, \ldots A_i,$ $\ldots A'_1, A'_2, \ldots A'_j$ distributed among several phases in any manner whatsoever and able to react one with another according to the equation:

[1] $\qquad n_1A_1 + n_2A_2 + \cdots + n_iA_i \rightleftharpoons n'_1A'_1 + n'_2A'_2 + \cdots + n'_jA'_j.$

The increment in free enthalpy dG for the system can be written as

[2] $\qquad dG = -S\,dT + V\,dP + \sum_i \mu_i\,dn_i + \sum_j \mu'_j\,dn'_j$

which at constant temperature and pressure becomes

[3] $\qquad dT = 0, \quad dP = 0, \quad dG = \sum_i \mu_i\,dn_i + \sum_j \mu'_j\,dn'_j.$

But the increments dn_i, dn'_j are not independent, since from (1) it follows that

[4] $\qquad \dfrac{dn_1}{n_1} = \dfrac{dn_2}{n_2} = \cdots = -\dfrac{dn'_1}{n'_1} = -\dfrac{dn'_2}{n'_2} = -dv.$

210

Equation (3) then becomes

$$dT = 0, \quad dP = 0, \quad dG = dv \left(\sum_j n'_j \mu'_j - \sum_i n_i \mu_i \right).$$

To simplify the writing of the summations put

[5] $$\sum_j n'_j \mu'_j = \Sigma n' \mu' \quad \text{and} \quad \sum_i n_i \mu_i = \Sigma n \mu$$

so that equation (3) becomes

$$dT = 0, \quad dP = 0, \quad dG = dv \, (\Sigma n' \mu' - \Sigma n \mu).$$

At constant temperature and pressure the condition for reversibility and therefore for equilibrium is $dG = 0$, which, since $dv \neq 0$, can be written as

[6] $$\Sigma n' \mu' - \Sigma n \mu = 0.$$

This is the most general statement of the equilibrium condition for a heterogeneous reaction. All the development below follows more or less immediately from this equation. In practice, moreover, it is often necessary to start from this equation, since the application of formulae such as the Law of Mass Action implies certain restrictions, ignorance or forgetfulness of which can lead to serious error.

1.2. The Law of Mass Action and equilibrium constants in gaseous systems.

1.2.1.—Equation (6) can be simplified for a homogeneous system entirely in the gas phase. For any component i

[7] $$\mu_i = \mu_i^0 + RT \ln f_i$$

then substitution in equation (6) yields

$$\Sigma n' \mu^{0'} - \Sigma n \mu^0 = RT \, (\Sigma n \ln f - \Sigma n' \ln f')$$

which can be rewritten as

[8] $$RT \ln \frac{f_1'^{n_1'} f_2'^{n_2'} \cdots}{f_1^{n_1} f_2^{n_2} \cdots} = \Sigma n \mu^0 - \Sigma n' \mu^{0'}$$

where μ^0 represents the chemical potential, and thus the molar free enthalpy, at unit fugacity. Therefore

$$\Sigma n \mu^0 = G^0 \quad \text{and} \quad \Sigma n' \mu^{0'} = G^{0'}$$

and, putting $G^{0'} - G^0 = (\Delta G)^0_T$, equation (8) becomes

[9] $$RT \ln \frac{f_1'^{n_1'} f_2'^{n_2'} \cdots}{f_1^{n_1} f_2^{n_2} \cdots} = -(\Delta G)^0_T$$

$(\Delta G)_T^0$ is the free enthalpy of reaction at temperature T and unit fugacity.

Now if K_f is defined by $\ln K_f = -\dfrac{(\Delta G)_T^0}{RT}$ equation (9) becomes

[10]
$$\frac{f_1'^{n_1'} f_2'^{n_2'} \cdots}{f_1^{n_1} f_2^{n_2} \cdots} = K_f$$

K_f being known as *the equilibrium constant with respect to fugacity;* it is independent of total fugacity and has a unique value for a given reaction at a given temperature.

1.2.2.—Equation (10) assumes an especially interesting form when the gases can be considered as perfect. Then $f_i = p_i$, where p_i is the partial pressure of component i in the mixture, and the Law of Mass Action is obtained in one of its classical forms:

[11]
$$\frac{p_1'^{n_1'} p_2'^{n_2'} \cdots}{p_1^{n_1} p_2^{n_2} \cdots} = K_p$$

where

[12]
$$\ln K_p = -\frac{(\Delta G)_T^0}{RT}.$$

K_p *is known as the equilibrium constant with respect to partial pressure.* It is independent of total pressure and of composition; it has a definite value for every temperature. $(\Delta G)_T^0$ is the free enthalpy of reaction at unit pressure at the temperature T.

1.2.3.—Partial pressures can of course be expressed in terms of the mol fractions of the various components in the mixture:

$$p_i = P x_i.$$

Equation (11) then becomes

[13]
$$\frac{x_1'^{n_1'} x_2'^{n_2'} \cdots}{x_1^{n_1} x_2^{n_2} \cdots} = K_p P^{-\Delta n} \qquad \text{where} \qquad \Delta n = \Sigma n' - \Sigma n.$$

Now if K_x is defined as $K_x = K_p P^{-\Delta n}$,

[14]
$$\frac{x_1'^{n_1'} x_2'^{n_2'} \cdots}{x_1^{n_1} x_2^{n_2} \cdots} = K_x.$$

K_x *is known as the equilibrium constant with respect to mol fraction;* unlike K_p, it is dependent on total pressure.

1.2.4.—Finally, for a perfect gas mixture another equilibrium constant K_c can be defined to refer to *molar concentrations* c_i, where

$$c_i = \frac{n_i}{V}$$

V being the total volume of the system. Since $p_i V = n_i RT$, substitution in equation (11) yields

[15]
$$\frac{c_1'^{n_1'} c_2'^{n_2'} \cdots}{c_1^{n_1} c_2^{n_2} \cdots} = K_p (RT)^{-\Delta n}$$

and putting $K_p (RT)^{-\Delta n} = K_c$,

[16]
$$\frac{c_1'^{n_1'} c_2'^{n_2'} \cdots}{c_1^{n_1} c_2^{n_2} \cdots} = K_c.$$

Like K_p, K_c is independent of total pressure.

It should be noticed that when $\Delta n = 0$, all three constants K_p, K_x, and K_c are independent of total pressure and moreover

$$K_p = K_x = K_c.$$

1.3. The Law of Mass Action and equilibrium constants in solution.

For reactions in solution an equation can be established that is exactly analogous to that developed earlier for gaseous systems:

[17]
$$\frac{a_1'^{n_1'} a_2'^{n_2'} \cdots}{a_1^{n_1} a_2^{n_2} \cdots} = K_a$$

where

[17']
$$\ln K_a = -\frac{(\Delta G)_T^P}{RT}$$

a_i being the activity of component i in the solution. K_a *is the equilibrium constant with respect to activity.* It is notable that, unlike the equilibrium constant with respect to fugacity for a gas system, K_a is dependent on pressure.

For a perfect solution $a_i = x_i$ and equation (17) becomes

[18]
$$\frac{x_1'^{n_1'} x_2'^{n_2'} \cdots}{x_1^{n_1} x_2^{n_2} \cdots} = K_x$$

where

[18']
$$\ln K_x = -\frac{(\Delta G)_T^P}{RT}$$

and K_x *is the equilibrium constant with respect to mol fraction.*

For an ideal non-perfect solution, *i.e.*, a very dilute solution, equation (18) remains valid since to a first approximation x for the solvent ~ 1, x_1, x_2, x_1', x_2' . . . represent the mol fractions of the solute components, and $(\Delta G)_T^P$ is the free enthalpy of reaction at pressure P and temperature T for solutes at infinite dilution and the solvent in the pure state. Again an equilibrium constant K_c referring to molar concentration can be defined, at least for very dilute ideal solutions. For a solute i

[19]
$$c_i = \frac{x_i}{x_S \overline{V}_S + \sum_i x_i \overline{V}_i} = \frac{n_i}{V}$$

where the subscript S refers to the solvent. If the solution is very dilute, equation (19) approaches

$$c_i \sim \frac{x_i}{V_S}$$

and substitution into equation (18) then yields

$$\frac{c_1'^{n_1'} \, c_2'^{n_2'} \, \cdots}{c_1^{n_1} \, c_2^{n_2} \, \cdots} = K_x V_S^{-\Delta n}$$

which on putting $K_c = K_x V_S^{-\Delta n}$ becomes

[20]
$$\frac{c_1'^{n_1'} \, c_2'^{n_2'} \, \cdots}{c_1^{n_1} \, c_2^{n_2} \, \cdots} = K_c.$$

1.4. Heterogeneous systems.

Consider a reaction involving a gas phase and condensed phases, the composition of the latter being constant, or, in other words, each condensed phase containing only one component. The case of a reaction involving a solution phase and condensed phases follows simply by analogy.

When gaseous components are present in a system, it has already been shown that the pressure dependence of the chemical potentials— and thus of the molar free enthalpies—of the condensed phases can be neglected. The reaction can be stated as

$$n_1A_1 + n_2A_2 + \cdots + m_1M_1 + m_2M_2 + \cdots \rightleftharpoons n_1'A_1'$$
$$+ n_2'A_2' + \cdots + m_1'M_1' + m_2'M_2' + \cdots$$

where the symbols A_i refer to gaseous components and M_i to the condensed phases. The condition for equilibrium is:

[21] $n_1\mu_{A_1} + n_2\mu_{A_2} + \cdots + m_1\mu_{M_1} + m_2\mu_{M_2} + \cdots$
$$= n_1'\mu_{A_1'} + n_1'\mu_{A_2'} + \cdots + m_1'\mu_{M_1'} + m_2'\mu_{M_2'} + \cdots.$$

Now suppose by way of simplification that the gases are perfect; then

$$\mu_A = \mu_A^0 + RT \ln p_A$$

and, since

$$\mu_M = \mu_M^0$$

the equilibrium condition becomes

[22]
$$\frac{p_{A_1'}^{'n_1'} p_{A_2'}^{'n_2'} \cdots}{p_{A_1}^{n_1} p_{A_2}^{n_2} \cdots} = K_p$$

where

$$\ln K_p = -\frac{(\Delta G)_T^0}{RT}.$$

The Law of Mass Action is therefore applicable to a case such as this in precisely the same manner as to an entirely gaseous equilibrium. Only the gaseous components appear on the left-hand side of the equation; but the right-hand side, K_p being a function of $(\Delta G)_T^0$, is concerned with all the components taking part in the reaction.

It follows that equation (22) will become invalid if the composition of any of the condensed phases can vary, since μ_M will then be dependent on the composition of phase M. Consider for instance a chemical reaction involving a perfect gas phase and a perfect solution; for the one

$$\mu_A = \mu_A^0 + RT \ln P + RT \ln x_A$$

and for the other

$$\mu_M = \mu_M^0 + RT \ln x_M$$

neglecting the pressure dependence of μ_M^0. The equilibrium condition is here:

$$\Sigma n\mu_A^0 + \Sigma m\mu_M^0 + RT \Sigma n \ln x_A + RT \Sigma m \ln x_M + RT \ln P\Sigma n$$
$$= \Sigma n'\mu_{A'}^0 + \Sigma m'\mu_{M'}^0 + RT \Sigma n' \ln x_{A'}' + RT \Sigma m' \ln x_{M'}' + RT \ln P\Sigma n'$$

which, on putting

$$\Sigma n' \mu_{A'}^{0'} + \Sigma m' \mu_{M'}^{0'} - \Sigma n \mu_A^0 - \Sigma m \mu_M^0 = (\Delta G)_T^0$$

and

$$\Sigma n' - \Sigma n = \Delta n$$

becomes

[23] $\displaystyle RT \ln \frac{x_{A1}'^{n'_1} x_{A2}'^{n'_2} \cdots x_{M1}'^{m'_1} x_{M2}'^{m'_2} \cdots}{x_{A1}^{n_1} x_{A2}^{n_2} \cdots x_{M1}^{m_1} x_{M2}^{m_2} \cdots} = -[(\Delta G)_T^0 + RT \, \Delta n \ln P].$

Therefore in this case the Law of Mass Action can be applied to all the constituents as though the system were homogeneous; but the equilibrium constant, defined in the usual way, then becomes K_x such that:

[24] $$\ln K_x = -\frac{(\Delta G)_T^0}{RT} - \Delta n \ln P$$

and

$$\frac{x_{A1}'^{n'_1} x_{A2}'^{n'_2} \cdots x_{M1}'^{m'_1} x_{M2}'^{m'_2} \cdots}{x_A^{n_1} x_{A2}^{n_2} \cdots x_{M1}^{m_1} x_{M2}^{m_2} \cdots} = K_x.$$

1.5. Dependence of equilibrium constants on T and P.

Only equilibrium constants referred to mol fractions will be considered here; the behavior of other equilibrium constants follows very simply.

Equation (18′) provides a statement of K_x at any temperature and pressure:

$$\ln K_x = -\frac{(\Delta G)_T^P}{RT}.$$

Therefore

[25] $$\ln K_x = -\frac{(\Delta H)_T^0}{RT} + \frac{(\Delta S)_T^0}{R} - \frac{1}{RT} \int_0^P (\Delta V)_T^P \, dP.$$

For reactions involving only condensed phases ΔV is constant to a first approximation and then

[26] $$\ln K_x = -\frac{(\Delta H)_T^0}{RT} + \frac{(\Delta S)_T^0}{R} - \frac{P(\Delta V)}{RT}.$$

And further, if ΔC_P can be neglected at temperatures above the temperature of the standard state,

[27] $$\ln K_x = -\frac{(\Delta H)_{298}^0}{RT} + \frac{(\Delta S)_{298}^0}{R} - \frac{P(\Delta V)}{RT}.$$

When gaseous components are also involved in the reaction, the dependence of the volume of the condensed phases on temperature and pressure can be neglected and if the gas phase is assumed to be perfect, it is evident that

$$[28] \qquad \ln K_x = -\frac{(\Delta H)^0_{298}}{RT} + \frac{(\Delta S)^0_{298}}{R} - \Delta n \ln P$$

where Δn is the change in the number of moles of gaseous components in reaction.

2. Examples of the use of the Law of Mass Action

Only five examples of the use of the Law of Mass Action will be discussed here: all five are concerned with the problem of the distribution of one or more elements among several phases. Other applications of the law are to be found among the varied problems of geological interest that are the subject of Chapter XIII.

The earliest work on the partition of a component between two distinct phases dates from 1891, when Roozeboom published a diagram showing the concentration of an element in each of two coexisting phases plotted on rectangular coordinates. The same kind of diagram is not infrequently used today by petrologists and geochemists, but all too frequently its discussion is restricted to quite vague correlations, and rarely is any attempt made at interpretation in terms of the Law of Mass Action.

2.1. Nernst's Distribution Law and its application to Barth's "geological thermometer."

2.1.1.—Consider a rock containing among its mineral phases two feldspathic phases, (1) an alkali feldspar $Ab_{x_1}Or_{1-x_1}$, and (2) a plagioclase feldspar $Ab_{x_2}An_{1-x_2}$, where

$$Or = KAlSi_3O_8 \text{ (end-member orthoclase)},$$
$$Ab = NaAlSi_3O_8 \text{ (end-member albite)},$$
$$An = CaAl_2Si_2O_8 \text{ (end-member anorthite)},$$

$$x_1 = \frac{Ab}{Ab + Or}, \qquad x_2 = \frac{Ab}{Ab + An}.$$

The two phases have a common component, albite, and at equilibrium the chemical potential of albite must be identical in the two feldspars; therefore

$$\mu_{Ab}^{01} + RT \ln a_1 = \mu_{Ab}^{02} + RT \ln a_2$$

where μ_{Ab}^{01} and μ_{Ab}^{02} are constants at given temperature and pressure. It follows that

[29] $$\frac{a_1}{a_2} = k_{Ab}$$

where

[30] $$\ln k_{Ab} = \frac{\mu_{Ab}^{02} - \mu_{Ab}^{01}}{RT}.$$

Expansion of the activities in equation (29) yields

[31] $$\frac{x_1}{x_2} = \frac{\gamma_2}{\gamma_1} k_{Ab}.$$

This equation simplifies if it is assumed that both feldspars approximate to perfect solutions, *i.e.*, if $\gamma_1 = \gamma_2 = 1$, to

[32] $$\frac{x_1}{x_2} = k_{Ab}.$$

This is Nernst's Distribution Law which controls the partition of

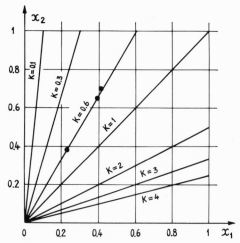

Fig. 51. Roozeboom diagram when Nernst's Distribution Law is obeyed. The three points plotted belong to the feldspars of the three 'normal' trachytes used by Barth. The axes are x_1 = mol fraction of Ab in alkali feldspar and x_2 = mol fraction of Ab in plagioclase.

a solute between two immiscible solvents, in this instance, the partition of albite between alkali feldspar and plagioclase. The partition coefficient k_{Ab} is a constant for given pressure and temperature. Thus under specified conditions, the ratio of the mol fractions of a solute in two solvents must be constant, provided the solutions are perfect; in consequence the Roozeboom diagram (fig. 51) for this situation is simply a set of straight lines passing through the origin.

2.1.2.—The association alkali feldspar—plagioclase is very common in a variety of rocks and T. F. W. Barth (1951) has proposed a "geological thermometer" based on the partition of albite between two coexisting feldspar phases.

The principle of the thermometer is very simple and is merely a direct application of Nernst's Distribution Law. Assuming, as in 2.1.1, that feldspars approximate to perfect solid solutions,

$$\frac{x_1}{x_2} = k_{Ab} \qquad \text{where} \qquad \ln k_{Ab} = \frac{\mu_{Ab}^{02} - \mu_{Ab}^{01}}{RT}.$$

and, putting

$$\mu_{Ab}^{02} - \mu_{Ab}^{01} = - (\Delta G)_T^P$$

it follows that

[33]
$$\frac{x_1}{x_2} = e^{-\frac{(\Delta G)_T^P}{RT}}.$$

where x_1 and x_2 are respectively the mol fractions of albite in the alkali feldspar and in the plagioclase. $(\Delta G)_T^P$ is the free enthalpy change accompanying the passage of one mole of albite from the plagioclase phase to the alkali feldspar phase.

Since the coefficients of compressibility are negligible, it can be supposed, as a first approximation, that $(\Delta G)_T^P$ is independent of pressure; whence

[34]
$$\frac{x_1}{x_2} = e^{-\frac{(\Delta G)_T^0}{RT}}$$

or, alternatively,

[35]
$$\ln k_{Ab} = \ln \frac{x_1}{x_2} = -\frac{(\Delta G)_T^0}{RT}.$$

If the dependence of $(\Delta G)_T^0$ on temperature is known, the experimental measurement of x_1 and x_2, determining k_{Ab}, enables the temperature of formation* of the rock to be determined from equation (35).

Unfortunately the data required for the calculation of $(\Delta G)^0_T$, and thus of k_{Ab}, are not available. This obstacle was however overcome by Barth with the help of some supplementary simplifications. Suppose that in the temperature range of interest to the petrologist, that is 200–1000°C, equation (35) can be simplified by the assumption that $\Delta C_P = 0$, then

$$[36] \qquad \ln k_{Ab} = \ln \frac{x_1}{x_2} = -\frac{(\Delta H)}{RT} + \frac{(\Delta S)}{R}$$

where (ΔH) and (ΔS) are constants independent of temperature. The graph of $\ln k_{Ab} = f\left(\frac{1}{T}\right)$ is then linear and is completely determined by knowledge of the slope and the coordinates of one point. Barth chose a point based on the compositions of the feldspars in three trachytes, whose temperature of formation he estimated on geological grounds to be of the order of 800°C; moreover the feldspars of the three trachytes chosen have closely similar partition coefficients, $k_{Ab} \sim 0.6$, in spite of wide differences in composition. The compositions of the three pairs of feldspars are shown in rows 2, 3, and 4 of the table below. The variability of the compositions of the chosen feldspars provides, of course, a quite stringent test of the applicability of equation (36). The line can then be drawn (fig. 52) from other data in the table, the temperatures of formation of various rocks being crudely known from their mineralogical, petrographic, and structural characters. The resultant line corresponds to the equation

$$[37] \qquad \ln k_{Ab} \sim \text{minus } \frac{1400}{T} + 0.8 \,,$$

assuming that $(\Delta H) \sim +2800$ cal mole^{-1} and $(\Delta S) \sim +1.6$ cal deg^{-1}

---

* The temperature so determined is not necessarily that of the crystallization of the rock, nor even of the feldspars in it, but rather the temperature at which the rock reached its last equilibrium state; on cooling to lower temperatures the rock would have remained *fixed* in a metastable state, all reaction having ceased.

The "thermometer" evidently also depends on the assumption that there is perfect solid solution between the end-members of each feldspar series. On p. 49 it was seen that the experiments of Kracek and Neuvonen indicate a lacuna in the plagioclase series and recent experiments of another sort appear to confirm that conclusion (Iiyama, Wyart, and Sabatier, 1963).

mole^{-1}, which are quite reasonable values for the differences in molar enthalpy and entropy of solution of albite in alkali feldspar and plagioclase.

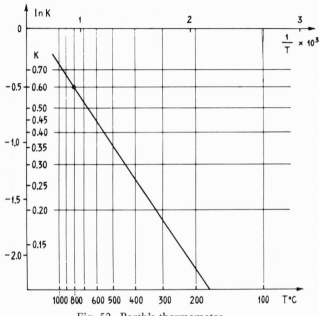

Fig. 52. Barth's thermometer.

Thus the temperature of formation of rocks* containing alkali feldspar and plagioclase can be obtained from equation (37) in the form $T = \dfrac{1400}{0.8 - \ln \dfrac{x_1}{x_2}}$ or more simply from the graph of fig. 52.

But it should not be forgotten that the basis of the method involves several simplifications: that $\Delta C_P = 0$, that anorthite cannot enter into solid solution with alkali feldspars (although alkali feldspars often contain a little Ca), and that the feldspars are approximately perfect solutions (although it is known that they are not precisely so). Great precision is therefore not to be expected, but in petrography great precision is not required, and, moreover, since there is no alternative thermometer, the Barth "thermometer" remains important.

* See note on p. 220.

	% Ab in alkali-feldspar	% Ab in plagio-clase	k_{Ab}	Approximate temperature
1 sanidinite	35	52	0.68	—
2 labradorite trachyte	23	38	0.61	800°C
3 oligoclase trachyte	39	65	0.60	—
4 oligoclase trachyte	41	70	0.60	—
5 rhyodacite	41	72	0.57	700–800°C
6 granite	29	72	0.40	500–600°C
7 granite	31	89	0.35	—
8 migmatite	31	85	0.36	450–550°C
9 augen-gneiss	27	77	0.35	—
10 pegmatite	27	78	0.36	400–500°C
11 pegmatite	20	59	0.34	—
12 pegmatite	32	97	0.33	—
13 pegmatite	23	83	0.28	350–450°C
14 pegmatite	14	57	0.25	—
15 pegmatite	18	80	0.23	—
16)alpine hydrothermal	21	96	0.22	200–300°C
16')adularia-bearing veins	9	96	0.10	—

2.2. Partition of Fe and Mg between olivine and pyroxene (after Ramberg and De Vore, 1951, and Ramberg, 1958).

This is rather more complicated than the preceding example in that it is concerned with the partition of two elements between two phases, but the principle remains the same.

The exchange of iron and magnesium between a phase of olivine structural type and a phase of pyroxene structural type can be represented by the equation:

forsterite   ferrosilite   fayalite   enstatite

[38] $Mg_2SiO_4 + 2FeSiO_3 \rightleftharpoons Fe_2SiO_4 + 2MgSiO_3.$

But it is important not to lose sight of the fact that forsterite and fayalite form solid solutions as do enstatite and ferrosilite. The equilibrium condition at given temperature and pressure must therefore be written, in conformity with equation (6), as:

[39] $\mu_{Fa}^{Ol} + 2\mu_{En}^{Py} - \mu_{Fo}^{Ol} - 2\mu_{Fs}^{Py} = 0.$ (*)

* And not as $(\Delta G) = G_{Fa} + 2G_{En} - 2G_{Fs} = 0$, an equation that would be valid only if solid solution were impossible between pairs of components.

Let x_1, $1 - x_1$, x_2, and $1 - x_2$ be the mol fractions of Mg and Fe in olivine and pyroxene respectively so that the composition of the olivine can be written as $(Mg_{x_1}Fe_{1-x_1})_2SiO_4$ and that of the pyroxene as $(Mg_{x_2}Fe_{1-x_2})SiO_3$. It is known that olivine and pyroxenes are sensibly perfect solid solutions, therefore

$$\mu_{Fo}^{Ol} = \mu_{Fo}^0 + RT \ln x_1$$
$$\mu_{Fa}^{Ol} = \mu_{Fa}^0 + RT \ln (1 - x_1)$$
$$\mu_{En}^{Py} = \mu_{En}^0 + RT \ln x_2$$
$$\mu_{Fs}^{Py} = \mu_{Fs}^0 + RT \ln (1 - x_2).$$

Substitution in equation (39) then yields:

[40] $$RT \ln \frac{(1 - x_1)x_2^2}{(1 - x_2)^2 x_1} = \mu_{Fo}^0 + 2\mu_{Fs}^0 - \mu_{Fa}^0 - 2\mu_{En}^0.$$

Now $(\Delta G)_T^P$, defined by $(\Delta G)_T^P = \mu_{Fa}^0 + 2\mu_{En}^0 - \mu_{Fo}^0 - 2\mu_{Fs}^0$, is the free enthalpy of reaction for equation (38) when all the reactants and products are pure and exist as separate phases. Equation (40) therefore becomes

[41] $$\ln \frac{(1 - x_1)x_2^2}{(1 - x_2)^2 x_1} = -\frac{(\Delta G)_T^P}{RT}$$

which becomes on putting $-\dfrac{(\Delta G)_T^P}{RT} = \ln K_x$

[42] $$\frac{(1 - x_1)x_2^2}{(1 - x_2)^2 x_1} = K_x.$$

Equation (42) is none other than the Law of Mass Action, derived here for a particular case, and K_x is the equilibrium constant with respect to mol fraction.*

Displayed on figure 53 are curves of $f(x_1, x_2) = K_x$ for various

* Ramberg and De Vore (1951) and Ramberg (1958) used instead of equation (42) the relationship

[42'] $$\frac{(1 - x_1)\, x_2}{(1 - x_2)\, x_1} = K_x$$

for the equilibrium

[38'] $$MgSi_{\frac{1}{2}}O_2 + FeSiO_3 \rightleftharpoons FeSi_{\frac{1}{2}}O_2 + MgSiO_3.$$

These equations are, as Bartholomé (1960, 1962, and private communications) has observed *a priori* just as valid as (38) and (42) above. However it would appear that only the latter are consistent with petrological observations.

values of K_x. It must always be kept in mind that at any given temperature and pressure, and therefore at a given value of K_x, there

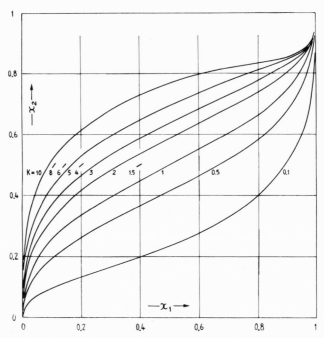

Fig. 53. Partition of Fe and Mg, mol fractions respectively x_1 and x_2, between olivine and pyroxene. The curves are drawn for selected values of the partition coefficient K.

exists an infinite number of possible distributions of Fe and Mg between the two phases. Thus for $K_x = 3$ all the assemblages set out below can theoretically be in equilibrium:

olivine	pyroxene
$(Mg_{0.16}Fe_{0.84})_2SiO_4$	$(Mg_{0.40}Fe_{0.60})SiO_3$
$(Mg_{0.25}Fe_{0.75})$	$(Mg_{0.50}Fe_{0.50})$
$(Mg_{0.64}Fe_{0.36})$	$(Mg_{0.70}Fe_{0.30})$
$(Mg_{0.84}Fe_{0.16})$	$(Mg_{0.80}Fe_{0.20})$.

For given values of x_1 and x_2, on the contrary, there evidently exists only one value of K_x that will satisfy equation (42). If the pressure of formation of a rock can be estimated, study of the distribution of Mg and Fe between its olivine and pyroxene phases can provide a means of estimating its temperature of formation. It suffices to determine x_1 and x_2, to calculate $K_x = \dfrac{(1 - x_1)x_2^2}{(1 - x_2)^2 x_1}$, and thence to evaluate $\ln K_x$. Now

$$\ln K_x = -\frac{(\Delta G)_T^P}{RT}$$

therefore

[43] $$\ln K_x \sim -\frac{(\Delta H)_T^0}{RT} + \frac{(\Delta S)_T^0}{R} - \frac{P(\Delta V)}{RT}.$$

The effect of pressure can probably be quite safely neglected since ΔV is small (-2.05 cm^3 according to the data quoted by Deer, Howie and Zussmann, 1962), and ΔC_P may likewise approximate to zero; with these assumptions, equation (43) simplifies to

[44] $$\ln K_x \sim -\frac{(\Delta H)}{RT} + \frac{(\Delta S)}{R}.$$

Now (ΔH) can be calculated from the data of Sahama and Torgeson (1949), discussed above on p. 49, as

$$(\Delta H) = -2310 \text{ cal.}$$

Therefore, taking $R \sim 2$ cal deg^{-1}, equation (44) becomes

[45] $$\ln K_x \sim \frac{1155}{T} + \frac{(\Delta S)}{2}$$

or, if the effect of pressure is taken into account,

$$\ln K_x \sim \frac{1155 + 0.025\,P}{T} + \frac{(\Delta S)}{2},$$

where T is in °K, P in atmospheres, and (ΔS) in cal deg^{-1}.

Regrettably the value of (ΔS) is not yet known with sufficient certainty for this geological thermometric method to be applied with much accuracy (Weisbrod, 1963). The standard entropies of three of the end-members have been determined to a satisfactory degree of accuracy and the measurement of the standard entropy of ferrosilite is all that is lacking; the determination of S_{Fs}^0 would evidently be of some practical utility, although ferrosilite is very rare and indeed almost a mineralogical curiosity.

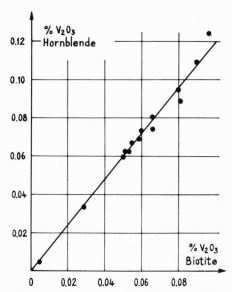

Fig. 54. Partition of vanadium between hornblende and biotite (after Kretz).

2.3. Distribution of a trace element (vanadium) between garnet, biotite, and hornblende (after Kretz, 1959).

The conclusions reached in the first part of Kretz's paper constitute the primary hypothesis on which this study is based. After a classical petrological study, dealing especially with mineral parageneses, Kretz concluded that most of the rocks that he had examined (assemblages containing quartz, plagioclase, alkali feldspar, biotite, garnet, hornblende, and accessory minerals in Grenville gneisses) could be considered to have attained equilibrium, and, moreover, at almost identical temperatures.

The three phases biotite, hornblende, and garnet contain small amounts, $\leqslant 1^0/_{00}$, of vanadium, the structural position of which is unknown in any of the three minerals; but vanadium can nevertheless be thought of in a general sense as entering into solid solution in these structures.

Construction of a Roozeboom diagram (fig. 54) for the partition of vanadium between biotite and hornblende* demonstrates that the

---

* Kretz reported the percentage of vanadium in the various phases. It would be rigorous to plot mol fractions in the Roozeboom diagram, but at such low concentrations the two quantities are very nearly proportional.

observational points lie, within the limits of experimental error, on a straight line; that is

$$\frac{m_V^{\text{Hbd}}}{m_V^{\text{Bt}}} \sim 1.2$$

and therefore

$$\frac{x_V^{\text{Hbd}}}{x_V^{\text{Bt}}} = K_V \,(T, P, n_j).$$

Nernst's Distribution Law is therefore properly applicable to this problem. That is not surprising since the temperature and pressure, although the latter may have no significant effect, may be supposed to be constant and the solution of vanadium in the two phases is certainly dilute enough to be approximately ideal. But it is necessary to bear in mind that the partition coefficient K_V may be dependent on the compositions of the phases, although that is not apparent in this case since K_V is found to be invariant while the compositions of the hornblende and biotite involved vary widely. In other words the value of the chemical potential of vanadium in biotite and in hornblende does not appear to be significantly dependent on the compositions of the solvent phases.

Figure 55 shows similarly the partition of vanadium between biotite and garnet and between hornblende and garnet respectively. The results obtained are very different from those for the previous pair in that the scatter of points appears to be almost random. Since the temperature and pressure of formation are identical for every specimen, it must be conceded that the composition of the garnet affects the chemical potential of the vanadium it carries in solid solution. An attempt may be made to discover the *perturbing* element by plotting $K_1 = \dfrac{\% \, V_2O_3 \text{ (garnet)}}{\% \, V_2O_3 \text{ (biotite)}}$ and $K_2 = \dfrac{\% \, V_2O_3 \text{ (garnet)}}{\% \, V_2O_3 \text{ (hornblende)}}$ against the mol fraction of Ca in the garnet phase, *i.e.*, $Ca/(Fe + Mg + Mn + Ca)$, and that is done in figure 56; the points so obtained are disposed on very similar curves of exponential aspect and it would appear that the Ca^{2+} content of garnet is in large measure responsible for the observed anomaly in vanadium distribution between garnet on the one hand and hornblende and biotite on the other. This seems all the more likely when it is recalled that the introduction of Ca is accompanied by considerable distortion of

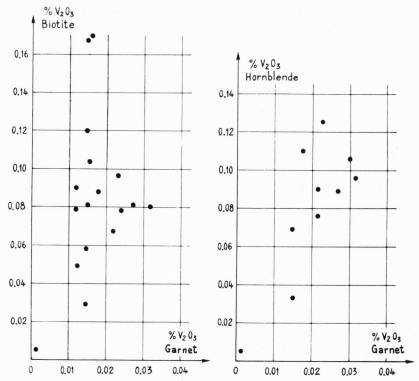

Fig. 55. Partition of vanadium between biotite and garnet and between hornblende and garnet.

the garnet structure, as evidenced by the anomalous optics of lime garnets, and that such distortion may be expected to facilitate the entry of vanadium ions into solid solution. Evidently the solution of vanadium in garnet cannot be regarded as approximating to ideality and Nernst's Distribution Law is not applicable. In biotite and in hornblende the change of composition is in large measure merely substitution of Fe for Mg and that is effected without any significant structural modification; therefore no marked effect on the chemical potential of vanadium in solid solution, nor on its partition coefficient is to be expected.

To conclude this section, a brief account will be given of the results obtained by Kretz for titanium. Partition between biotite and hornblende again obeys Nernst's Law with $\dfrac{x_{Ti}^{Bt}}{x_{Ti}^{Hbd}} \sim 2.0$ with a rather

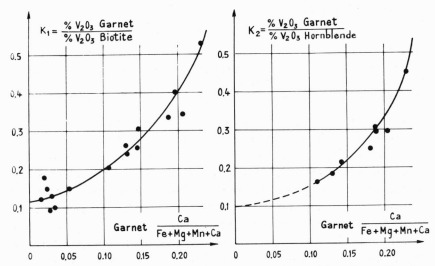

Fig. 56. Effect of calcium concentration in garnet on the partition of vanadium between garnet and biotite and between garnet and hornblende.

greater dispersion than in the case of vanadium. The increased dispersion is undoubtedly due to the common presence of exsolved
rutile, for which inadequate allowance was made in adjusting the
analyses. Partition of Ti between garnet and biotite (or hornblende)
obeys no obvious law; here again it is possible that the Ca content
of the garnet exerts a controlling influence, but the problem is
complicated by exsolution of Ti-bearing minerals, such as rutile and
ilmenite, in almost all the garnets studied.

*2.4. The use of oxygen isotope ratios in geological thermometry.**

Oxygen has two stable isotopes O^{16} and O^{18}, which are present
in the Earth in proportions of the order of $99.8:0.2$. Clearly the
proportion will not vary greatly from one oxy-compound to another,

* Paragraphs XI–*2.4* and XI–*2.5* have been specially written for this English edition
by the translator.

but there will be a small variation since the two nuclei differ in structure and consequently there will be a difference in the bonding properties of their valence electrons; it follows that the free enthalpy of a compound XO^{16} will differ slightly from that of XO^{18}. Exchange reactions of the type

$$XO^{16} + YO^{18} \rightleftharpoons XO^{18} + YO^{16}$$

can therefore be set up. In general ΔG for such reactions will be dependent on T and P. The nature of the resemblance between the isotopes however makes $\left(\dfrac{\partial \Delta G}{\partial P}\right)_T$ negligible and the pressure-dependence of ΔG will be ignored in the sequel. The temperature-dependence of ΔG is real and, although small, observable since the techniques of mass-spectrometry are so advanced that very small variations in the proportions of oxygen isotopes present in an oxy-compound are measurable to a high degree of accuracy. The form of the temperature dependence of ΔG can be established theoretically by statistical thermodynamic methods outside the scope of this work, but for solids and liquids the constants in the theoretical equations cannot be evaluated and recourse must be had to empirical equations that are consistent with the general theoretical equations. It can be shown that for oxygen isotopic equilibrium between a pair of minerals such as quartz (q) and hematite (h)

$$\ln K_{qh} = A_{qh} T^{-2} - B_{qh},$$

where $K_{qh} = \dfrac{(O^{18}/O^{16})_q}{(O^{18}/O^{16})_h}$, and A_{qh} and B_{qh} are constants independent of temperature.

For some of the most convenient pairs of oxy-minerals the parameters A and B have not yet been determined experimentally, and indeed, their experimental determination would often be a problem of almost insuperable difficulty, since the rate of attainment of oxygen isotopic equilibrium between solids must be exceedingly slow. Various ways of circumventing this difficulty in order to produce oxygen isotopic thermometers have been devised and we shall, by way of example, consider here the treatment by Clayton and Epstein (1961) of equilibria involving the phases quartz (q), calcite (c), hematite (h), and water (w). Six isotopic exchange equilibria are involved, their equilibrium constants being given by:

[46] $\ln K_{qc} = A_{qc} T^{-2} - B_{qc}$

[47] $\ln K_{qh} = A_{qh} T^{-2} - B_{qh}$

[48] $\ln K_{qw} = A_{qw} T^{-2} - B_{qw}$

[49] $\ln K_{ch} = A_{ch} T^{-2} - B_{ch}$

[50] $\ln K_{cw} = A_{cw} T^{-2} - B_{cw}$

[51] $\ln K_{hw} = A_{hw} T^{-2} - B_{hw}.$

Only the parameters in equation (50) have been determined experimentally: as

[52] $A_{cw} = 2730, \quad B_{cw} = 0.00256.$

Isotopic analysis of five quartz-calcite-hematite rocks, thought on textural evidence to be equilibrium assemblages, yielded the relationship

$$\ln K_{qh} = 1.388 \ln K_{ch},$$

whence

[53] $A_{qh} = 1.388 A_{ch}$ and $B_{qh} = 1.388 B_{ch}.$

Clayton and Epstein (1961) next considered equilibria between quartz and calcite in hydrothermal environments and found a linear relationship between $\ln K_{qc}$ and a parameter that they designated $d_c = \ln \left\{ \dfrac{(O^{18}/O^{16})_c}{(O^{18}/O^{16})^0} \right\}$, where $(O^{18}/O^{16})^0$ refers to some arbitrary substance in its standard state:

$$d_c = 3.04 \ln K_{qc} + 0.0033.$$

Now it follows from the definitions of K_{cw}, d_c, and d_w that

$$\ln K_{cw} = \ln \left\{ \frac{(O^{18}/O^{16})_c}{(O^{18}/O^{16})_w} \right\}$$

$$= \ln \left\{ \frac{(O^{18}/O^{16})_c}{(O^{18}/O^{16})^0} \right\} - \ln \left\{ \frac{(O^{18}/O^{16})_w}{(O^{18}/O^{16})^0} \right\}$$

$$= d_c - d_w$$

[54] $\therefore \quad \ln K_{cw} = 3.04 \ln K_{qc} + 0.0033 - d_w$

and it follows that

[55] $A_{cw} = 3.04 A_{qc}$ and $B_{cw} = 3.04 B_{qc} - 0.0033 + d_w.$

Of the six fractionation equations (46)–(51) only three are independent. Six constants therefore have to be determined, two of which are given by equations (52). Between the remaining four constants we have three relationships given by equations (53) and (54) in terms of the undetermined parameter d_w. Thus for the A parameters:

from (52) $A_{cw} = 2730,$

from (55) $A_{qc} = \dfrac{A_{cw}}{3.04} = 899,$

$A_{qw} = A_{qc} + A_{cw} = 3629,$

from (53) $A_{qh} = 1.388A_{ch} = 1.388(-A_{qc} + A_{qh}) = \dfrac{1.388}{0.388} A_{qc}$

$= 3216$

$\therefore$ $A_{ch} = \dfrac{A_{qh}}{1.388} = 2317,$

and $A_{hw} = -A_{qh} + A_{qw} = 413.$

And for the B parameters:

from (52) $B_{cw} = 0.00256,$

from (55) $B_{qc} = \dfrac{1}{3.04} \{B_{cw} + 0.0033 - d_w\},$

$= 0.33(0.0059 - d_w),$

$\therefore$ $B_{qw} = B_{qc} + B_{cw} = 0.00256 + 0.33(0.0059 - d_w);$

from (53) $B_{qh} = 1.388B_{ch} = 1.388(-B_{qc} + B_{qh}) = \dfrac{1.388}{0.388} B_{qc}$

$= 1.17(0.0059 - d_w),$

$\therefore$ $B_{ch} = \dfrac{B_{qh}}{1.388} = 0.84(0.0059 - d_w),$

and $B_{hw} = -B_{qh} + B_{qw}$

$= 0.00256 - 0.84(0.0059 - d_w).$

The magnitude of d_w remains undetermined, but there are some statistical thermodynamic grounds for supposing that $B_{\alpha\beta} = 0$, when α and β are solid phases; B_{qc}, B_{qh}, and B_{ch} can be made equal to zero if d_w is put equal to 0.0059 and this will be done. It follows that the six fractionation equilibrium constants are given by:

[46′] $\ln K_{qc} = 899\ T^{-2}$

[47′] $\ln K_{qh} = 3216\ T^{-2}$

[48'] $\qquad \ln K_{qw} = 3629\ T^{-2} - 0.00256$

[49'] $\qquad \ln K_{ch} = 2317\ T^{-2}$

[50'] $\qquad \ln K_{cw} = 2730\ T^{-2} - 0.00256$

[51'] $\qquad \ln K_{hw} = 413\ \ T^{-2} - 0.00256.$

It is not claimed by Clayton and Epstein that the parameters in these equations are highly accurate. But the equations (46'), (47'), and (49') can be used to give geologically useful estimates of the temperatures at which rocks containing any two of the three phases— quartz, calcite, hematite—crystallized, or at least reached a temperature too low for the effective exchange of oxygen isotopes. By way of example these authors quote five examples for which both K_{qh} and K_{ch} could be evaluated:

	t°C from K_{qh}	t°C from K_{ch}
Balmat, New York	95	100
Port Radium, Canada	120	115
Iron Mountain, Montana	280	300
Republic, Michigan	330	350
Iron Springs, Utah	690	590.

These results show that the fractionation of oxygen isotopes can be used now as an approximate method of geological temperature determination, and this is a method that can be expected to increase in precision with the improvement of experimental data.

2.5. Crossing of tie-lines between solid solutions in compositional phase diagrams.

Equilibrium in a series of metamorphic rocks composed of several phases, only two of which, α and β, are of variable composition and those only variable with respect to two components, labeled 1 and 2, has been considered by Phinney (1963) and by Greenwood, Doe, and Phinney (1964). The approach of these authors is founded in the generalized discussion given by Prigogine and Defay (1954, pp. 278-9) and is of some interest outside the bounds of the specific problem, itself important, that they have considered.

At equilibrium between two phases α and β, that are both variable with respect to components 1 and 2,

[56] $\qquad \mu_1^\alpha = \mu_1^\beta \quad \text{and} \quad \mu_2^\alpha = \mu_2^\beta.$

Now μ_1^α is a perfect differential and therefore

$$d\mu_1^\alpha = \left(\frac{\partial \mu_1^\alpha}{\partial T}\right)_{Px^\alpha} dT + \left(\frac{\partial \mu_1^\alpha}{\partial P}\right)_{Tx^\alpha} dP + \left(\frac{\partial \mu_1^\alpha}{\partial x^\alpha}\right)_{PT} dx^\alpha,$$

where x^α is the mol fraction of component 2 in phase α. It follows from equations (37) and (39) of Chapter IX that

$$d\mu_1^\alpha = -\bar{S}_1^\alpha dT + \bar{V}_1^\alpha dP + \left(\frac{\partial \mu_1^\alpha}{\partial x^\alpha}\right)_{PT} dx^\alpha.$$

But, from equation (56), at equilibrium $d\mu_1^\alpha = d\mu_1^\beta$ and therefore

$$-(\bar{S}_1^\alpha - \bar{S}_1^\beta)\, dT + (\bar{V}_1^\alpha - \bar{V}_1^\beta)\, dP + \left(\frac{\partial \mu_1^\alpha}{\partial x^\alpha}\right)_{PT} dx^\alpha - \left(\frac{\partial \mu_1^\beta}{\partial x^\beta}\right)_{PT} dx^\beta = 0$$

[57] $\therefore$ $-\Delta\bar{S}_1 dT + \Delta\bar{V}_1 dP + \left(\dfrac{\partial \mu_1^\alpha}{\partial x^\alpha}\right)_{PT} dx^\alpha - \left(\dfrac{\partial \mu_1^\beta}{\partial x^\beta}\right)_{PT} dx^\beta = 0,$

where $\Delta\bar{S}_1 = \bar{S}_1^\alpha - \bar{S}_1^\beta$ and $\Delta\bar{V}_1 = \bar{V}_1^\alpha - \bar{V}_1^\beta = 0$. And similarly

[58] $-\Delta\bar{S}_2 dT + \Delta\bar{V}_2 dP + \left(\dfrac{\partial \mu_2^\alpha}{\partial x^\alpha}\right)_{PT} dx^\alpha - \left(\dfrac{\partial \mu_2^\beta}{\partial x^\beta}\right)_{PT} dx^\beta = 0.$

Elimination of dx^β yields

$$\left[-\Delta\bar{S}_1 dT + \Delta\bar{V}_1 dP + \left(\frac{\partial \mu_1^\alpha}{\partial x^\alpha}\right)_{PT} dx^\alpha\right]\left(\frac{\partial \mu_2^\beta}{\partial x^\beta}\right)_{PT}$$

$$= \left[-\Delta\bar{S}_2 dT + \Delta\bar{V}_2 dP + \left(\frac{\partial \mu_2^\alpha}{\partial x^\alpha}\right)_{PT} dx^\alpha\right]\left(\frac{\partial \mu_1^\beta}{\partial x^\beta}\right)_{PT}.$$

Now by the Gibbs-Duhem relation (p. 172)

$$(1 - x^\beta)\, d\mu_1^\beta + x^\beta\, d\mu_2^\beta = 0$$

$$(1 - x^\beta)\left(\frac{\partial \mu_1^\beta}{\partial x^\beta}\right)_{PT} + x^\beta\left(\frac{\partial \mu_2^\beta}{\partial x^\beta}\right)_{PT} = 0\,.$$

Therefore

$$\left[-\Delta\bar{S}_1 dT + \Delta\bar{V}_1 dP + \left(\frac{\partial \mu_1^\alpha}{\partial x^\alpha}\right)_{PT} dx^\alpha\right](1 - x^\beta)$$

$$+ \left[-\Delta\bar{S}_2 dT + \Delta\bar{V}_2 dP - \frac{(1 - x^\alpha)}{x^\alpha}\left(\frac{\partial \mu_1^\alpha}{\partial x^\alpha}\right)_{PT} dx^\alpha\right] x^\beta = 0,$$

whence

[59] $-[(1 - x^\beta)\,\Delta\bar{S}_1 + x^\beta\,\Delta\bar{S}_2]\, dT + [(1 - x^\beta)\,\Delta\bar{V}_1 + x^\beta\,\Delta\bar{V}_2]\, dP$

$$+ \left[(1 - x^\beta) - \frac{(1 - x^\alpha)}{x^\alpha} x^\beta\right]\left(\frac{\partial \mu_1^\alpha}{\partial x^\alpha}\right)_{PT} dx^\alpha = 0.$$

If we are concerned only with phase assemblages that have developed at quite small distances from one another, constancy of pressure may reasonably be assumed and equation (59) will become, on rearrangement,

$$\left(\frac{\partial x^\alpha}{\partial T}\right)_P = \frac{x^\alpha[(1 - x^\beta)\,\Delta\bar{S}_1 + x^\beta\,\Delta\bar{S}_2]}{[(1 - x^\beta)\,x^\alpha - (1 - x^\alpha)\,x^\beta](\partial\mu_1^\alpha/\partial x^\alpha)_{PT}}.$$

$$\therefore \quad \left(\frac{\partial x^\alpha}{\partial T}\right)_P = \frac{x^\alpha[(1 - x^\beta)\,\Delta\bar{S}_1 + x^\beta\,\Delta\bar{S}_2]}{(x^\alpha - x^\beta)\,(\partial\mu_1^\alpha/\partial x^\alpha)_{PT}}$$

[60] $$\qquad \therefore \quad \left(\frac{\partial x^\alpha}{\partial T}\right)_P = \frac{x^\alpha[(1 - x^\beta)\,\Delta\bar{S}_1 + x^\beta\,\Delta\bar{S}_2]}{\Delta x\,(\partial\mu_1^\alpha/\partial x^\alpha)_{PT}}$$

where $\Delta x = x^\alpha - x^\beta$. And similarly the equation

[61] $$\left(\frac{\partial x^\beta}{\partial T}\right)_P = \frac{x^\beta[(1 - x^\alpha)\,\Delta\bar{S}_1 + x^\alpha\,\Delta\bar{S}_2]}{\Delta x\,(\partial\mu_1^\beta/\partial x^\beta)_{PT}}$$

can be derived from equation (58).

Now if $\left(\dfrac{\partial x^\alpha}{\partial T}\right)_P$ and $\left(\dfrac{\partial x^\beta}{\partial T}\right)_P$ have the same sign, the tie-line joining the compositions of the coexisting phases α and β at some temperature T_1 cannot intersect the corresponding tie-line for some other temperature T_2. On the other hand if the two derivatives differ in sign, the tie-lines for T_1 and T_2 *must* cross. These contrasting situations are illustrated in figures 57 and 58; they can be traced back to the

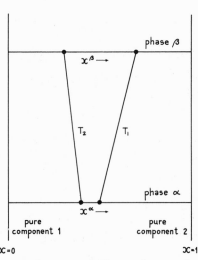

Fig. 57. Tie-lines joining two phases α and β in non-intersecting relationship for two temperatures T_2 and T_1; $T_2 > T_1$, $\left(\dfrac{\partial x^\alpha}{\partial T}\right)_P < 0$, $\left(\dfrac{\partial x^\beta}{\partial T}\right)_P < 0$.

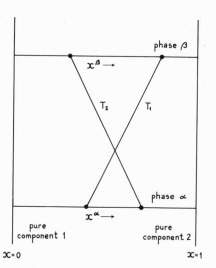

Fig. 58. Tie-lines joining two phases α and β in crossed relationship for two temper-atures T_2 and T_1; $T_2 > T_1$, $\left(\dfrac{\partial x^\alpha}{\partial T}\right)_P > 0$, $\left(\dfrac{\partial x^\beta}{\partial T}\right)_P < 0$.

mutual relationship of $\Delta \bar{S}_1$ and $\Delta \bar{S}_2$ by the argument that follows.

Let us assume crossed tie-lines with $\left(\dfrac{\partial x^\alpha}{\partial T}\right)_P > 0$ and $\left(\dfrac{\partial x^\beta}{\partial T}\right)_P < 0$.

The terms x^α and x^β must always be positive, while $\left(\dfrac{\partial \mu_1^\alpha}{\partial x^\alpha}\right)_{PT}$ and $\left(\dfrac{\partial \mu_1^\beta}{\partial x^\beta}\right)_{PT}$ must always be negative. The term Δ_x, common to both equations (60) and (61), may be either positive or negative; it will be assumed to be positive. It follows that

$$(1 - x^\beta)\,\Delta \bar{S}_1 + x^\beta\,\Delta \bar{S}_2 > 0 \qquad \text{and} \qquad (1 - x^\alpha)\,\Delta \bar{S}_1 + x^\alpha\,\Delta \bar{S}_2 < 0$$

i.e., $\quad \Delta \bar{S}_1 - x^\beta(\Delta \bar{S}_1 - \Delta \bar{S}_2) > 0 \qquad \text{and} \qquad \Delta \bar{S}_1 - x^\alpha(\Delta \bar{S}_1 - \Delta \bar{S}_2) < 0$

i.e., $\quad x^\beta < \dfrac{\Delta \bar{S}_1}{\Delta \bar{S}_1 - \Delta \bar{S}_2} \qquad \text{and} \qquad x^\alpha > \dfrac{\Delta \bar{S}_1}{\Delta \bar{S}_1 - \Delta \bar{S}_2}$

or $\quad x^\beta > \dfrac{\Delta \bar{S}_1}{\Delta \bar{S}_1 - \Delta \bar{S}_2} \qquad \text{and} \qquad x^\alpha < \dfrac{\Delta \bar{S}_1}{\Delta \bar{S}_1 - \Delta \bar{S}_2}.$

But $0 \leqslant x^\beta \leqslant 1$ and $0 \leqslant x^\alpha \leqslant 1$, therefore

$$0 \leqslant \dfrac{\Delta \bar{S}_1}{\Delta \bar{S}_1 - \Delta \bar{S}_2} \leqslant 1$$

and consequently $\Delta \bar{S}_1$ and $\Delta \bar{S}_2$ must be of opposite sign.

This result can alternatively be obtained by writing

$$\Delta\bar{S}_1 = \bar{S}_1^\alpha - \bar{S}_1^\beta = -\left(\frac{\partial\mu_1^\alpha}{\partial T}\right) + \left(\frac{\partial\mu_1^\beta}{\partial T}\right)$$

$$= -\left(\frac{\partial\mu_1^\alpha}{\partial x^\alpha}\right)\left(\frac{\partial x^\alpha}{\partial T}\right) + \left(\frac{\partial\mu_1^\beta}{\partial x^\beta}\right)\left(\frac{\partial x^\beta}{\partial T}\right).$$

Now we have postulated crossed tie-lines with $\left(\dfrac{\partial x^\alpha}{\partial T}\right)_P > 0$ and $\left(\dfrac{\partial x^\beta}{\partial T}\right)_P < 0$. The derivatives $\left(\dfrac{\partial\mu_1^\alpha}{\partial x^\alpha}\right)$ and $\left(\dfrac{\partial\mu_1^\beta}{\partial x^\beta}\right)$ are both bound to be < 0. Therefore $\Delta\bar{S}_1 > 0$. And correspondingly

$$\Delta\bar{S}_2 = \bar{S}_2^\alpha - \bar{S}_2^\beta = -\left(\frac{\partial\mu_2^\alpha}{\partial x^\alpha}\right)\left(\frac{\partial x^\alpha}{\partial T}\right) + \left(\frac{\partial\mu_2^\beta}{\partial x^\beta}\right)\left(\frac{\partial x^\beta}{\partial T}\right),$$

but $\left(\dfrac{\partial\mu_2^\alpha}{\partial x^\alpha}\right)$ and $\left(\dfrac{\partial\mu_2^\beta}{\partial x^\beta}\right)$ are both bound to be > 0. Therefore $\Delta\bar{S}_2 < 0$.

Thus pairs of minerals that have crystallized at different temperatures along the same continuous thermal gradient at constant pressure *must* show crossing of tie-lines if no other phases of variable composition with respect to the same pair of components coexist. The argument has been extended by Greenwood *et al.* (1964) to systems in which more than two phases of variable composition coexist: in such circumstances they have shown that tie-lines between pairs of coexisting minerals of variable composition cross only if terms such as $\Delta\bar{S}^{\alpha\beta}$, $\Delta\bar{S}^{\beta\gamma}$, $\Delta\bar{S}^{\gamma\alpha}$ obey certain restrictions of sign which may not be so in all systems.

XII

The Phase Rule
and Phase Diagrams

1.　Introduction

Equilibrium conditions can, as has been seen in earlier chapters, be expressed in a variety of ways, beginning with their most abstract formulation in terms of the entropy of the system (pp. 58, 60), and reaching their most concrete mode of expression in the Law of Mass Action (p. 210), various more or less explicit statements of equilibrium being noticed on the way (pp. 66, 102, 105); all these expressions amount in essence to the Second Law in the form enunciated by Clausius (p. 58).

There exists yet another mode of implicit expression of equilibrium conditions, that is the so-called *Phase Rule* of J. Willard Gibbs,* which is a theorem derived without added restrictions from the Second Law, which relates the number of parameters of state capable of independent variation to the number of components occurring in equilibrium in a given number of phases. Clearly this expression is especially important for the graphical representation of completely generalized equilibrium conditions. The Phase Rule is the basis on which phase diagrams are constructed, but in view of its abstract character the mode of its application may not always be obvious.

---

* The Phase Rule is unlike the statements customarily described as *rules* in that it is just as infallible as the Second Law.

2.   The Phase Rule

2.1. *Theory.*

Let $\mathfrak{N}$ be the total number of components identifiable in the various phases of the system and $M_1, M_2, \ldots M_i \ldots M_1', M_2' \ldots M_j'$ their molar masses. The $\mathfrak{N}$ components can enter into $\mathfrak{R}$ independent reactions such as

$$\left\{ \begin{array}{l} \sum_i {}_1n_i M_i \rightleftharpoons \sum_j {}_1n_j' M_i' \\[2mm] \sum_i {}_2n_i M_i \rightleftharpoons \sum_j {}_2n_j' M_j' \\[2mm] \sum_i {}_{\mathfrak{R}}n_i M_i \rightleftharpoons \sum_j {}_{\mathfrak{R}}n_j' M_j'. \end{array} \right.$$

The number $\mathfrak{R}$ of such equations is finite if only independent reactions are counted.* In the course of such reactions φ phases are formed, the $\mathfrak{N}$ components being partitioned between the phases.

If it is desired to alter *a priori* these $\mathfrak{R}$ equilibria then there is a choice of $\mathfrak{N} + 2$ parameters of state that may be adjusted. The concentrations of $\mathfrak{N}$ components and in addition the two classical parameters† T and P can be adjusted. These parameters of state must satisfy certain conditions. The first of which evidently must be the conditions controlling the concentrations of the $\mathfrak{N}$ components in the φ phases, $\alpha, \beta, \ldots$ In terms of mol fractions,

[1] $$\underbrace{\sum_i x_i^\alpha = 1; \qquad \sum_i x_i^\beta = 1 \ldots \sum_i x_i^\varphi = 1.}_{\varphi \text{ conditions}}$$

The second set of conditions are those controlling equilibrium in the form of $\mathfrak{R}$ equations relating to chemical potential:

---

* The number of independent reactions can be verified as $\mathfrak{R}$ if none of these $\mathfrak{R}$ reactions can be derived from the remaining $(\mathfrak{R} - 1)$ equations. Thus the three reactions

$$CaO(s) + CO_2(g) \rightarrow CaCO_3(s),$$
$$MgCO_3(s) + CaO(s) \rightarrow CaCO_3(s) + MgO(s),$$
$$MgO(s) + CO_2(g) \rightarrow MgCO_3(s)$$

are not independent since the third can be derived by subtraction of the other two.
† Other parameters of state may also be considered, *e.g.*, the surface area s_φ of the φ phases, the position h of the system in the gravitational field, and so on.

$$[2] \qquad \Re \text{ conditions} \left\{ \begin{array}{l} \sum_i {}_1n_i\,{}_1\mu_i = \sum_j {}_1n'_j\,{}_1\mu'_j \\[6pt] \sum_i {}_2n_i\,{}_2\mu_i = \sum_j {}_2n'_j\,{}_2\mu'_j \\ \cdots\cdots\cdots\cdots\cdots\cdots \\ \cdots\cdots\cdots\cdots\cdots\cdots \\ \sum_i {}_{\Re}n_{i\Re}\mu_i = \sum_j {}_{\Re}n'_{j\Re}\mu'_j. \end{array} \right.$$

Thus $\Re + 2$ *parameters of state* ($\Re$ *concentrations*, P, *and* T) *are restricted by* $\Re + \varphi$ *conditions, that is*

$$[3] \qquad \qquad \overline{\mathcal{V} = \Re + 2 - (\Re + \varphi)}$$

where $\mathcal{V}$ *is the number of parameters that can be varied at equilibrium with retention of equilibrium** *and of the stoichiometry†* *of the phases;* $\mathcal{V}$ *is known as the number of degrees of freedom, or the variance of the system.*

Equation (3) may be written alternatively as $\varphi = \Re + 2 - (\Re + \mathcal{V})$, when it is immediately apparent that *a system of* $\Re$ *components subjected to* $\mathcal{V}$ *external restraints can comprise at least* φ *phases at equilibrium.* If on the other hand all the conditions of equilibrium (2) are not satisfied, $\Re$ will be decreased and a number of phases in excess of that required by the equilibrium conditions will be present.

2.2. Examples.

A very simple system will be dealt with first and then the precautions that must be taken when the Phase Rule is applied to more elaborate systems will be examined.

2.2.1. Phases of fixed composition.—Consider for example the polymorphic transformations in silica (p. 115)

$$\left. \begin{array}{l} \alpha\text{-quartz} \rightleftharpoons \beta\text{-quartz} \\ \alpha\text{-quartz} \rightleftharpoons \quad \text{tridymite} \\ \alpha\text{-quartz} \rightleftharpoons \quad \text{cristobalite} \\ \alpha\text{-quartz} \rightleftharpoons \quad \text{coesite} \\ \alpha\text{-quartz} \rightleftharpoons \quad \text{liquid} \end{array} \right\} \; 5 \text{ independent reactions.}$$

A single component SiO_2 is distributed among 6 phases, therefore $\Re = 6$ components and $\Re = 5$ equilibrium conditions, whence

$$\mathcal{V} = 3 - \varphi.$$

* See second note on p. 239.
† See first note on p. 239.

For $\varphi = 1$, a single phase, the variance of the system is 2: the phase is therefore stable over a P, T area and each of the polymorphs occupies a field in the P, T plane.

If two phases coexist in equilibrium, the variance is 1, that is if P (or T) is given, then T (or P) is necessarily fixed. In a Clapeyron plot, $T = f(P)$, this equilibrium condition is represented by a curve separating the fields of two polymorphs, solid and liquid, solid and gas, or liquid and gas.

If three phases coexist in equilibrium the variance is zero; three phases can coexist in equilibrium only if pressure and temperature have each simultaneously a certain value corresponding to what is known as the triple point; at the triple point gas + liquid + solid, gas + 2 polymorphs, liquid + 2 polymorphs, or 3 polymorphs can coexist.

2.2.2. Multicomponent systems.—The formation of wollastonite by the reaction

$$\text{quartz} + \text{calcite} \rightleftharpoons \text{wollastonite} + CO_2$$

was discussed on p. 141. Here $\mathfrak{N} = 4$ and, since there is a single equilibrium condition, $\mathfrak{R} = 1$, it follows from equation (3) that

$$\mathfrak{v} = 5 - \varphi.$$

At equilibrium with four coexisting phases $\mathfrak{v} = 1$. If the parameters P and T are fixed, the partial pressure of CO_2 is determined and there exists an equation of the form $p_{CO_2} = f(P, T)$.

The space P, T, p_{CO_2} is therefore divided by an *equilibrium surface*, on one side of which the three phase assemblages quartz—calcite—wollastonite or quartz—calcite—CO_2 can occur in equilibrium and on the other side the three phase assemblages wollastonite—CO_2—quartz or wollastonite—CO_2—calcite.

2.3. Parameters of state other than T *and* P.

In establishing the Phase Rule in the form of equation (3) it was supposed *a priori* that the number, $\mathfrak{N} + 2$, of variables represented $\mathfrak{N}$ components, P, and T. Other variables, such as magnetic field, electrical field, gravitational field, surface tension, lithostatic pressure, and so on, could, however, be considered. In such cases it is simplest to write the Phase Rule in the general form

[4] $\mathcal{U}$ = (variables *a priori*) − (restrictions imposed on the variables)

and to particularize for each case that arises.

2.3.1. Lithostatic pressure.—When simultaneously a pressure P_F acts on the fluids and a pressure P_S on the solids (p. 92) of a system, the number of *a priori* variables must* be $\mathfrak{N}$ components, P_F, P_S, and T, *i.e.*, $\mathfrak{N}$ + 3. The restrictions imposed on these variables are the same as in equation (3), that is $(\mathfrak{R} + \varphi)$ since equilibrium is still controlled by $\mathfrak{R}$ chemical potential equations and stoichiometric equations. The Phase Rule in these circumstances becomes:

[5] $\mathcal{U} = \mathfrak{N} + 3 - (\mathfrak{R} + \varphi).$

If however the lithostatic pressure determines the fluid pressure (p. 93) an equation of the type $P_F = \lambda P_S$ must apply and the number of restrictive conditions increases to $(\mathfrak{R} + \varphi + 1)$; the Phase Rule now becomes

$$\mathcal{U} = \mathfrak{N} + 2 - (\mathfrak{R} + \varphi),$$

identical with equation (3).

2.3.2. Gravitational field.—If the position h of the system in the gravitational field is introduced as an additional variable, the number of *a priori* variables becomes $\mathfrak{N}$ + 3, but the number of restrictions remains $\mathfrak{R} + \varphi$. On p. 187 it was seen that the $\mathfrak{R}$ equations in chemical potential persist when a general field is considered. Therefore

[6] $\mathcal{U} = \mathfrak{N} + 3 - (\mathfrak{R} + \varphi).$

3.   The Mineralogical Phase Rule

Equation (3) can be rearranged as

[3′] $\varphi = \mathfrak{N} + 2 - (\mathfrak{R} + \mathcal{U}),$

to give, as V. Goldschmidt (1911) first observed, information about the number of phases possible in any paragenesis.

---

* If only isotropic pressures are considered.

3.1. Goldschmidt's Rule.

According to Goldschmidt (1911) the variance of a natural system must be at least two, $v \leqslant 2$, which amounts to saying that during the production of any paragenesis the temperature T and the pressure P can vary independently. Therefore the stability field of a paragenesis is effectively at least an area of the P, T plane; it would be highly improbable that it could have developed at fixed pressure and temperature or along a $T = f(P)$ curve. Therefore in these circumstances equation (3′) yields

[7]
$$\overline{\varphi < \mathfrak{N} - \mathfrak{R},}$$

that is, *the number of mineral phases present in a rock at equilibrium cannot exceed the number of independent components,** $\mathfrak{C}$, *where* $\mathfrak{C} = \mathfrak{N} - \mathfrak{R}$.

The concept of the number $\mathfrak{C}$ of independent components depends not only on the concept of the component, as the equation $\mathfrak{C} = \mathfrak{N} - \mathfrak{R}$ implies, but also on the concept of equilibrium, since $\mathfrak{R}$ is the number of equilibrium equations that have to be satisfied. Thus for the paragenesis

$$CaSO_4 \cdot 2\ H_2O \rightleftharpoons 2\ H_2O + CaSO_4$$
$$\text{gypsum} \qquad \text{water } (l) \qquad \text{anhydrite}$$

in a closed system, $\mathfrak{N} = 3$ and $\mathfrak{R} = 1$. Therefore from equation (7)

[7]
$$\mathfrak{C} \leqslant 2.$$

Possible equilibrium parageneses are then: gypsum, gypsum + water, gypsum + anhydrite, water + anhydrite.

If the supplementary reaction

$$CaSO_4 + \tfrac{1}{2}\ H_2O \rightleftharpoons CaSO_4 \cdot \tfrac{1}{2}\ H_2O$$
$$\text{anhydrite} \qquad \text{water } (l) \qquad \text{hemihydrate}$$

is also taken into account, again in a closed system, $\mathfrak{N} = 4$, $\mathfrak{R} = 2$, and equation (7) again yields $\varphi \leqslant 2$. Possible parageneses are: gypsum, gypsum + water, hemihydrate, hemihydrate + water,

---

* As was observed on p. 241, a system at equilibrium contains the minimum number of phases; disequilibrium assemblages contain a greater number of mineral phases.

anhydrite + water,   gypsum + hemihydrate,   gypsum + anhydrite, hemihydrate + anhydrite.

When the number of phases predicted by Goldschmidt's Rule is exceeded, it must be concluded:

(a) that equilibrium was not attained and there must have been either metastable equilibrium or complete disequilibrium, the latter amounting to a mechanical aggregation of minerals as in a detrital sediment, or

(b) that several stable equilibria are juxtaposed but are mutually unstable; this is the *mosaic equilibrium* of Korzhinskii (1957).

Goldschmidt's Rule is not affected by considering other variables such as lithostatic pressure. If Goldschmidt's statement $\upsilon \geqslant 2$ is replaced by $\upsilon \geqslant 3$, then simultaneously $\mathfrak{N} + 2$ becomes $\mathfrak{N} + 3$ and equation (7) is again obtained. In the example discussed above the same number of mineral phases will occur in the paragenesis, their nature being changed, however, by the effect of lithostatic pressure (p. 242).

3.2. Korzhinskii's Rule.

Korzhinskii (1957) found it convenient to distinguish, in an *open system*, two types of component, a distinction that has already been made in discussing the open system calcite + wollastonite + $CO_2(g)$ + silica (p. 206):

(a) *inert components* that at given T and P are characterized by their extensive parameters, such as free enthalpy. They undergo no change, except their appearance or disappearance when the system gains or loses matter, and

(b) *mobile components*, that at given T and P, vary in a manner that can be described by the variation of their chemical potential.* The recognition of some components as inert and the remainder as mobile, a distinction that has to be made *a priori*, must result in some modification of Goldschmidt's Rule stated in equation (7). This can only be done satisfactorily by re-examining the foundations of the Gibbs Phase Rule (paragraph *2.1*).

---

* Or what amounts to the same statement, by variation of their concentration.

On preceding pages, discussion has been in terms of $\mathfrak{N}$ components and $\mathfrak{C} = \mathfrak{N} - \mathfrak{R}$ independent components, $\mathfrak{R}$ being the number of equilibrium conditions for the system. Korzhinskii however distinguishes $\mathfrak{N} + 2$ *a priori* variables, that is $\mathfrak{N}$ components, P, and T. Therefore by analogy the number of independent variables is *a priori:*

$$\mathfrak{N} + 2 - \mathfrak{R} = \mathfrak{C} + 2.$$

Of these variables, a number f_{int} are intensive factors and the remainder f_{ext} are extensive parameters:

[8] $$f_{int} + f_{ext} = \mathfrak{N} + 2 - \mathfrak{R} = \mathfrak{C} + 2.$$

Korzhinskii has assumed that the intensive parameters (T, P, μ_i) can vary independently in an open mineralogical system; therefore

$$\upsilon \geqslant f_{int}$$

in contrast to Goldschmidt's Rule $\upsilon \geqslant 2$, with T and P as the essential independent variables. Now Gibbs' Phase Rule (equation (3)) taken in conjunction with equation (8) yields

[9] $$\varphi \leqslant f_{ext}.$$

But only the inert components are characterized by extensive factors and consequently, if $\mathfrak{C}_i$ is defined as the number of inert components

[10] $$\varphi \leqslant \mathfrak{C}_i.$$

Equation (10) is *Korzhinskii's Rule:* the number of minerals in a paragenesis of an open system in equilibrium must be less than or equal to the number of inert components.

The calcium sulphate—water system discussed in *3.1* has three inert components, gypsum, anhydrite, and hemihydrate, and of these only two are independent; therefore

$$\mathfrak{C}_i = 2 \quad \text{and} \quad \varphi \leqslant 2$$

the stable mineral assemblages being anhydrite + gypsum, gypsum + hemihydrate, or hemihydrate + anhydrite; water does not count as a mineral phase.

A further example is provided by the system SiO_2, calcite, wollastonite, CO_2 under open or closed conditions. Goldschmidt's Rule, equation (7), yields $\mathfrak{N} = 4$, $\mathfrak{R} = 1$, whence $\varphi \leqslant 3$; the parageneses would then be calcite + quartz + wollastonite, calcite + CO_2 + wollastonite, quartz + calcite + CO_2, or quartz + CO_2 + wollastonite according to the prevailing conditions. Korzhinskii's Rule, equation (10), however indicates that if CO_2 and SiO_2 are mobile components, calcite and wollastonite inert components, then $c_i = 2$ and $\varphi \leqslant 2$; this is equivalent to saying in Goldschmidt's terms that SiO_2 and CO_2 do not count as phases (see also p. 206).

4.   Phase diagrams

The Phase Rule becomes less mysterious when one becomes used to using phase diagrams, to which the Rule is related merely as an arithmetic control. Three types of diagram are in common use: intensive, extensive, and composite diagrams.

4.1. Intensive diagrams.

The commonest are plane diagrams with two of the variables T, P, μ_i as coordinates.

4.1.1.—T, P diagrams, also called *Clapeyron diagrams*, follow immediately from the Gibbs Phase Rule.* Equation (3),

$$\mathfrak{V} = \mathfrak{N} - \mathfrak{R} + 2 - \varphi$$

with $c = \mathfrak{N} - \mathfrak{R}$, the number of independent components, leads to the variance table below:

$\mathfrak{V}$	φ	Geometrical representation of the coexistence of φ phases
0	$c + 2$	a point with fixed P, T.
1	$c + 1$	a line P = f(T)
2	c	a field (area)

Figure 59 illustrates the representation on the T, P phase of the conditions of coexistence of φ phases. Here all the chemical potentials μ_i,

* See for instance Niggli (1937).

to the number $\mathfrak{N}$, are constant, being completely fixed for components whose concentration is constant in the several phases.

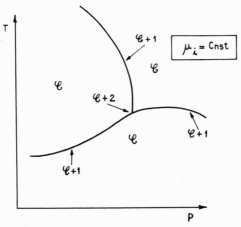

Fig. 59. Clapeyron, or P, T diagram for a generalized system of not more than $\mathfrak{C} + 2$ phases, the chemical potentials of the $\mathfrak{N}$ components being maintained constant.

It is convenient to display in juxtaposition the diagram (fig. 60) for the three components MgO, CO_2, H_2O, for which

$$\mathfrak{v} = 5 - \varphi.$$

In such a P, T diagram the field of each phase corresponds to an area and the diagram is valid only if the chemical potentials μ_i remain

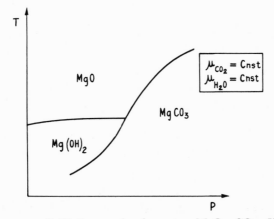

Fig. 60. Clapeyron, or P, T diagram for the system MgO—CO_2—H_2O, the chem-
·ical potentials of CO_2 and H_2O being fixed.

constant; it is therefore necessary to put $\mu_{CO_2} = k$, $\mu_{H_2O} = k'$, μ_{MgO} being of necessity always fixed. It is evident from figure 60 that areas on the diagram are occupied separately by the three phases MgO, $MgCO_3$, $Mg(OH)_2$, that at the triple point all three phases coexist in stable equilibrium, and that along the curves the following equilibria occur:

(1) $MgO + CO_2 \rightleftharpoons MgCO_3$; ΔH_1, ΔV_1

(2) $Mg(OH)_2 + CO_2 \rightleftharpoons MgCO_3 + H_2O$; ΔH_2, ΔV_2

(3) $MgO + H_2O \rightleftharpoons Mg(OH)_2$; ΔH_3, ΔV_3 .

It is easy to show that tangents to the equilibrium curves are given by the Clapeyron equation as

$$\frac{dP}{dT} = \frac{(\Delta H)}{T(\Delta V)}$$

where (ΔH) and (ΔV) are respectively the change in H and V in each of the three reactions.

4.1.2.—Another type of diagram has been introduced into common usage by Korzhinskii (1957). The variables P and T, as well as all the chemical potentials μ_i, except for two, denoted μ_1 and μ_2, are fixed and μ_1 is plotted against μ_2 as on figure 61, where polyphasic

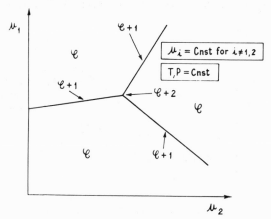

Fig. 61. Korzhinskii, or μ_1—μ_2, diagram for a generalized system of not more than $\mathcal{C} + 2$ phases, pressure, temperature, and the chemical potentials of all components other than 1 and 2 being maintained constant.

fields of ℮ phases, the triple point, and equilibrium curves can be recognized as on figure 59. The diagram of figure 60 for CO_2—H_2O—MgO can then be converted to that of figure 62 at

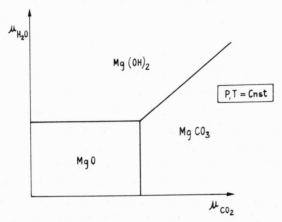

Fig. 62. Korzhinskii diagram for the system MgO—CO_2—H_2O at constant pressure and temperature.

constant P, T, and with μ_{H_2O} and μ_{CO_2} as coordinates; its appearance is simple because the equilibrium curves are straight lines, since

$$dG = \mu_{H_2O}\ dn_{H_2O} + \mu_{CO_2}\ dn_{CO_2}$$

at constant P and T, so that a linear equation

$$\mu_{H_2O} = -\mu_{CO_2}\ \frac{dn_{CO_2}}{dn_{H_2O}} = a\ \mu_{CO_2}$$

corresponds to equilibrium ($dG = 0$). Now the slopes of the equilibrium lines for the three reactions involved (labeled as on p. 251) are given by

(1) $\qquad dn_{H_2O} = \quad 0; \qquad dn_{CO_2} = -1: \qquad a = \infty$

(2) $\qquad dn_{H_2O} = \quad 1; \qquad dn_{CO_2} = -1: \qquad a = 1$

(3) $\qquad dn_{H_2O} = -1; \qquad dn_{CO_2} = \quad 0: \qquad a = 0.$

An example of the use of Korzhinskii diagrams is provided by the work of Fonteilles (1962), on the skarns of Kamioka, Japan, where several skarn series can be recognized, one of which, the "A-skarn series" develops at contacts between marble and gneisses or acid

migmatites and exhibits three types of paragenetic sequence between
its internal and external limits:

(A₁)   calcite + diopside | wollastonite + diopside | plagioclase
                              + diopside | quartz + plagioclase + diopside | .

(A₂)   calcite + diopside | wollastonite + diopside | idocrase
                              + diopside | plagioclase + diopside | quartz
                              + plagioclase + diopside | .

(A₃)   calcite + diopside | idocrase + diopside | plagioclase
                              + diopside | quartz + plagioclase + diopside | .

Also found, especially in suite A₂, are the assemblages grossular +
idocrase and grossular + idocrase + diopside. After an elaborate
discussion Fonteilles was able to establish the conditions of formation
of these skarns not only in terms of pressure and temperature, but
also p_{CO_2} and p_{H_2O} which seemed not to have varied during the formation of the observed assemblages. He concluded therefore that
metasomatic activity between the marble and the surrounding quartz-
bearing rocks was primarily responsible for the observed assemblages
and that elements such as Ca and Mg were not apparently transported, while SiO_2 and Al_2O_3 had to be regarded as mobile, their
movement being always in one direction only.

The problem therefore reduces to the establishment of the theoretical equilibrium diagram for all the observed parageneses with the
aid of stoichiometric equations; and then to the deduction of an
explanation for their appearance along the contact of marble with
quartz-bearing rocks.

The abbreviations that will be used are:

$$An = anorthite \qquad Gr = grossular$$
$$Wo = wollastonite \qquad Id = idocrase$$
$$Ca = calcite \qquad Di = diopside$$

It is to be noted that the last assemblage listed for each of the
three suites is of little interest, since $\mu_{SiO_2} = G_{quartz} =$ Constant, and
therefore

$$T = Constant, \quad P = Constant, \quad p_{CO_2}(or \ \mu_{CO_2}) = Constant$$

$$p_{H_2O} \ (or \ \mu_{H_2O}) = Constant \ .$$

The equilibrium diagram will be developed in several stages by consideration of three groups of three reactions capable of yielding the assemblages that have to be explained.

[1]   Wo + SiO$_2$ + Al$_2$O$_3 \rightleftharpoons$ An.

The equilibrium condition is

$$G_{Wo} - G_{An} + \mu_{SiO_2} + \mu_{Al_2O_3} = 0.$$

Therefore

$$\frac{d\mu_{SiO_2}}{d\mu_{Al_2O_3}} = -1.$$

[2]   Ca + 2 SiO$_2$ + Al$_2$O$_3 \rightleftharpoons$ An + CO$_2$.

Therefore at equilibrium

$$G_{Ca} - G_{An} - \mu_{CO_2} + 2\mu_{SiO_2} + \mu_{Al_2O_3} = 0$$

and

$$\frac{d\mu_{SiO_2}}{d\mu_{Al_2O_3}} = -\frac{1}{2}.$$

[3]   Ca + SiO$_2 \rightleftharpoons$ Wo + CO$_2$.

Therefore at equilibrium

$$G_{Ca} - G_{Wo} - \mu_{CO_2} + \mu_{SiO_2} = 0$$

and

$$\frac{d\mu_{SiO_2}}{d\mu_{Al_2O_3}} = 0.$$

The slope of each equilibrium line for the three reactions is therefore now known and figure 63a can be drawn when it is recalled that the three lines must pass through a common point, the triple point at which Ca + Wo + An are in equilibrium. Combination of the conditions of equilibrium for (1) and (2) yields

$$G_{Ca} - G_{Wo} - \mu_{CO_2} + \mu_{SiO_2} = 0$$

the equilibrium condition for reaction (3).

It is now necessary to turn to the reactions:

[4]   Id + 18 SiO$_2$ + $\frac{19}{2}$ Al$_2$O$_3 \rightleftharpoons$ 15 An + 3 Di + $\frac{5}{2}$ H$_2$O

for which at equilibrium

$$\frac{d\mu_{SiO_2}}{d\mu_{Al_2O_3}} = -\frac{19}{36};$$

[5] $15\ Wo + 3\ Di + \frac{11}{2}\ Al_2O_3 + \frac{5}{2}\ H_2O \rightleftharpoons Id + 3\ SiO_2,$

for which at equilibrium

$$\frac{d\mu_{SiO_2}}{d\mu_{Al_2O_3}} = \frac{11}{6};$$

and

[6] $15\ Ca + 3\ Di + 12\ SiO_2 + \frac{11}{2}\ Al_2O_3 + \frac{5}{2}\ H_2O \rightleftharpoons Id + 15\ CO_2,$

for which at equilibrium

$$\frac{d\mu_{SiO_2}}{d\mu_{Al_2O_3}} = -\frac{11}{24}.$$

It is to be noted that the equilibrium lines (5) and (6) will cut that for reaction (3) since subtraction of the equilibrium conditions for reactions (5) and (6)

[5] $15\ G_{Wo} + 3\ G_{Di} + \frac{11}{2}\ \mu_{Al_2O_3} + \frac{5}{2}\ \mu_{H_2O} - G_{Id} - 3\ \mu_{SiO_2} = 0$

[6]

$15\ G_{Ca} + 3\ G_{Di} + 12\ \mu_{SiO_2} + \frac{11}{2}\ \mu_{Al_2O_3} + \frac{5}{2}\ \mu_{H_2O} - G_{Id} - 15\ \mu_{CO_2} = 0$

yields

$$G_{Ca} - G_{Wo} - \mu_{CO_2} + \mu_{SiO_2} = 0,$$

the equilibrium condition for reaction (3). Likewise (5) minus (4) and (6) minus (4) yield (1) and (2) respectively. The diagram of figure 63b can thus be constructed.

Finally, the garnet-bearing assemblages can be derived by the equations:

[7] $3\ An \rightleftharpoons Gr + 3\ SiO_2 + 2\ Al_2O_3,$

for which at equilibrium

$$\frac{d\mu_{SiO_2}}{d\mu_{Al_2O_3}} = -\frac{2}{3};$$

[8] $3\ Wo + Al_2O_3 \rightleftharpoons Gr,$

for which at equilibrium

$$\frac{d\mu_{SiO_2}}{d\mu_{Al_2O_3}} = \infty \qquad (\therefore d\mu_{SiO_2} = 0);$$

and

[9] $\qquad\qquad$ 3 Ca + 3 SiO$_2$ + Al$_2$O$_3$ $\rightleftharpoons$ Gr + 3 CO$_2$,

for which at equilibrium

$$\frac{d\mu_{SiO_2}}{d\mu_{Al_2O_3}} = -\frac{1}{3}.$$

The comments made about the relative positions of the lines corresponding to equations (4), (5), (6) apply also to the relative positions of those for (7), (8), (9) and (1), (2), (3). To complete the diagram it remains to place the lines corresponding to (7), (8), (9) in relation to those for (4), (5), (6); this can be done by supposing that the stability field of grossular is completely contained by that of idocrase, a reasonable assumption for idocrase-free grossular-bearing skarns are never found. Figure 63c can thus be constructed.

The simultaneous variation of μ_{SiO_2} and $\mu_{Al_2O_3}$ can in addition be shown on the completed diagram (fig. 63c) so as to display the possible formation of the paragenetic sequences A$_1$, A$_2$, and A$_3$.

4.1.3.—In the study of ore formation the Korzhinskii diagram is being used increasingly as a result of the work of Garrels (1960) and the existence of relevant experimental data. Garrels' technique is to plot the partial pressures p_1 and p_2 of two components on logarithmic scales on rectangular coordinates on a plane diagram, maintaining all other parameters constant. By way of example, consider the following equilibria in the system Cu—O—S:

[1] $\qquad\qquad$ 2 Cu(s) + $\frac{1}{2}$ O$_2$(g) $\rightleftharpoons$ Cu$_2$O, $\qquad$ cuprite

[2] $\qquad\qquad$ 2 Cu(s) + $\frac{1}{2}$ S$_2$(g) $\rightleftharpoons$ Cu$_2$S, $\quad$ chalcocite

[3] $\qquad\qquad$ Cu$_2$O(s) + $\frac{1}{2}$ O$_2$(g) $\rightleftharpoons$ 2 CuO, $\qquad$ tenorite

[4] $\qquad\qquad$ Cu$_2$S(s) + $\frac{1}{2}$ S$_2$(g) $\rightleftharpoons$ 2 CuS, $\qquad$ covellite

[5]
$$CuO(s) + \frac{1}{2} S_2(g) \rightleftharpoons CuS(s) + \frac{1}{2} O_2(g)$$

[6]
$$2\ CuO(s) + \frac{1}{2} S_2(g) \rightleftharpoons Cu_2S(s) + O_2(g).$$

The Law of Mass Action applied to heterogeneous systems (p. 215, equation (22)) leads to six relations between p_{O_2} and p_{S_2} that can most conveniently be written in logarithmic form. Knowledge of the free enthalpies of the six reactions then enables the equilibrium constants to be calculated for the six reactions listed above and for the subordinate reaction

[7]
$$Cu_2O(s) + \frac{1}{2} S_2 \rightleftharpoons Cu_2S(s) + \frac{1}{2} O_2.$$

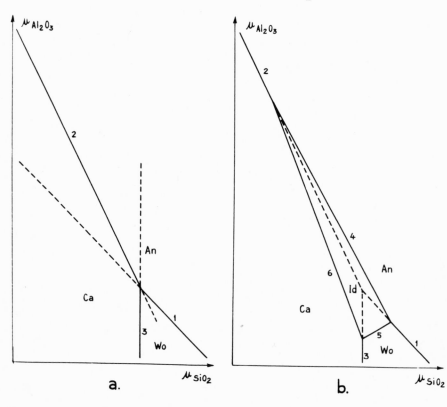

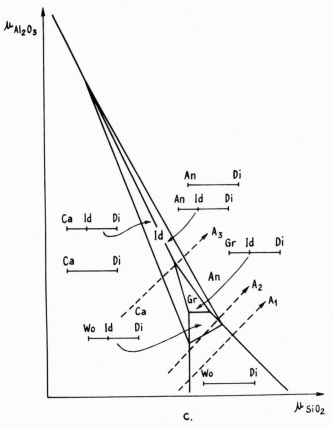

Fig. 63a, b, c. Construction of a Korzhinskii diagram for parageneses at the contact of limestone and quartziferous rocks (after Fonteilles, 1962).

The standard free enthalpies of the substances involved are given by Garrels (1960, p. 221) as:

Substance	Cu(s)	O₂(g)	S₂(g)	Cu₂O(s)	CuO(s)	Cu₂S(s)	CuS(s)
ΔG^0_{298} kcal mole⁻¹	0	0	+19.13	−34.98	−30.4	−20.6	−11.7

From these data the calculation shown in the table below can be made for reactions (1) through (7):

Reaction	(1)	(2)	(3)	(4)
$(\Delta G)^0_{298}$ kcal	-35.0	-30.0	-25.8	-12.4
$\log K$ $= \dfrac{-0.43(\Delta G)^0_{298}}{RT}$	$+26$	$+22$	$+19$	$+9.1$
At equilibrium	$-\log p_{O_2}$ $= 52$	$-\log p_{S_2}$ $= 44$	$-\log p_{O_2}$ $= 38$	$-\log p_{S_2}$ $= 18$

The resultant equilibrium equations are displayed, with some inconsistencies smoothed out, on figure 64, where each phase may be seen to occupy a definite stability field.

It should be noted that Garrels diagrams differ only slightly from Korzhinskii diagrams. Instead of writing down the chemical potential equations and then displaying them on a diagram as a summary of the stoichiometry of the reactions, Garrels applies the Law of Mass Action directly and then works back to obtain his equations in

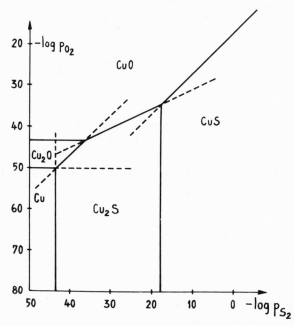

Fig. 64. p_{O_2}—p_{S_2} diagram for the system Cu—O—S (after Garrels, 1960).

(5)	(6)	(7)
+9.0	+30.6	+4.8
−6.6	−22.5	−3.5
$-\log p_{O_2}$ $= 13 - \log p_{S_2}$	$-\log p_{O_2}$ $= 22 - \frac{1}{2}\log p_{S_2}$	$-\log p_{O_2}$ $= 7.0 - \log p_{S_2}$

logarithms to the base 10. His diagrams therefore are also chemical potential diagrams but, unlike Korzhinskii's, they are explicit and indeed quantitative, as can be seen on p. 282 below.

4.1.4.—The intensive diagram has many variants but, since it is only really helpful when one is completely familiar with it, an individual worker will tend always to use one variant only.

In this book rather limited use is made of $\mu - T$ and $\mu - P$ diagrams, and that is in the study of the formation of wollastonite in an open system (p. 206).

4.2. Extensive, or compositional, diagrams.

If all the intensive parameters are fixed, so that only a number of extensive parameters remain variable, it is possible to construct a type of diagram, of which the only important examples are those on which the compositions of a system are represented.

If $n_1, n_2, \ldots n_i$ are the numbers of moles (normalized to 100 so as to be molar percentages with $n_1 + n_2 + \cdots + n_i = 100$) of the $\mathcal{C}$ components that are taken as the *a priori* variables, space of $\mathcal{C} - 1$ dimensions will be necessary for the representation of composition. In such a diagram any point represents a definite chemical composition and the whole diagram can have thermodynamic significance or be merely descriptive. Thus two kinds of diagram are distinguished: thermodynamic diagrams and paragenesis or assemblage diagrams.

4.2.1. Linear diagrams.—If $\mathcal{C} = 2$, a one-dimensional space suffices for representation. A straight line is drawn with its extremities representing pure components 1 and 2; any point on the line between 1 and 2 has coordinates n_1 and n_2 with $n_1 + n_2 = 100$. Figure 65 represents the system halite—water at constant T, P, and μ_i. Halite is soluble up to 40% by weight; the point S on the diagram represents the composition of the saturated solution. The two fields between the

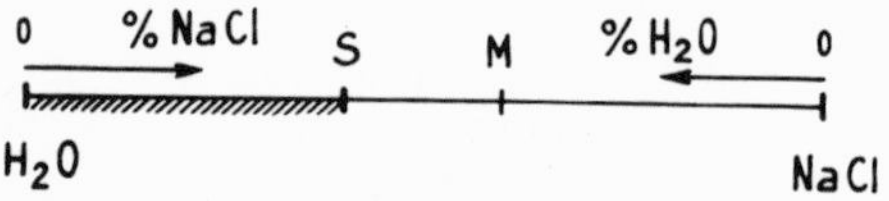

Fig. 65. Linear diagram showing the solubility of NaCl in pure water at given P, T.

extremities of the diagram are thus occupied by solution (hachured) and by saturated solution and NaCl crystals. The diagram thus contains thermodynamic information, the solubility of NaCl in water at given P, T.

   A petrological example is given in figure 30 on p. 130 for the system quartz—jadeite—albite—nepheline. There are four reactions:

$$1 \text{ Ne} + 1 \text{ Q} \rightarrow 1 \text{ Jd}$$
$$1 \text{ Jd} + 1 \text{ Q} \rightarrow 1 \text{ Ab}$$
$$1 \text{ Ab} + 1 \text{ Ne} \rightarrow 2 \text{ Jd}$$
$$1 \text{ Ne} + 2 \text{ Q} \rightarrow 1 \text{ Ab.}$$

By choosing as limits quartz (Q) and nepheline (Ne) the linear diagram of figure 66 is produced. At this stage the diagram contains no

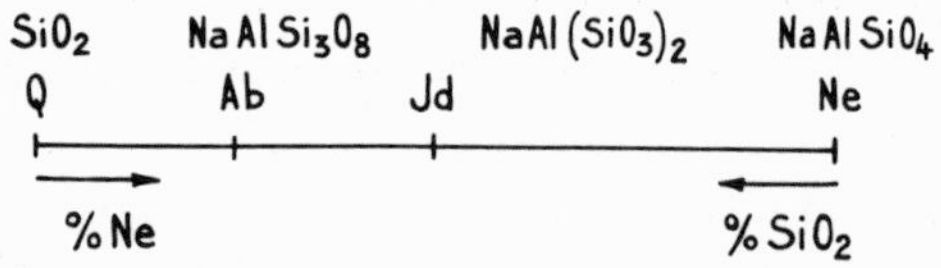

Fig. 66. Linear diagram of two-phase assemblages in the system quartz-albite.

other information than the stoichiometry of the four reactions listed above. Following Eskola, petrologists have become accustomed to making use of such diagrams to represent two-phase assemblages. This can be done here, for at equilibrium two phases coexist (p. 130). Thus figure 66 acts as a reminder, if the Ab point is removed, that possible parageneses are Ne + Jd or Q + Jd; or if the Jd point is removed, that Ne + Ab or Q + Ab are possible assemblages.

4.2.2. Plane diagrams.—If $c = 3$ it is necessary to make use of two-dimensional space. Three points 1, 2, 3 are taken at the vertices of a triangle, usually an equilateral triangle. Allowing the height of the triangle to represent 100 units, any point on the diagram corresponds to

$$n_1 + n_2 + n_3 = 100$$

if n_1, n_2, n_3 are the distances from the edges opposite the vertices labelled 1, 2, 3 (fig. 67). If the height of the triangle is $100\sqrt{3}/2$,

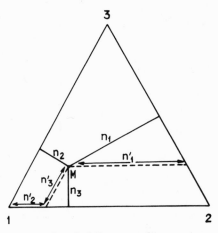

Fig. 67. The use of normal and oblique coordinates on ternary diagrams.

that is if its sides are 100 units, each point can be labeled n'_1, n'_2, n'_3, which are now the oblique coordinates in the triangle (fig. 67); again $n'_1 + n'_2 + n'_3 = 100$.

In 4.3 an example of a ternary diagram with thermodynamic significance will be discussed. Here an example of a three-phase mineral association diagram will be exhibited. The equilibrium

quartz + calcite → wollastonite + CO_2

is, as was seen on p. 147, represented in P—T—p_{CO_2} space. It has two fields, each occupied by three phases. In the first field, two assemblages are possible:

Q + Ca + gas
Q + Ca + Wo,

and in the second

Wo + Q + gas
Wo + Ca + gas .

If the chemical compounds SiO_2, CaO, CO_2 are represented by the vertices of an equilateral triangle, the points representing the four phases Q, Ca, Wo, gas can readily be plotted (fig. 68a).

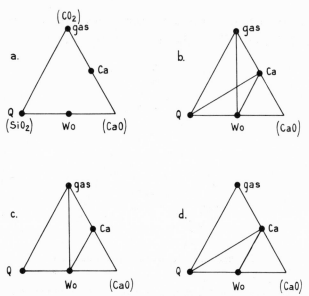

Fig. 68a, b, c, d. Triangular diagrams displaying three-phase assemblages in the system CaO—SiO_2—CO_2 under various conditions.

In this sort of problem that concerns three-phase assemblages it suffices to join the points representing phase compositions by straight lines (fig. 68b) in order to show that four triangles of interest arise; they correspond to the four three-phase mineral assemblages listed above. Figures 68c and 68d represent the two fields of the T—P—p_{CO_2} diagram.

It should be noted that such mineral association diagrams are only conventional, whereas on thermodynamic diagrams every line possesses a quantitative significance. Such paragenetic diagrams do however have considerable petrological interest. Eskola has shown that knowledge of the total chemical composition of a rock represented on a particular triangular diagram, especially the A.C.F. diagram as used by Turner and Verhoogen (1960) or Lafitte (1957), taken together with the petrographic finding of three minerals,

enables the rock to be assigned to a particular degree of metamorphism.

4.2.3. Space-diagrams.—If $c = 4$ the representation-space required is
three-dimensional. The four poles 1, 2, 3, 4 are most commonly
disposed at the corners of a regular tetrahedron. If n_1, n_2, n_3, n_4 are respectively the distances to the faces 2-3-4, 1-3-4, 1-2-4, 1-2-3, then

$$n_1 + n_2 + n_3 + n_4 = 100,$$

the height of the tetrahedron corresponding to 100 units. Oblique
coordinates can equally well be used if the tetrahedron edge is taken
as 100 units.

Here again there are two types of diagram: the thermodynamic
diagram, which is little used because its establishment is too difficult
a task, and the mineral association diagram. The latter enables four-
phase assemblages to be represented, planes here playing the same
role as lines in *4.2.2.*

4.3. Composite diagrams.

As their name indicates, these have intensive and extensive factors
among their variables. Examples are many and the reader is referred
to the following figures:

specific heat diagrams: figs. 18, 19, 28, 29,
enthalpy diagrams: figs. 6, 7, 24, 25,
partial molar volume diagram: fig. 37.

Another type is an extensive diagram with a supplementary T
or P axis, for example n_1, n_2, T diagrams:

fusion diagrams: figs. 42, 43,
unmixing diagrams: figs. 46, 47.

An n_1, n_2, P, T diagram is shown in perspective on fig. 48.

For three components n_1, n_2, n_3, and T, the triangular n_1, n_2, n_3
diagram of paragraph *4.4* may have added to it a T-axis perpendicular to the plane of the compositional triangle. Figure 69 gives,
in projection on the compositional triangle, the exsolution limits of
Ab, Or, An at the 500, 600, 700, and 900°C isotherms. On the

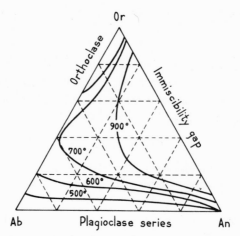

Fig. 69. The ternary system Or—Ab—An showing isothermal contours on the surface of unmixing.

An—Or edge of the triangle an immiscibility field extending above
900°C is recognizable.

When the three components n_1, n_2, n_3 are not of comparable significance, the triangular representation becomes inappropriate. For
aqueous systems, such as KCl—NaCl—H_2O, it suffices to plot on
orthogonal axes, n_1 = g of KCl/100 g of H_2O, n_2 = g of NaCl/100 g
of H_2O, and T.

For information on the construction and use of phase diagrams
the reader is referred to Findlay (1951) and for Eskola-diagrams to
Korzhinskii (1957).

XIII

Some Problems
of Mineralogical
and Petrological Interest

1. Calcite-Aragonite

Some attempt will be made here to solve some of the problems related to the two principal polymorphs of $CaCO_3$ and in particular to account for their relative solubility, their conditions of formation, and their transformation from one to another.

1.1. Solubility of the carbonates of calcium in water.

The solution of calcium carbonate in water can be represented by the equation

[1]
$$CaCO_3 \text{ (cryst.)} \rightarrow CO_3^{2-} + Ca^{2+},$$

if it is assumed that there is complete ionization in solution.

The Law of Mass Action for heterogeneous systems can be applied to crystalline $CaCO_3$ in equilibrium with its saturated solution thus:

[2]
$$a_{CO_3^{2-}} \, a_{Ca^{2+}} = K_1$$

where K_1 is the equilibrium constant with reference to activity; K_1 is known as the *solubility product* of calcium carbonate and can simply be evaluated from

[3]
$$\ln K_1 = -\frac{(\Delta G)_T^P}{RT}$$

263

where $(\Delta G)_T^P$ is the free enthalpy of solution according to equation (1). In the standard conditions (p. 70),

$$(\Delta G)_{298}^0 = + \text{ 11,404 Cal for calcite}$$
$$(\Delta G)_{298}^0 = + \text{ 11,055 Cal for aragonite.}$$

Therefore K_1 at 1 atm and 298°K has the values:

$$K_1 = 10^{-8.36} \text{ for calcite}$$
$$K_1 = 10^{-8.17} \text{ for aragonite.}$$

Now if the saturated solution is, as it will be shown to be in due course, extremely dilute, equation (2) can be rewritten as

[4]
$$c_{CO_3^{2-}} \; c_{Ca^{2+}} = K_1.$$

But $c_{CO_3^{2-}}$ and $c_{Ca^{2+}}$ are restricted by another equation, since the electrical neutrality of the system is preserved:

[5]
$$c_{CO_3^{2-}} = c_{Ca^{2+}}.$$

From equations (4) and (5),

$$c_{Ca^{2+}} = c_{CO_3^{2-}} = (K_1)^{1/2}$$

and therefore at 1 atm and 298°K,

[6]
$$\begin{cases} c_{Ca^{2+}} = 10^{-4.18} \text{ for calcite} \\ c_{Ca^{2+}} = 10^{-4.08} \text{ for aragonite.} \end{cases}$$

To a first approximation then, comparison with equation (6) yields

[7]
$$\begin{cases} c_{calcite} = (10^{-4.18}/18) \text{ mole liter}^{-1} \\ c_{aragonite} = (10^{-4.08}/18) \text{ mole liter}^{-1}, \end{cases}$$

both concentrations of the order of 0.01 g. liter^{-1}, aragonite, the unstable phase, being more soluble than calcite.

It must be stressed that all the results so far obtained for the equilibrium

[1]
$$CaCO_3 \text{ (cryst.)} \rightleftharpoons CO_3^{2-} + Ca^{2+}$$

are valid only to a first approximation. Water itself is known to be slightly dissociated:

[8] $H_2O \text{ (liq)} \rightleftharpoons H^+ + OH^-$ whence $c_{H^+} \, c_{OH^-} = K_2 = 10^{-14}.$

Three additional reactions then become possible:

[9] $HCO_3^- \rightleftharpoons H^+ + CO_3^{2-}$ whence $\dfrac{c_{H^+} \, c_{CO_3^{2-}}}{c_{HCO_3^-}} = K_3 = 10^{-10.3}$

[10]

$$H_2CO_3 \text{ (aq.)} \rightleftharpoons H^+ + HCO_3^- \qquad \text{whence} \qquad \frac{c_{H^+} \, c_{HCO_3^-}}{c_{H_2CO_3}} = K_4 = 10^{-6.4}$$

[11] $\qquad\qquad\qquad Ca^{2+} + 2OH^- \rightleftharpoons Ca(OH)_2.$

In other words there can be reaction between CO_3^{2-} and Ca^{2+} ions produced by the solution of the carbonate and H^+ and OH^- ions produced by the dissociation of water. Reaction (11) can in practice be omitted because it goes almost completely from right to left. But the taking into consideration of reactions (8), (9), and (10) does modify slightly the results obtained previously. The calculation will be worked out in detail in the next paragraph; here it suffices to compare the results so obtained for the dissociation of the calcium carbonates in pure water with the approximate results (equation (6)):

$$\begin{cases} \text{calcite:} & c_{CO_3^{2-}} = 10^{-4.41}; \quad c_{Ca^{2+}} = 10^{-3.95} \\ \text{aragonite:} & c_{CO_3^{2-}} = 10^{-4.30}; \quad c_{Ca^{2+}} = 10^{-3.87}. \end{cases}$$

The accuracy of these concentrations depends mainly on that of the equilibrium constants and is of the order of $10^{\pm 0.01}$.

1.2. Solubility of the calcium carbonates in the presence of a CO_2-containing atmosphere (after Garrels, 1960).

This is analogous to the problem of the preceding paragraph, but here the presence of CO_2 in the atmosphere above the solution will be taken into account.

The reactions involved and their equilibrium constants at $298°K$ and 1 atm are:

(1) solution of crystalline carbonate: $CaCO_3 \rightleftharpoons Ca^{2+} + CO_3^{2-}$

$\qquad K_1 = c_{CO_3^{2-}} \, c_{Ca^{2+}} = 10^{-8.36}$ (calcite) $\qquad$ or $\qquad 10^{-8.17}$ (aragonite)

(8) dissociation of water: $H_2O \rightleftharpoons H^+ + OH^-$

$$K_2 = c_{H^+} \, c_{OH^-} = 10^{-14}$$

(9) dissociation of HCO_3^-: $HCO_3^- \rightleftharpoons H^+ + CO_3^{2-}$

$$K_3 = \frac{c_{H^+} \, c_{CO_3^{2-}}}{c_{HCO_3^-}} = 10^{-10.3}$$

(10) dissociation of H_2CO_3: $H_2CO_3 \rightleftharpoons H^+ + HCO_3^-$

$$K_4 = \frac{c_{H^+} \, c_{HCO_3^-}}{c_{H_2CO_3}} = 10^{-6.4}$$

(12) solution of CO_2: $CO_2(g) + H_2O(\ell) \rightleftharpoons H_2CO_3(\ell)$

$$K_5 = \frac{c'_{H_2CO_3}}{p_{CO_2}} = 10^{-1.5}.$$

In order to make the argument clear, let $c_{H_2CO_3}$ be the concentration of H_2CO_3 resulting from the solution of $CaCO_3$ and $c'_{H_2CO_3}$ the concentration of H_2CO_3 resulting from the solution of CO_2.

The equilibrium constant K_4 of reaction (10) is then

[10′]
$$\frac{c_{H^+} \, c_{HCO_3^-}}{c_{H_2CO_3} + c'_{H_2CO_3}} = K_4 = 10^{-6.4}.$$

The electrical neutrality of the solution must also be taken into account:

[13] $$2c_{Ca^{2+}} + c_{H^+} = c_{OH^-} + c_{HCO_3^-} + 2c_{CO_3^{2-}}.$$

Finally the concentration of carbonate ions derived from calcite (or aragonite) are related to the concentration of calcium ions by

[14] $$c_{Ca^{2+}} = c_{CO_3^{2-}} + c_{HCO_3^-} + c_{H_2CO_3}.$$

Thus seven equations are available for the determination of seven unknowns,

$$c_{Ca^{2+}}, \; c_{CO_3^{2-}}, \; c_{HCO_3^-}, \; c_{H_2CO_3}, \; c'_{H_2CO_3}, \; c_{H^+}, \; c_{OH^-},$$

the partial pressure of CO_2 in the atmosphere being the chosen variable parameter. The solution of this set of simultaneous equations presents no theoretical difficulty, but is nevertheless very laborious. Here the results will merely be stated.

The curves shown on figure 70 give the variation in pH (defined as $-\log a_{H^+}$) of the solutions as a function of p_{CO_2} for calcite and aragonite. In the absence of atmospheric CO_2, it can be seen that the pH is close to 10 (9.95 for calcite, 10.0 for aragonite). The pH falls only slowly from those values for $p_{CO_2} < 10^{-3}$ atm and then it decreases rapidly towards 7 (corresponding to a neutral solution) as p_{CO_2} approaches 10^{-1} atm.

The analogous behavior of HCO_3^- ions is seen in figure 71. Figure 72 displays similarly the variation of $c_{Ca^{2+}}$ and $c_{CO_3^{2-}}$ with p_{CO_2}.

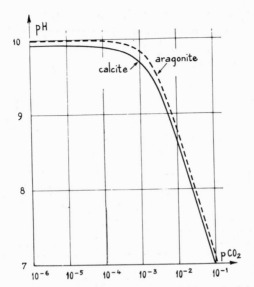

Fig. 70. Partial pressure of CO_2 over an aqueous solution of calcite or aragonite as a function of the pH of the solution.

These are most informative about the solubility of calcite and aragonite, since $c_{Ca^{2+}}$ represents the concentration of dissolved carbonate.

An apparent paradox is obvious: the concentration of carbonate

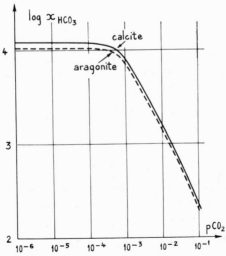

Fig. 71. Concentration of bicarbonate ions in an aqueous solution of calcite or aragonite as a function of the partial pressure of CO_2 over the solution.

ions in the solution decreases as the atmosphere is enriched in CO_2. However, as would be expected, the solubility of the calcium carbonates increases with the partial pressure of CO_2. Moreover, the solubility of aragonite exceeds that of calcite at all values of p_{CO_2}, but

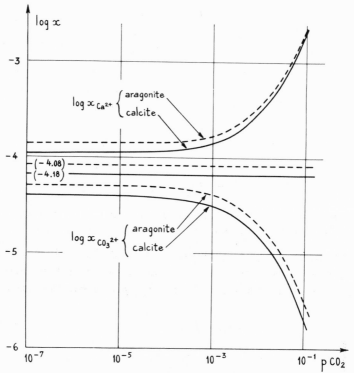

Fig. 72. Solubility of calcite and aragonite in water as a function of the partial pressure of CO_2 in the atmosphere above the solution.

the difference in solubility of the two polymorphs becomes less as p_{CO_2} increases.

1.3. Crystallization of calcite and aragonite.

Consider any body of water which in the course of its underground circulation passes through a limestone horizon in the presence of a CO_2-rich medium. It will take up Ca^{2+} ions in equilibrium with CO_3^{2-} in accordance with

[15] $$c_{Ca^{2+}} \, c_{CO_3^{2-}} = K_1; \, (pCO_2)$$

where p_{CO_2} is the partial pressure of CO_2 in the limestone horizon. Suppose that from there the water flows into a region with a CO_2-poor atmosphere, such as an aerated cave or the open air. The Ca^{2+} content of the water will remain unchanged at $c_{Ca^{2+}}$, but since the new partial pressure of CO_2, $p'_{CO_2} < p_{CO_2}$, the concentration of CO_3^{2-} will assume a new value $c_{CO_3^{2-}} + \Delta c_{CO_3^{2-}} > c_{CO_3^{2-}}$; therefore

[16] $$c_{Ca^{2+}} \, (c_{CO_3^{2-}} + \Delta c_{CO_3^{2-}}) = k > K_1.$$

The solution will no longer be in equilibrium; either calcite or aragonite must be precipitated in order that the equations

[17] $$\begin{cases} c'_{Ca^{2+}} \, c'_{CO_3^{2-}} = K_1; \ (p'_{CO_2}) \text{ for calcite} \\ c''_{Ca^{2+}} \, c''_{CO_3^{2-}} = K'_1; \ (p'_{CO_2}) \text{ for aragonite} \end{cases}$$

shall be obeyed. Before crystallization begins, the solution will be supersaturated; in this condition it can be characterized by its degree of supersaturation or its excess function defined as β by

[18] $$\beta = \frac{c_{CO_3^{2-}} + \Delta c_{CO_3^{2-}}}{c_{CO_3^{2-}}} = \frac{k}{K_1} > 1.$$

The excess function, due here to change of partial pressure of CO_2, could equally well have been caused by evaporation, change of temperature, or some other change.

In other words calcite can crystallize from the solution only if it has a supersaturation $\beta_{Cal} = \dfrac{k}{K_1} > 1$ and similarly for aragonite the supersaturation must be $\beta_{Arag} = \dfrac{k}{K'_1} > 1$. From equation (18) it follows that

[19] $$\beta_{Cal} = \frac{k}{K_1} = 1 + \frac{\Delta c_{CO_3^{2-}}}{c_{CO_3^{2-}}}$$

and therefore calcite can crystallize as soon as $\Delta c_{CO_3^{2-}}$ becomes positive, by however small a margin. However, for aragonite

$$\beta_{Arag} = \frac{k}{K'_1} = \frac{c_{Ca^{2+}}(c_{CO_3^{2-}} + \Delta c_{CO_3^{2-}})}{K'_1}$$

and, since $c_{Ca^{2+}}$ is equal to the mol fraction of calcium carbonate introduced by the solution of calcite from the limestone beds traversed previously, it follows that

$$\beta_{Arag} = \frac{K_1 + c_{Ca^{2+}} \Delta c_{CO_3^{2-}}}{K_1'}$$

and the condition $\beta_{Arag} > 1$ becomes

$$\frac{\Delta c_{CO_3^{2-}}}{c_{CO_3^{2-}}} > \frac{K_1' - K_1}{K_1}.$$

Thus for aragonite to be able to crystallize, it is necessary that the change of atmosphere should produce a change in the CO_3^{2-} content of the order of 60% at least. This will happen for instance when $p_{CO_2} \sim 10^{-2}$ atm and $p'_{CO_2} \sim 10^{-3.5}$ atm (corresponding to the ordinary open air). In short it is evident that waters sufficiently rich in Ca^{2+} and CO_3^{2-} ions can deposit either calcite or aragonite at ordinary temperatures and pressures.

It will be seen in the following paragraph that the stable polymorph of calcium carbonate under these conditions is calcite and that aragonite is theoretically unstable. It is no less true that aragonite has often been observed to crystallize at ordinary temperatures and pressures; that is an instance of *metastable synthesis*, the crystallization of a mineral outside its stability field. The study of such phenomena belongs to the field of crystal growth kinetics, which will not be dealt with here. A few comments may however be appropriate. It is necessary that aragonite should crystallize faster than calcite under conditions of adequate supersaturation: this is not impossible *a priori*, for classical thermodynamic data do not control the kinetics, but rather the *activation energy for nucleation*, which depends *inter alia* on the surface energies of the minerals. It is also necessary that the aragonite so crystallized should not undergo spontaneous polymorphic transformation to calcite, or at least that it should only do so infinitely slowly. This is not an assumption that raises any difficulty, since aragonite crystals can persist unchanged at ordinary pressures and temperatures for very long periods of time.

1.4. Calcite-aragonite stability relations.

It remains to examine the equilibrium conditions for the polymorphic transformation

$$\text{calcite} \rightarrow \text{aragonite}.$$

The thermodynamic functions for the transformation are all very small and it is necessary for them to be known to quite a high order of accuracy before the equilibrium diagram can be drawn. The most accurate method of determination depends on measurement of the respective solubilities of the two minerals.

Consider the cycle

$$\text{calcite} \rightarrow \text{aragonite} \rightarrow CaCO_3 \text{ solution} \rightarrow \text{calcite}$$

for which $(\Delta G_{transf})_T^P = (\Delta G_{soln \, of \, cal})_T^P - (\Delta G_{soln \, of \, arag})_T^P$, that is

$$(\Delta G_{transf})_T^P = RT \, (\ln K_1' - \ln K_1),$$

where K_1 and K_1' are the solubility products of calcite and aragonite at temperature T and pressure P.

The condition for calcite and aragonite to coexist in equilibrium is $(\Delta G_{transf})_T^P = 0$, that is

$$K_1(T, \, P) = K_1'(T, \, P).$$

An ingenious device based on the electrical behavior of the two saturated solutions and developed by Jamieson (1953, 1957) enables all the pairs of P, T values for which the solubilities are equal, that is for which calcite and aragonite are in equilibrium, to be measured; the results are:

T °K	P Kg/cm^2
302.1	3980
311.2	4130
325.6	4500
350.1	4800

The points so determined lie on a straight line with an empirical equation:

$$P = 17.86 \, T - 1405 \, ,$$

where P is in kg cm^{-2} and T in °K (fig. 73).

Knowledge of the dependence of (ΔV) on P and T makes it possible to determine, with the aid of the Clapeyron equations, $(\Delta H)_T^P$ and $(\Delta S)_T^P$:

$$17.864 = \frac{dP}{dT} = \frac{(\Delta H)}{T(\Delta V)} = \frac{(\Delta S)}{(\Delta V)}.$$

T °K	$(\Delta H)_T^P$ cal/mole	$(\Delta S)_T^P$ cal/deg/mole
302.1	+ 375	+ 1.24
311.2	385	1.24
325.6	401	1.23
350.2	426	1.22

These results have been confirmed by the more recent work of Clark (1957) in a different P, T field in the course of a direct study of the conditions of the calcite-aragonite transformation. And MacDonald (1956) has also determined the calcite-aragonite phase

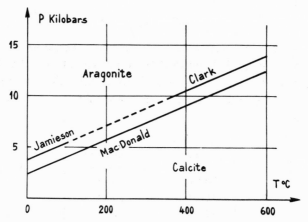

Fig. 73. Calcite-aragonite stability relations.

diagram, the line he obtained having a similar slope to that determined by the previous writers, although the two lines are significantly displaced from one another. The discrepancy undoubtedly derives from inaccuracy of pressure measurements and in part from MacDonald's experiments being under directed stress (fig. 73).

It is, however, clear from both sets of data that aragonite is unstable at atmospheric pressure at all temperatures, its transformation to calcite being described as monotropic. Its crystallization under ordinary atmospheric conditions, such as was envisaged in the preceding paragraph, is therefore in effect a metastable synthesis. It is evident therefore that the calcite-aragonite pair represent a dangerous kind of geological thermometer.

2. Gypsum-Anhydrite

2.1. Introduction.

Calcium sulphate can exist in six anhydrous or hydrous forms, each characterized by its X-ray diffraction pattern and thermodynamic properties. In order to establish the equilibrium diagram for these six forms, it suffices to calculate the free enthalpy change $(\Delta G)_T^P$ for each of the reactions:

$CaSO_4 \cdot 2\ H_2O$ (gypsum) $\rightleftharpoons CaSO_4$ (anhydrite) $+\ 2\ H_2O(\ell)$

$\rule{4cm}{0.4pt} \rightleftharpoons CaSO_4 \cdot \frac{1}{2}\ H_2O$ (hemihydrate-α) $+\ \frac{3}{2}\ H_2O(\ell)$

$\rule{4cm}{0.4pt} \rightleftharpoons CaSO_4 \cdot \frac{1}{2}\ H_2O$ (hemihydrate-β) $+\ \frac{3}{2}\ H_2O(\ell)$

$\rule{4cm}{0.4pt} \rightleftharpoons CaSO_4$ (soluble α-anhydrite) $+\ 2H_2O(\ell)$

$\rule{4cm}{0.4pt} \rightleftharpoons CaSO_4$ (soluble β-anhydrite) $+\ 2H_2O(\ell)$

Only the first of these equilibria, gypsum $\rightleftharpoons$ anhydrite $+\ H_2O$, will be discussed here. $(\Delta G)_T^0$ can be calculated, by the method that has been used many times above, from the following data taken from Kelley (1960) and Kelley and King (1961):

Specific heats:

gypsum	$C_P = 21.84 + 0.076\ T$ cal deg^{-1} mole^{-1}
anhydrite	$C_P = 14.10 + 0.033\ T$ " " "
water (ℓ)	$C_P = 18.02$ " " "
$\therefore$	$\Delta C_P = 28.30 - 0.043\ T$ " " " .

Standard entropies:

gypsum	$S^0_{298} = 46.4$ cal deg^{-1} mole^{-1}
anhydrite	$S^0_{298} = 25.5$ " " "
$H_2O(\ell)$	$S^0_{298} = 16.8$ " " " .

Heat of reaction for gypsum $\rightarrow$ anhydrite $+\ H_2O(\ell)$

$$\Delta H^0_{298} = 4030\ \text{cal.}$$

The usual sequence of calculations makes it possible to show that

$$(\Delta G)_T^0 = -2495 - 65.17 \log T + 0.0215 \, T^2 + 163.9 \, T \, ;$$

the curve of $(\Delta G)_T^0 = f(T)$ is plotted on figure 74. It deviates only slightly from a straight line and $(\Delta G)_T^0 = 0$ at $T = 313°K$ (40°C).

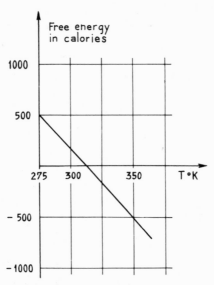

Fig. 74. Free enthalpy of reaction for the dehydration of gypsum in water.

At 1 atm pressure, gypsum is in equilibrium with anhydrite and water at a temperature of 40°C. Above 40°C, $(\Delta G)_T^0 < 0$ and then anhydrite becomes stable in the presence of water. Below 40°C lies the stability field of gypsum. These conclusions are consistent with those deduced from solubility measurements: below 40°C anhydrite is more soluble than gypsum. Also consistent are the vapor pressure measurements of Van't Hoff (1911).

2.2. Influence of hydrostatic pressure.

Suppose for the time being that the same hydrostatic pressure is applied uniformly to the solid phases and to water. The equilibrium condition is then:

$$(\Delta G)_T^P = 0$$

and, if the dependence of (ΔV) on P and T is neglected, it follows that

$$(\Delta G)_T^0 + P(\Delta V) = 0$$

whence, for $(\Delta V) = 6.66$ cm^3,

$$-2495 - 65.17 \, T \log T + 0.0215 \, T^2 + 163.9 \, T + \frac{6.66}{41.3} \, P = 0.$$

From this expression the equilibrium pressure at any temperature can simply be evaluated. Since $\Delta V > 0$, increase in pressure must evidently favor the formation of gypsum.

2.3. Influence of lithostatic pressure (after MacDonald, 1953).

In practice the problem does not arise quite in this way and it is necessary to dissociate hydrostatic from lithostatic pressure. If ΔV_S is the change in volume of the solid phases and ΔV_L that of the liquid,

$$(\Delta G)_T^{Ps,PL} = (\Delta G)_T^0 + (\Delta V_S)P_S + (\Delta V_L)P_L$$

where

P_S = lithostatic pressure
P_L = hydrostatic pressure
$\Delta V_S = V_{anhyd} - V_{gyps} = -29.48$ cm^3
$\Delta V_L = 2V_{H_2O} = 36.14$ cm^3.

Therefore

$$(\Delta G)_T^{Ps,PL} = (\Delta G)_T^0 - \frac{29.48}{41.3} \, P_S + \frac{36.14}{41.3} \, P_L \, .$$

If it is supposed that the subjacent rock is permeable right up to the surface, then

$$P_S \sim 2.4 P_L \, ,$$

2.4 being the mean density of crystalline rocks.

It must be noted however that calcium sulphate deposits are often enclosed in clays or marls. The column is then not completely permeable and the equation $P_S \sim 2.4 P_L$ must be replaced by

$$\lambda P_S = P_L \, ,$$

where $\dfrac{1}{2.4} < \lambda < 1$.

The new equilibrium condition is therefore

$$(\Delta G)^0_T + \frac{36.14 - 2.4 \times 29.48}{41.3}\, P_L = 0$$

i.e.,

$$(\Delta G)^0_T - 0.84\, P_L = 0\ .$$

Now an increase in pressure favors the dehydration of gypsum and stabilizes the assemblage anhydrite + water.

At one value of $\dfrac{1}{\lambda} = \dfrac{P_s}{P_L}$, equal to 1.2, pressure plays no part in the equilibrium, since then $(\Delta G)^0_T = 0$.

All these results are summarized by the equilibrium diagram,

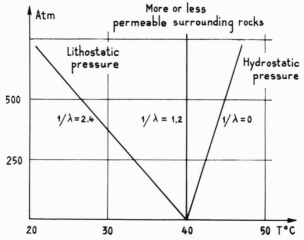

Fig. 75. Equilibrium diagram for the assemblage gypsum-anhydrite-water showing the effect of variation of the ratio of lithostatic to hydrostatic pressure.

figure 75. It should be noticed that the curves on the diagram follow directly from the Clapeyron equation (p. 102).

2.4. Influence of brine composition.

The equilibrium condition for the reaction

$$\text{gypsum} \rightarrow \text{anhydrite} + \text{water}$$

as it has been written in terms of free enthalpy in the preceding paragraphs is valid only if the composition of the phases is invariant. This is so for gypsum and for anhydrite, but water on the other hand can hold an appreciable amount of the various salts in solution.

The equilibrium condition is more correctly written therefore as

$$2\mu_{H_2O} + \mu_{anhyd} = \mu_{gyps} \quad \text{or} \quad 2\mu_{H_2O} + G_{anhyd} - G_{gyps} = 0.$$

The chemical potential of water at temperature T and pressure P can be expressed in terms of the activity a_{H_2O} of the aqueous solvent of the solution as

$$\mu_{H_2O} = \mu^0_{H_2O} + RT \ln a_{H_2O} = G_{H_2O} + RT \ln a_{H_2O}.$$

Therefore

$$2\,RT \ln a_{H_2O} + 2\,G_{H_2O} + G_{anhyd} - G_{gyps} = 0$$

and, putting

$$2\,G_{H_2O} + G_{anhyd} - G_{gyps} = (\Delta G)^P_T$$

the equilibrium condition becomes

$$2\,RT \ln a_{H_2O} + (\Delta G)^P_T = 0$$

or

$$2\,RT \ln \gamma_{H_2O}\, x_{H_2O} + (\Delta G)^P_T = 0.$$

The activity coefficient γ_{H_2O} of water in the presence of dissolved NaCl has already been calculated (p. 194). With the aid of the values obtained then, the equilibrium temperature can be evaluated for various concentrations of NaCl at a constant pressure of 1 atm. Substitution of the value obtained previously for $(\Delta G)^0_T$ leads to

$$2\,RT \ln (\gamma_{H_2O}\, x_{H_2O}) - 2495 - 65.17\,T \log T + 0.0215\,T^2$$
$$+ 163.9\,T = 0.$$

The curve shown on figure 76, constructed point by point from

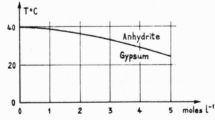

Fig. 76. Influence of salinity on the equilibrium temperature of the gypsum-anhydrite transformation.

this equation, illustrates the result. It is evident that the gypsum-anhydrite transformation temperature is lowered in the presence of a dissolved salt. And the effect of dissolved magnesium salts is even more marked, a point of some significance in consideration of the genesis of calcium sulphate deposits.

3.   The crystallization of some simple copper minerals

We are concerned, in essence, with the reactions produced by the circulation of a dilute aqueous Cu^{2+} solution. In the course of flowing through a limestone horizon, for instance, such a solution would become more basic (see p. 265). If it contains in addition to Cu^{2+} ions such as OH^-, Cl^-, SO_4^{2-}, CO_3^{2-}, copper minerals may be deposited and the purpose of these paragraphs is to examine, in the light of the available experimental data, the conditions under which they might crystallize.

3.1. Brochantite, tenorite.

The addition of a base to a solution of copper sulphate produces brochantite according to the reaction:

[1] $4\ Cu^{2+} + 6\ OH^- + SO_4^{2-} \rightleftharpoons Cu_4(OH)_6SO_4(s).$

The Law of Mass Action applied to a heterogeneous reaction, as this is, yields

[1] $a_{Cu^{2+}}^{-4}\ a_{OH^-}^{-6}\ a_{SO_4^{2-}}^{-1} = K_1.$

In a more basic environment brochantite decomposes to yield tenorite according to the equation

[2] $Cu_4(OH)_6SO_4(s) + 2\ OH^- \rightleftharpoons 4\ CuO(s) + SO_4^{2-} + 4\ H_2O,$

for which

[2] $a_{SO_4^{2-}}\ a_{OH^-}^{-2} = K_2.$

Tenorite can alternatively be formed directly from the primary solution, the equation for the reaction corresponding simply to (1) + (2), that is

[3] $Cu^{2+} + 2\ OH^- \rightleftharpoons CuO(s) + H_2O,$

with equilibrium constant K_3 given by:

[3] $$K_3^{-1} = a_{Cu^{2+}} \, a_{OH^-}^2.$$

Since the reactions (1), (2), (3) are not independent, K_3 is related to K_1 and K_2 by

[4] $$K_3 = (K_1 K_2)^{\frac{1}{4}}.$$

Equation (4) is of interest because reaction (3) is not directly accessible to experiment and thus its constant K_3 can only be evaluated by determination of K_1 and K_2, followed by application of equation (4).

K_1 and K_2 have been determined by Barton and Bethke (1960). For separate solutions in which equilibria (1) and (2) were set up, Cu^{2+} and SO_4^{2-} were determined chemically and OH^- by pH-meter; then the constants $\mathcal{K}_1$ and $\mathcal{K}_2$ were evaluated from

[1'] $$c_{Cu^{2+}}^4 \, c_{OH^-}^6 \, c_{SO_4^{2-}} = \mathcal{K}_1^{-1}$$
[2'] $$c_{SO_4^{2-}}^{-\frac{1}{2}} \, c_{OH^-}^2 = \mathcal{K}_2^{-1}.$$

Further determinations for more dilute solutions enable the results to be extrapolated, by familiar graphical methods, to infinite dilution. Now $a_i = \gamma_i c_i$, therefore

$$K_1 = \mathcal{K}_1 \, \gamma_{Cu^{2+}}^4 \, \gamma_{OH^-}^6 \, \gamma_{SO_4^{2-}},$$

and since $\gamma_i \to 1$ as $c_i \to 0$,

$$\lim_{c_i \to 0} K_1 = \mathcal{K}_1.$$

At 298°K, experimental determinations give

$$K_1 = 10^{68.4}, \qquad K_2 = 10^{10.2}$$

and consequently, from (4),

$$K_3 = 10^{19.6}.$$

Sufficient data have now been assembled for the stabilities of brochantite and tenorite to be predicted. In view of the necessarily low concentrations of the relevant ions in solution, mol fractions may be identified with activities. For brochantite to crystallize, its solubility product must be exceeded, therefore

$$c_{Cu^{2+}}^{+4} \; c_{SO_4^{2-}} \geqslant K_1^{-1} c_{OH^-}^{-6}.$$

If it is supposed that all the SO_4^{2-} ions derive from $CuSO_4$ (*see below*), then

$$c_{Cu^{2+}} = c_{SO_4^{2-}}$$

whence

$$c_{Cu^{2+}} \geqslant K_1^{-\frac{1}{2}} \, c_{OH^-}^{-3} \qquad\qquad \text{for brochantite crystallization}$$

and

$$c_{Cu^{2+}} \geqslant K_3^{-1} \, c_{OH^-}^{-2} \qquad\qquad \text{for tenorite crystallization.}$$

It is evident that the relative stability of the two minerals depends not only on the concentration of Cu^{2+} ions in the circulating body of water, but also on the alkalinity of the solution. A convenient diagram for displaying this relationship is that showing $\log x_{Cu^{2+}}$ as a function of pH.

Since $pH = -\log a_{H^+}$ by definition and the ionic product of water, whether the solution contains foreign ions or not, is

$$a_{H^+} \, a_{OH^-} = 10^{-14}$$

the inequalities become

$$\left.\begin{aligned} \log c_{Cu^{2+}} &\geqslant -\frac{68.4}{5} - \frac{6}{5}(-14 + pH) \\[4pt] i.e., \qquad \log c_{Cu^{2+}} &\geqslant 3.1 - \frac{6}{5}\,pH \end{aligned}\right\} \text{ for brochantite}$$

and

$$\left.\begin{aligned} \log c_{Cu^{2+}} &\geqslant -19.6 - 2(-14 + pH) \\ i.e., \qquad \log c_{Cu^{2+}} &\geqslant 8.4 - 2\,pH \end{aligned}\right\} \text{ for tenorite}$$

Figure 77 shows the stability fields of the two minerals, that of tenorite being very restricted in the shaded area of the diagram, which corresponds to solutions on the alkaline side of neutrality. Tenorite therefore crystallizes as a primary mineral from very dilute solutions of Cu^{2+}, more dilute than those crystallizing brochantite.

In contrast to such primary crystallization of tenorite is its formation as a secondary mineral from brochantite by reaction (2). For brochantite to persist, it is necessary in the absence of Cu^{2+} ions that

$$c_{SO_4^{2-}} > K_2\, c_{OH^-}^2.$$

At $pH = 7$ this implies that the concentration of sulphate ions should not fall below

$$c_{SO_4^{2-}} = 10^{-3.8}.$$

The circulating waters in general will contain other ions, which, without being directly involved in the equilibria concerned, never-

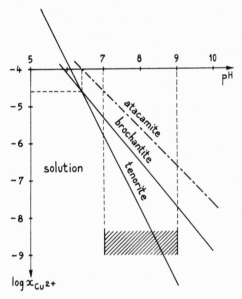

Fig. 77. Crystallization diagram for brochantite and tenorite as a function of Cu^{2+} concentration and pH of the crystallizing solutions.

theless exert some influence on the primary crystallization of both minerals. At sufficiently high concentrations such ions affect the activity coefficients γ_i of SO_4^{2-}, Cu^{2+}, and OH^-. The activity coefficients γ_i becoming then less than unity, some slight downward displacement of the brochantite line on figure 77 can be predicted.

A more important effect is that of variation of SO_4^{2-} concentration on the formation of brochantite; this is what is called a *homoionic effect*, which will decrease the solubility of brochantite without affecting the crystallization of tenorite by reaction (3). Thus the field of brochantite is extended downward so that the field of tenorite may miss the zone of common alkaline waters. Tenorite is therefore a mineral that is formed from solutions containing only low concentrations at once of Cu^{2+} and SO_4^{2-}.

3.2. Atacamite.

Atacamite poses a problem exactly analogous to that of brochantite. In an alkaline solution,

[5] $4\ Cu^{2+} + 6\ OH^- + 2\ Cl^- \rightleftharpoons Cu_4(OH)_6Cl_2(s)$

and, according to Barton and Bethke (1960), this reaction has an equilibrium constant $K_5 = 10^{69.4}$ at 298°K.

A pure solution of $CuCl_2$ has

$$c_{Cu^{2+}} = \frac{1}{2}\ c_{Cl^-}$$

and therefore the stability field of atacamite therein is given by

$$\log c_{Cu^{2+}} \geqslant 2.4 - pH.$$

Clearly then the stability field of atacamite is near that of brochantite, as shown by the broken line on fig. 77. One or other of these two

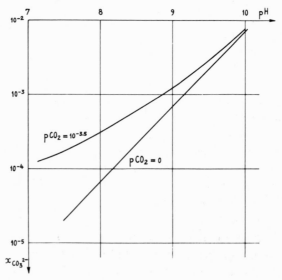

Fig. 78. pH of an aqueous solution of CO_2 in the presence of limestone.

minerals will therefore be formed according to whether the solution contains Cl^- or SO_4^{2-}, all other conditions being very similar.

3.3. Malachite-Azurite.

The two preceding paragraphs have dealt with crystallization from waters made alkaline, in the range pH 7–9, by passage through limestone strata. It is clear, however, from figure 78 (see also p. 266) that in such circumstances the CO_3^{2-} content of the waters may be of the order of 10^{-4}, and, on exposure to the open air, of the order of 10^{-5}.

The possibility of primary crystallization of malachite and azurite cannot therefore be ignored. The relevant reactions are:

$$2 \ Cu^{2+} + CO_3^{2-} + 2 \ OH^- \rightleftharpoons Cu_2(OH)_2CO_3; \quad \text{(malachite)},$$
$$3 \ Cu^{2+} + 2 \ CO_3^{2-} + 2 \ OH^- \rightleftharpoons Cu_3(OH)_2(CO_3)_2; \quad \text{(azurite)}.$$

The free enthalpy of reaction can be calculated for both from data given by Rossini et al. (1952) and Garrels and Dreyer (1952):

	Malachite	Azurite	Cu^{2+}	OH^-	CO_3^{2-}
ΔG_{298}^0 Kcal/mole	− 216.44	− 343.73	+ 15.53	− 37.595	− 126.22

Therefore

$$(\Delta G)_{298}^0 = - 46.09 \text{ Kcal mole}^{-1} \text{ for malachite}$$
$$(\Delta G)_{298}^0 = - 62.69 \text{ Kcal mole}^{-1} \text{ for azurite.}$$

The equilibrium constant for each reaction is given by

$$\ln K_{298} = -\frac{(\Delta G)_{298}^0}{298 \ R}$$

that is

$$\log K = 33.5 \text{ for malachite crystallization}$$

and

$$\log K = 46.5 \text{ for azurite crystallization.}$$

Application of the Law of Mass Action for heterogeneous systems yields:

$$c_{Cu^{2+}}^2 \ c_{CO_3^{2-}} \ c_{OH^-}^2 = 10^{-33.5}; \quad \text{(malachite)}$$
$$c_{Cu^{2+}}^3 \ c_{CO_3^{2-}}^2 \ c_{OH^-}^2 = 10^{-46.5}; \quad \text{(azurite)}.$$

Knowledge of the relationship between $c_{CO_3^{2-}}$, c_{OH^-} (or pH), and the partial pressure of CO_2 in the atmosphere above the solution (fig. 77) makes it possible to express the stability fields of malachite and azurite in terms of the pH and $c_{Cu^{2+}}$ in the solution at various partial pressures of CO_2 (fig. 79). It is clear from the figure that malachite

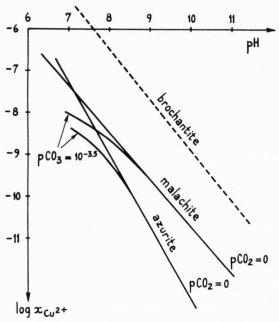

Fig. 79. Stability diagram for malachite and azurite. The concentration of CO_2 has only a very slight effect on relative stability.

and azurite will crystallize under very similar conditions, which are only slightly dependent on p_{CO_2}.

In short, it can be stated that dilute cupric solutions in their passage through a limestone formation will crystallize brochantite or atacamite if the Cu^{2+} concentration is high enough. At very low Cu^{2+} concentration, on the other hand, azurite, malachite, or tenorite will be precipitated and in such circumstances the CO_2 content of the atmosphere above the solution has scarcely any influence on the precipitation of these mineral phases.

4. Ferrous-ferric equilibrium in a lava*

4.1. Experiments on basalts.

The experimentalist who has tried to recrystallize a basalt in the laboratory knows how difficult it is to maintain the Fe^{2+}/Fe^{3+} ratio constant during the experiment. If he performs the experiment in the open air all the ferrous iron will oxidize, and if, on the contrary, he works in a vacuum, the ferric iron will be reduced to the ferrous condition or even to metallic iron. The only means of maintaining the ratio constant is to work in a controlled atmosphere with a definite partial pressure of oxygen at any given temperature.

4.1.1. Preliminary calculations.

—The requisite experimental conditions can be predicted by means of a straightforward calculation. The equilibrium involved, a very familiar one, is:

$$2\ Fe_2O_3(s) \rightleftharpoons 4\ FeO(s) + O_2(g).$$

The Law of Mass Action for a heterogeneous system gives

$$K_1 = \frac{a_{FeO}^4\ a_{O_2}}{a_{Fe_2O_3}^2}$$

where a_i represents the activity of a solid or gaseous phase. If the silicates concerned can be considered as ideal solid solutions and the gas phase as an ideal mixture, then

$$K_1 = \frac{x_{FeO}^4 x_{O_2}}{x_{Fe_2O_3}^2} = \frac{x_{FeO}^4 p_{O_2}/P}{x_{Fe_2O_3}^2}.$$

K_1 depends on the total pressure P and it is therefore convenient to define K_1' as

$$K_1' = \frac{x_{FeO}^4 p_{O_2}}{x_{Fe_2O_3}^2}$$

with $K_1 = K_1'/P$, K_1' being an equilibrium constant independent of total pressure. The temperature dependence of K_1' is given (p. 216) by

$$d \ln K_1'/dT = (\Delta H)/RT^2.$$

* After Kennedy, 1948.

Now at 298°K the standard enthalpies concerned are:

$$\Delta H_{Fe_2O_3} = -\ 198.5 \text{ Kcal mole}^{-1}$$
$$\Delta H_{FeO} = -\ \ 64.3 \text{ Kcal mole}^{-1}$$
$$\Delta H_{O_2} = 0 \quad (\text{by definition for an element}) ,$$

whence

$$(\Delta H)_{298} = +\ 69.9 \text{ Kcal per mole of Fe}_2O_3 \text{ reduced .}$$

And the mean specific heats are:

$$(C_P)_{Fe_2O_3} = 56.7 \text{ cal deg}^{-1} \text{ mole}^{-1}$$
$$(C_P)_{FeO} = 14.4 \text{ cal deg}^{-1} \text{ mole}^{-1}$$
$$(C_P)_{O_2} = \ \ 7.2 \text{ cal deg}^{-1} \text{ mole}^{-1} ,$$

whence $\Delta C_P = -24.3$ cal deg^{-1} and at, say 1350°C (1623°K), the heat of reaction is to a first approximation given by

$$(\Delta H)_{1623} = +\ 37.6 \text{ Kcal per two moles of Fe}_2O_3 \text{ reduced,}$$

assuming ΔC_P constant between 298 and 1620°K.

4.1.2. Experimental data.—Kennedy did not content himself with making this simple calculation which would, as it happens, have led to the conclusions he eventually drew. But in order to convince himself that an equation involving only the oxides could be applicable to Fe^{2+} and Fe^{3+} dissolved in the solid phases of a basalt, he performed the following experiment.

A basalt from the San Juan Mountains, Colorado, was analyzed and converted into a homogeneous glass by heating in a furnace in a controlled atmosphere. The homogeneity was tested by measurements of refractive index and a chemical analysis showed that no stoichiometric change had occurred during the short period of heating. The crushed glass was placed in platinum-iridium crucibles and heated at accurately determined temperatures for various times at a partial pressure of oxygen of 0.2 atm. Kennedy found that equilibrium could only be obtained in runs of convenient duration (10–20 hours) at temperatures above 1200°C. His experiments were therefore limited to the range 1200–1400°C. Equilibrium attained, he quenched the charge and analyzed it for total iron, $Fe^{2+} + Fe^{3+}$. His mean results, for a total pressure P = 1 atm, are detailed below:

T °C	p_{O_2}	% FeO	% Fe$_2$O$_3$	K$_1'$ 10^4
1400	0.2	3.20	9.02	1.055
1300	0.2	2.30	9.97	0.246
1200	0.2	1.59	10.82	0.0439

The equilibrium constant K$_1'$ is here given by

$$K_1' = \frac{x_{\text{FeO}}^4 \; 0 \cdot 2}{x_{\text{Fe}_2\text{O}_3}^2}.$$

A graph of log K$_1'$ against T^{-1} yields a straight line of slope $-(\Delta H)/R$, whence $(\Delta H) = +37.05$ Kcal per mole of Fe$_2$O$_3$ between 1200 and 1400°C, a value perfectly consistent with that obtained directly by calculation. Thus the solid solutions into which Fe$_2$O$_3$ can be supposed to enter in a basalt must be approximately perfect solutions and the simple equation in terms of oxides can conveniently be used to represent the process (fig. 80). The constant K$_1'$ cannot be determined

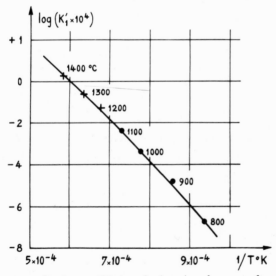

Fig. 80. Oxidation-reduction equilibrium for iron in a lava as a function of temperature.

experimentally below 1200°C, but calculation enables the experimental results to be extrapolated to lower temperatures with confidence.

4.2. Application to geology.

4.2.1.—*Partial pressure of oxygen arising from the dissociation of iron oxides in a magma.*—The fresh basalt studied earlier contained initially 8.87 molecular % FeO and 0.6% of Fe_2O_3; and by taking into account the experimentally determined temperature dependence of K_1', the partial pressure of oxygen obtaining at the time of its sudden quenching on extrusion can be calculated. This is simply a matter of the converse application of the Law of Mass Action.

°C	p_{O_2}
1400	7.07×10^{-5} atm
1300	1.65×10^{-5}
1200	2.94×10^{-6}
1100	3.36×10^{-7}
1000	2.66×10^{-8}
900	9.25×10^{-10}
800	2.02×10^{-11}

It is noticeable from the table that the partial pressure necessary to maintain a given Fe^{2+}/Fe^{3+} ratio decreases with decreasing temperature.

The calculation could be objected to on the grounds that it applies only to a molten lava; this is, however, an invalid objection since the value observed directly at 1200°C is in excellent agreement with that calculated for 1200°C on this assumption. Now at 1200°C the lava is solid and contains a magnesian magnetite and a lime feldspar. The lava begins to crystallize at 1285 ± 5°C. Between 1170 and 1140°C the lava contains 70% of crystalline solids, in the main hypersthene. Therefore the calculation is valid whatever the physical state of the lava.

This leads to an important result: the Fe^{2+}/Fe^{3+} ratio in such a rock maintains a constant value and physicochemical conclusions can be drawn directly from the determination of the ratio in different basalts.

4.2.2. *Hydrogen content of volcanic gases and its relation to the* Fe^{2+}/Fe^{3+} *of a lava.*—Since the magnitude of the ferrous-ferric ratio is significant in a quenched lava, it would appear to be worthwhile to try to relate the ratio to the hydrogen content of the associated volcanic gases.

The partial pressure of oxygen necessary to establish equilibrium between Fe^{2+} and Fe^{3+} can arise from the well-known dissociation of water vapor at high temperatures:

$$2 H_2(g) + O_2(g) \rightleftharpoons 2 H_2O(g).$$

The Law of Mass Action for a homogeneous reaction gives:

$$\frac{f_{H_2O}^2}{f_{H_2}^2 f_{O_2}} = K_2 \qquad \text{or} \qquad \frac{x_{H_2O}^2}{x_{H_2}^2 x_{O_2}} \frac{1}{P} = K_2;$$

where K_2 is independent of the total pressure P. Values of K_2 for various temperatures at 1 atm total pressure have been calculated and verified experimentally:

T °C	K_2
900	2.19×10^{16}
1000	3.72×10^{14}
1100	1.18×10^{13}
1200	7.41×10^{11}
1300	4.47×10^{10}
1400	5.57×10^{9}
1500	6.46×10^{8}

The reaction is certainly pressure sensitive since three moles appear on one side of the equation and only two on the other. The partial pressure of oxygen can, moreover, be calculated quite simply as a function of T and P. Let μ be the number of moles of O_2 formed; then 2μ moles of H_2 will be formed simultaneously and $1 - 2\mu$ moles of water vapor remain unchanged. The total number of moles in the system will then be:

$$\mu + 2\mu + 1 - 2\mu = 1 + \mu.$$

Therefore at a total pressure P,

$$p_{H_2O} = \frac{1 - 2\mu}{1 + \mu} P; \qquad p_{O_2} = \frac{\mu}{1 + \mu} P; \qquad p_{H_2} = \frac{2\mu}{1 + \mu} P$$

and the Law of Mass Action yields

$$K_2 = \frac{\left(\dfrac{1 - 2\mu}{1 + \mu}\right)^2 P^2}{\left(\dfrac{2\mu}{1 + \mu}\right)^2 P^2 \left(\dfrac{\mu}{1 + \mu}\right) P} \sim \frac{1}{4\mu^3 P}$$

therefore

$$\nu \sim \frac{1}{\sqrt[3]{4K_2P}}$$

and if $\mu \ll 1$

$$p_{O_2} \sim \frac{P^{2/3}}{\sqrt[3]{4K_2}}.$$

The partial pressure of oxygen due to the dissociation of water vapor is proportional to the 2/3 power of the total pressure.

Kennedy's argument can be extended by considering the two simultaneous reactions

[1] $$2\ Fe_2O_3 \rightleftharpoons 4\ FeO + O_2$$

for which

$$K_1 = \frac{x_{FeO}^4}{x_{Fe_2O_3}^2}\ x_{O_2}$$

and

[2] $$2\ H_2 + O_2 \rightleftharpoons 2\ H_2O$$

for which

$$K_2 = \frac{x_{H_2O}^2}{x_{H_2}^2\ x_{O_2}\ P}.$$

Both reactions are sensitive to the external pressure: the former is repressed as the total pressure increases and the latter is favored by increased total pressure.

The overall oxidation-reduction reaction for Fe in the presence of water vapor at temperature T and pressure P is obtained by addition of (1) and (2):

[3] $$2\ Fe_2O_3(s) + 2\ H_2 \rightleftharpoons 2\ H_2O + 4\ FeO(s).$$

This reaction is not dependent on the total pressure P applied to the system, a point of some significance that was apparently not noticed by Kennedy. In fact reaction (3) is accompanied by a volume change $\Delta V_3 = -10.5$ cm^3 mole^{-1} if the gases are assumed to be perfect; such a volume of reaction is utterly negligible in comparison with that for reaction (2), $\Delta V_2 = +22,400$ cm^3 mole^{-1}. The equilibrium constant for the heterogeneous reaction (3) is given by

$$K_3 = \frac{x_{H_2O}^2\ x_{FeO}^4}{x_{H_2}^2\ x_{Fe_2O_3}^2} = K_1'K_2$$

or if μ is the number of moles of H_2 and $1 - \mu$ the number of moles of H_2O formed,

$$K_3 = \frac{(1 - \mu)^2}{\mu^2} \frac{x_{FeO}^4}{x_{Fe_2O_3}^2} \sim \frac{1}{\mu^2} \frac{x_{FeO}^4}{x_{Fe_2O_3}^2}.$$

The number of moles of H_2 present in the system at temperature T and any pressure is given by

$$\mu = \frac{x_{FeO}^2}{x_{FeO_2}} (K_1'K_2)^{-\frac{1}{2}},$$

where K_1' and K_2 are functions only of T.

The significance of this equation can be seen by considering a fresh Halemaumau basalt with molar percentages of FeO 8.87% and Fe_2O_3 0.64%; for this lava

$$\mu = \frac{(8.87)^2}{(0.64)} (0.04 \times 7.0 \times 10^{11})^{-1/2} \sim 0.062 \text{ mol } \% \text{ } H_2.$$

The constants K_1' and K_2 have been evaluated for 1200°C, the temperature at and below which the lava has a fixed oxidation ratio, as the experimental work described earlier, indicated. At 1400°C μ is evaluated as

$$\mu = 0.2 \text{ mol } \% \text{ } H_2.$$

This latter value accords well with the gas analyses made by Jaggar at Halemaumau, the mean of 14 of the best analyses of volcanic gases being 0.222 mol % H_2.

Kennedy found a different result for 1200°C and 10 atm, but, as has already been noted, the total pressure exerts no significant effect on the controlling equilibrium.

In the final part of his paper, Kennedy attacked the problem of the gabbros. Knowledge of the Fe^{2+}/Fe^{3+} ratio for a Californian gabbro enabled him to show that, at 1200°C in the presence of a gas of the same composition as the Halemaumau gas, the total water vapor pressure applied to the gabbro must be of the order of 250 atm. He remarked on the other hand that reference to Goranson's data for the solubility of water in granitic melts yields, on extrapolation to 1200°C and 250 atm, a content of 2% of water in such a gabbro. This sort of argument is to be encouraged, but in this particular case it leads to a manifestly false conclusion since the Fe^{2+}/Fe^{3+} ratio is independent of the total pressure of water vapor.

Bibliography

ABELSON, P. H., editor (1959). Researches in Geochemistry. New York, John Wiley & Sons.

ADAMS, L. H. (1953). A Note on the stability of jadeite. Amer. Journ. Sci., vol. 251, pp. 299–308.

BARTH, T. F. W. (1951). The feldspar geologic thermometers. N. Jahrb. Min., Abh. vol. 82, pp. 143–154.

———— (1962). The feldspar geologic thermometers. Norsk. Geol. Tids., vol. 42.2, pp. 330–339.

BARTHOLOMÉ, P. (1960). L'interprétation pétrogénétique des associations d'olivine et d'orthopyroxène. Ann. Soc. Géol. Belgique, vol. 83, pp. 319–344.

———— (1962). Iron-magnesium ratio in associated pyroxenes and olivines. Petrologic studies: A volume in honor of A. F. Buddington. New York, Geol. Soc. Amer., pp. 1–20.

BARTON, P. B., and *BETHKE, P. M.* (1960). Thermodynamic properties of some synthetic zinc and copper minerals. Amer. Journ. Sci., vol. 258A, pp. 21–34.

BIRCH, F. (1955). Physics of the Crust. *In* Crust of the Earth, A. Poldervaart, editor. Geol. Soc. Amer. Special Paper 62, pp. 101–118.

————, *SCHAIRER, J. F.*, and *SPICER, H. C.*, editors (1942). Handbook of Physical Constants. Geol. Soc. Amer., Special Paper 36.

BOWEN, N. L., and *SCHAIRER, J. R.* (1935). The system $MgO—FeO—SiO_2$. Amer. Journ. Sci., ser. 5, vol. 29, pp. 151–217.

BOYD, F. R., and *ENGLAND, J. L.* (1960). The quartz-coesite transition. Journ. Geophys. Res., vol. 65, pp. 749–756.

BUERGER, M. J. (1948). The role of temperature in mineralogy. Amer. Min., vol. 33, pp. 101–121.

CLARK, S. P. (1957). A note on calcite-aragonite equilibrium. Amer. Min., vol. 42, pp. 564–566.

CLAYTON, R. N., and *EPSTEIN, S.* (1961). The use of oxygen isotopes in high-temperature geological thermometry. Journ. Geol., vol. 69, pp. 447–452.

COLE, W. F., SÖRUM, H. and *TAYLOR, W. H.* (1951). The structures of the plagioclase feldspars, I. Acta Cryst., vol. 4, pp. 20–29.

CORRENS, C. W., and *STEINBORN, W.* (1939). Über die Messung der sogenannten Kristallisationskraft. Fortschr. Min. Krist. u. Petr., vol. 23, pp. CV–CVIII.

DANIELSSON, A. (1950). Das calcit-wollastonitgleichgewicht. Geochim. et Cosmochim. Acta, vol. 1, pp. 55–59.

DEER, W. A., HOWIE, R. A., and ZUSSMANN, J. (1962-3). Rock-forming Minerals. London, Longmans, Green & Co., 5 volumes.

DENBIGH, K. G. (1955). The Principles of Chemical Equilibrium. Cambridge University Press. (Intended for chemical engineers, the treatment is such as to emphasize the application of classical and statistical thermodynamics to a wide range of practical problems, many of which are relevant, by analogy, to petrology.)

DE VORE, G. W. (1959). Role of minimum interfacial free energy in determining the macroscopic features of mineral assemblages. I. The model. Journ. Geol., vol. 67, pp. 211–227.

EITEL, W. (1952). Thermochemical Methods in Silicate Investigation. New Jersey, Rutgers University Press. (An authoritative text on experimental thermochemistry.)

ELLIS, A. J., and FYFE, W. S. (1956). A note on the calcite-wollastonite equilibrium. Amer. Min., vol. 41, pp. 805–807.

EMSCHWILLER, G. (1951). Chimie Physique, I, II, III. Paris, Presses universitaires de France. (An advanced book of chemical thermodynamics.)

FINDLAY, A. (1951). The Phase Rule and Its Applications, 9th ed. New York, Dover.

FONTEILLES, M. (1962). Contribution a l'étude des skarns de Kamioka, Prefecture de Gifu, Japon. Journ. Fac. Sci. Univ. Tokyo, sect. II, vol. 14, pp. 153–227.

FYFE, W. S., TURNER, F. J., and VERHOOGEN, J. (1958). Metamorphic reactions and metamorphic facies. Geol. Soc. Amer. Memoir 73.

GARRELS, R. M. (1960). Mineral Equilibria at Low Temperature and Pressure. New York, Harper & Row.

———, and CHRIST, C. L. (1965). Solutions, Minerals, and Equilibria. New York, Harper & Row.

GARRELS, R. M., and DREYER, R. M. (1952). Mechanism of limestone replacement at low temperatures and pressures. Bull. Geol. Soc. Amer., vol. 63, pp. 325–379.

GOGUEL, J. (1948). Introduction à l'étude mécanique des déformations de l'écorce terrestre. Mémoires pour servir à l'explication de la carte géologique détaillée de la France.

GOLDSCHMIDT, V. M. (1911). Die Kontaktametamorphose in Kristianiagebiet. Oslo Vidensk. Skr., I, Mat.-Naturv. Kl., no. 11.

——— (1912). Die Gesetze der Gesteinsmetamorphose. Oslo Vidensk. Skr., I, Mat.-Naturv. Kl., no. 22.

GREENWOOD, H. J., DOE, B. R., and PHINNEY, W. C. (1964). Phase equilibria in the metamorphic rocks of St. Paul Island and Cape North, Nova Scotia. Journ. Petrol., vol. 5, pp. 189–194.

GRUBENMANN, U., and NIGGLI, P. (1924). Die Gesteinsmetamorphose. Berlin, Borntraeger.

GUGGENHEIM, E. A. (1959). Thermodynamics, 4th ed. Amsterdam, North-Holland

Publishing Co. (A rigorous and lucid, but advanced, exposition of classical thermodynamics, paying especial attention to chemical aspects and applications.)

HARKER, R. I., and TUTTLE, O. F. (1956). Experimental data on the $P_{CO_2} - T$ curve for the reaction: calcite + quartz — wollastonite + carbon dioxide. Amer. Journ. Sci., vol. 254, pp. 239–256.

HOCART, R., and KERN, R. (1967). Problèmes de Chimie générale et de Cristallo-chimie, 2nd ed. Paris, Gauthiers-Villars.

IIYAMA, J. T., WYART, J., and SABATIER, G. (1963). Equilibre des feldspaths alcalins et des plagioclases a 500, 600, 700 et 800°C sous une pression d'eau de 1000 bars. C. R. Acad. Sci., Paris, vol. 256, pp. 5016–5020.

JAMIESON, J. C. (1953). Phase equilibrium in the system calcite-aragonite. Journ. Chem. Phys., vol. 21, pp. 1385–1390.

———— (1957). Introductory studies of high-pressure polymorphism to 24,000 bars by X-ray diffraction with some comments on calcite II. Journ. Geol., vol. 65, pp. 334–343.

KAMB, W. B. (1959). Theory of preferred crystal orientation developed by crystallization under stress. Journ. Geol., vol. 67, pp. 153–170.

KELLEY, K. K. (1941). The specific heats at low temperatures of ferrous silicates, etc. Journ. Amer. Chem. Soc., vol. 63, pp. 750–752.

———— (1943). Specific heats at low temperatures of magnesium orthosilicate and metasilicate. Journ. Amer. Chem. Soc., vol. 65, pp. 339–341.

————, (1960). Contributions to the data on theoretical metallurgy XIII. High-Temperature Heat-Content, Heat-Capacity, and Entropy Data for the Elements and Inorganic Compounds. U.S. Bureau of Mines, Bull. 584. (This is the latest in a series of such compilations and supersedes Bull. 371 (1934) and Bull. 476 (1949).)

————, and KING, E. G. (1961). Contributions to the data on theoretical metallurgy XIV. Entropies of the Elements and Inorganic Compounds. U.S. Bureau of Mines, Bull. 592. (This likewise supersedes earlier publications in the same series, viz. Bull. 350 (1932), Bull. 394 (1936), Bull. 434 (1941), and Bull. 477 (1950).)

KENNEDY, G. C. (1948). Equilibrium between volatiles and iron oxides in igneous rocks. Amer. Journ. Sci., vol. 246, pp. 529–549.

———— (1954). Pressure–volume–temperature relations in CO_2 at elevated temperatures and pressures. Amer. Journ. Sci., vol. 252, pp. 225–241.

KIRKWOOD, J. G., and OPPENHEIM, I. (1961). Chemical Thermodynamics. New York, McGraw-Hill.

KLOTZ, I. M. (1964). Chemical Thermodynamics. New York, W. A. Benjamin Inc.

KORZHINSKII, D. S. (1959). Physicochemical Basis of the Analysis of the Paragenesis of Minerals. Translated from the Russian edition, 1957. New York, Consultants Bureau Inc.

KRACEK, F. C., and NEUVONEN, J. J. (1952). Thermochemistry of plagioclase and alkali feldspar. Amer. Journ. Sci., Bowen vol., pp. 293–318.

——, NEUVONEN, J. J., and BURLEY, G. (1951). A thermodynamic study of the stability of jadeite. Washington Acad. Sci. Journ., vol. 41, pp. 373–383.

KRETZ, R. (1959). Chemical study of garnet, biotite, and hornblende from gneisses of southwestern Quebec, with emphasis on distribution of elements in coexisting minerals. Journ. Geol., vol. 67, pp. 371–402.

KUBASCHEWSKII, O., and EVANS, E. LL. (1958). Metallurgical Thermochemistry, 3rd ed. London and New York, Pergamon Press. (Many of the metallurgical problems treated here have their counterpart in petrology.)

KULLERUD, G. (1953). The FeS–ZnS system: a geological thermometer. Norsk. Geol. Tidssk., vol. 32, pp. 61–147.

LAFFITTE, P. (1957). Introduction à l'étude des roches métamorphiques et des gites métallifères: physico-chimie et thermodynamique. Paris, Masson.

—— (1958). Propagation de la chaleur dans les roches autour d'une source chaude sphérique. Bull. Soc. Franç. Min. Crist., vol. 81, pp. 147–149.

LAVES, F. (1952). Phase relations of the alkali feldspars. Journ. Geol., vol. 60, pp. 436–450, 549–574.

LEWIS, G. H., and RANDALL, M. (1961). Thermodynamics, 2nd ed., revised by K. S. Pitzer and Leo Brewer. New York, McGraw-Hill. (This is one of the classics of thermodynamics and is an invaluable source of information and ideas about the application of thermodynamics to chemical problems.)

MACDONALD, G. J. F. (1953). Anhydrite-gypsum equilibrium relations. Amer. Journ. Sci., vol. 251, pp. 884–898.

—— (1956). Experimental determination of calcite-aragonite equilibrium relations at elevated temperatures and pressures. Amer. Min., vol. 41, pp. 744–756.

—— (1957). Thermodynamics of solids under non-hydrostatic stress with geologic applications. Amer. Journ. Sci., vol. 255, pp. 266–281.

MEISSNER, H. P. (1948). Chemical reaction equilibria: estimating standard entropy changes. 2nd. Eng. Chem., vol. 40, pp. 904–908.

MIYASHIRO, A. (1960). Thermodynamics of reactions of rock-forming minerals with silica. Japanese Journ. Geol. and Geogr., vol. 31, pp. 71–78, 78–84, 107–111, 113–120, 241–246, 247–252.

—— (1961). Evolution of metamorphic belts. Journ. Petrol., vol. 2, pp. 277–311.

MOSESMAN, M. A., and PITZER, K. S. (1941). Thermodynamic properties of the crystalline forms of silica. Journ. Amer. Chem. Soc., vol. 63, pp. 356–438.

NEUVONEN, J. J. (1952). Thermochemical investigation of the åkermanite-gehlenite series. Bull. Comm. Géol. Finlande, no. 158, 50 pp.

NIGGLI, P. (1937). Das Magma und seine Produkte. Leipzig, Akademische Verlagsgesellschaft.

ORR, R. L. (1953). High-temperature heat contents of magnesium and ferrous ortho-silicates. Journ. Amer. Chem. Soc., vol. 75, pp. 528–529.

ORVILLE, P. M. (1962). Comments on the two-feldspar geothermometer. Norsk. Geol. Tidsskr., vol. 42, pp. 340–346.

PHINNEY, W. C. (1963). Phase equilibria in the metamorphic rocks of St. Paul Island and Cape North, Nova Scotia. Journ. Petrol., vol. 4, pp. 90–130.

PRIGOGINE, I., and DEFAY, R. (1954). Chemical Thermodynamics. Translated and revised by D. H. Everett. London, Longmans, Green & Co. (A rigorous advanced treatise on classical chemical thermodynamics following the methods of the great Belgian School.)

RAMBERG, H. (1947). The force of crystallization as a well definable property of crystals. Geol. For. Forh., vol. 69, pp. 189–194.

———— (1952). The origin of metamorphic and metasomatic rocks. Univ. Chicago Press.

————, and DE VORE, G. W. (1951). The distribution of Fe^{2+} and Mg^{2+} in coexist-ing olivines and pyroxenes. Journ. Geol., vol. 59, pp. 193–210.

ROBERTSON, E. C., BIRCH, F., and MACDONALD, G. J. F. (1957). Experimental determination of jadeite stability relations to 25,000 bars. Amer. Journ. Sci., vol. 255, pp. 115–137.

ROSSINI, F. D. (1950). Chemical Thermodynamics. New York, John Wiley & Sons; London, Chapman and Hall. (More elementary than either Guggenheim or Prigogine and Defay.)

————, WAGMAN, D. D., EVANS, W. H., LEVINE, S., and JAFFE, I. (1961). Selected Values of Chemical Thermodynamic Properties. Nat. Bur. Standards, Circular 500, 1952, reprinted 1961. (Enthalpies, entropies, and free enthalpies of formation, together with thermodynamic data for polymorphic transforma-tions and for changes of state are listed.)

———— (1962). Handbook of Chemistry and Physics, 44th ed. Cleveland, Ohio, Chemical Rubber Publishing Co. (Revised and republished annually; pp. 1882–1918 of the 1962 edition is a list of "Values of Chemical Thermodynamic Properties" extracted from Rossini et al. (q.v.).)

ROTH, W. A., BERENDT, H., and WIRTHS, G. (1941). Die Bildungswärmen einiger mineralischer und künstlicher Carbonate. Zeits. Elektrochem., vol. 47, pp. 185–190.

SAHAMA, Th. G., and TORGESON, D. R. (1949). Some examples of the applica-tion of thermochemistry to petrology. Journ. Geol., vol. 57, pp. 255–262.

SENG, H. (1937). Für das Riecke'sche Prinzip! N. Jahrb. Min. Geol., Beil. Bd. 73, Abt. A, pp. 239–308.

Tables annuelles de Constantes et Données Numériques. Paris, Gauthier-Villars; New York, McGraw-Hill.

THOMPSON, J. B., Jr. (1955). The thermodynamic basis for the mineral facies concept. Am. J. Sci. 253, pp. 65–103.

—————— (1959). Equilibrium in metasomatic processes, pp. 427–457 of Researches in Geochemistry, P. H. Abelson, editor. New York, John Wiley & Sons.

TORGESON, D. R., and SAHAMA, Th. G. (1948). A hydrofluoric acid solution calorimeter and the determination of the heats of formation of Mg_2SiO_4, $MgSiO_3$, $CaSiO_3$. Journ. Amer. Chem. Soc., vol. 70, pp. 2156–2160.

TURNER, F. J., and VERHOOGEN, J. (1960). Igneous and Metamorphic Petrology, 2nd ed. New York, McGraw-Hill.

TUTTLE, O. F., and BOWEN, N. L., (1958). Origin of granite in the light of experimental studies in the system $NaAlSi_3O_8$—$KAlSi_3O_8$—SiO_2—H_2O. Geol. Soc. Amer., Memoir 74.

TUTTLE, O. F., and HARKER, R. I. (1957). Synthesis of spurrite and the reaction wollastonite + calcite = spurrite + carbon dioxide. Amer. Journ. Sci., vol. 255, pp. 226–234.

VAN'T HOFF, J. H. (1912). Untersuchungen über die Bildungsverhältnisse der ozeanischen Salzablagerungen insbesonder des Stassfurter Salzlargers. Leipzig.

VERHOOGEN, J. (1951). The chemical potential of a stressed solid. Amer. Geophys. Union, Trans., vol. 32, pp. 251–258.

WEISBROD, A. (1963). Étude thermodynamique de l'équilibre quartz + olivine → 2 pyroxènes. Bull. Soc. Franç. Min. Crist., vol. 86, pp. 278–285.

YODER, H. S. (1950). High-low quartz inversion up to 10,000 bars. Amer. Geophys. Union, Trans., vol. 31, pp. 827–835.

—————, and WEIR, C. E. (1951). Change of free energy with pressure of the reaction nepheline + albite = 2 jadeite. Amer. Journ. Sci., vol. 249, pp. 683–694.

Indices

1. Thermodynamic index

2.   Geologic index

3. Index of authors' names